PREFACE

The elementary volume of this treatise deals with vector algebra and differentiation with respect to one scalar variable, showing how they may be usefully applied to Geometry and Mechanics. The present volume begins with partial differentiation of a vector function of several variables, and introduces right at the outset the gradient of a scalar point-function, and the divergence and curl of a vector function. The important theorems connecting line, surface, and space integrals are considered in the second chapter; but the theory of linear vector functions and dyadics is postponed till Chapters V. and VII. These four chapters contain all the advanced vector analysis that is ordinarily required.

The remaining portion of the book, dealing with applications of the above theory, forms a fairly complete introduction to Mathematical Physics. Naturally, it is only the three-dimensional work that is mentioned explicitly; but two-dimensional problems may be treated as particular cases of the general ones here discussed. In a short space it has been possible to go a considerable distance into each of the subjects taken up; and it will be apparent to the reader that a great saving is effected in all respects by vector methods. I have endeavoured to make the treatment of each subject continuous; and nothing has been assumed except a knowledge of the elementary phenomena of electricity and magnetism. Nearly the whole of Chapter IX. is independent of the theory of dyadics, and can be read if desired immediately after the discussion of the Potential Theory. The order of the book was adopted partly because of the introduction of dyadics in Arts. 107 and 116, and partly to keep the two chapters on Electricity consecutive. The historical introduction to the subject given in the author's *Elementary Vector Analysis* was intended to cover the present volume also; and it has not been thought necessary to add anything further in that direction.

My indebtedness to Professor J. H. Michell is as great in this case as in connection with the earlier volume. He was kind enough to read the original MS. and make many valuable suggestions, which I was glad to adopt. The point of view here taken agrees substantially with Professor Michell's. His University lectures in Mixed Mathematics have been a great help; and in Chapters VI. and VIII. I have followed his treatment fairly closely. But for his influence and inspiration the present volume would never have been even contemplated. I wish also to acknowledge a debt of gratitude to Mr R. A. Herman, M.A., of Trinity College, Cambridge, whose lectures in Applied Mathematics I had the privilege of attending while at that University. In the preparation of this book I have been influenced both consciously and unconsciously by Mr Herman's teaching.

The notation employed is that introduced by the late Professor Willard Gibbs; and I have chosen his theory of dyadics as being the most convenient for the treatment of the linear vector function. In this connection I owe a great deal to Professor E. B. Wilson, who, through his book, was one of my earliest instructors on the subject. This volume came to me as a stimulus and inspiration in mathematical work, and I have since been constantly under its influence. In particular my own presentation of the theory of dyadics has been considerably influenced by Professor Wilson's admirable discussion.

As to other literature, I derived considerable help from Professor Webster's *Dynamics*, which I consulted very often and in several parts of the subject. In my discussion of the elementary theory of Electricity and Magnetism I made frequent reference to Mr F. B. Pidduck's book; while in connection with the equations of Maxwell and Lorentz and the Lorentz-Einstein transformation I found Dr Silberstein's *Theory of Relativity* and Professor Lorentz's *Theory of Electrons* very helpful. In the vectorial expression of the transformation of coordinates I have followed Dr Silberstein fairly closely. Other works that were consulted during the writing of this book are mentioned in the bibliographical list below.

My thanks are also due to the Syndics of the Cambridge University Press, and to the University and Colleges of Cambridge, for permission to include among the Examples of this book a number of questions set in their examinations; to the *Mathematical Gazette* for permission to reprint as appendices two short articles which I contributed to that journal; and to Professor E. B. Wilson for allowing me to use a few Examples from his book. From Professor W. P. Milne, the editor of this series, I received several excellent suggestions, which I was very pleased to adopt; and I take this opportunity of thanking Mr A. D. Ross, B.A., a former student of Ormond College, whose kindness in reading the whole of the proofs was very helpful and much appreciated.

In conclusion, I wish to thank the Publishers for their courtesy, and the Printers for the excellence of their work.

C. E. WEATHERBURN.

September 1923.

CONTENTS

CHAPTER I.

THE DIFFERENTIAL OPERATORS.

CHAPTER II.

LINE, SURFACE, AND SPACE INTEGRALS.

CHAPTER III.

ELEMENTS OF THE POTENTIAL THEORY. EQUATION OF THERMAL CONDUCTION.

I. *Newtonian Potential.*

II. *Equation of Thermal Conduction.*

CHAPTER IV.

MOTION OF FRICTIONLESS FLUIDS.

Irrotational Motion.

Vortex Motion.

CHAPTER V.

LINEAR VECTOR FUNCTIONS. CENTRAL QUADRIC SURFACES.

I. *Dyadics.*

II. *Central Quadric Surfaces.*

CHAPTER VI.

THE RIGID BODY. INERTIA DYADIC. MOTION ABOUT A FIXED POINT.

I. *The Inertia Dyadic.*

II. *Motion about a Fixed Point.*

CHAPTER VII.

DYADICS INVOLVING ∇.

Transformation of Integrals.

CHAPTER VIII.

EQUILIBRIUM OF DEFORMABLE BODIES. MOTION OF VISCOUS FLUIDS.

I. *Strain Relations.*

II. *Stress Relations.*

III. *Isotropic Bodies.*

IV. *Motion of Viscous Fluids.*

CHAPTER IX.

ELEMENTARY THEORY OF ELECTRICITY AND MAGNETISM.

Intensity and Potential.

CHAPTER X.

THE EQUATIONS OF MAXWELL AND LORENTZ. THE LORENTZ-EINSTEIN TRANSFORMATION.

I. *The Electromagnetic Equations.*

BIBLIOGRAPHY

The following books have been consulted during the preparation of this volume:

BASSET, *Treatise on Hydrodynamics.*

CARSLAW, *Mathematical Theory of the Conduction of Heat.*

COFFIN, *Vector Analysis.*

CUNNINGHAM, *The Principle of Relativity.*

GANS, *Einführung in die Vektoranalysis.*

GIBBS, *Collected Papers.*

IGNATOWSKY, *Die Vektoranalysis.*

LAMB, *Hydrodynamics.*

LAUE, *Das Relativitätsprinzip.*

LORENTZ, *Theory of Electrons.*

LOVE, *Mathematical Theory of Elasticity.*

MARCOLONGO, *Calcul Vectoriel. Teoria Matematica dello Equilibrio dei Corpi Elastici.*

MAXWELL, *Treatise on Electricity and Magnetism.*

PIDDUCK, *A Treatise on Electricity.*

POINCARE, *Potentiel Newtonien.*

RAMSEY, *Hydrodynamics.*

RICHARDSON, *Electron Theory of Matter.*

ROUTH, *Rigid Dynamics. Analytical Statics*, vol. ii.

SILBERSTEIN, *Vectorial Mechanics. Theory of Relativity.*

WEBSTER, *Dynamics of Particles, and of Rigid, Elastic, and Fluid Bodies.*

WILSON, *Vector Analysis.*

TABLE OF NOTATIONS *

	Vector.	Scalar product.	Vector product.	Dyad.	Gradient.	Divergence.	Curl.
Gibbs, Wilson	**a**	**a·b**	**a**×**b**	**ab**	∇	$\nabla\cdot$ = div	curl = $\nabla\times$
Heaviside .	**a**	**ab**	*V***ab**	**a.b**	∇	div	curl
Abraham .	$\mathfrak{A}$	$\mathfrak{A}\mathfrak{B}$	$[\mathfrak{A}\mathfrak{B}]$		∇	div	curl
Ignatowsky .	$\mathfrak{A}$	$\mathfrak{A}\mathfrak{B}$	$[\mathfrak{A}\mathfrak{B}]$	$\mathfrak{A}\,;\,\mathfrak{B}$	∇	div.	rot
Lorentz .	**A**	(**A.B**)	[**A.B**]		grad	div	rot
Burali - Forti and Marcolongo.	**a**	**a**×**b**	**a** ∧ **b**		grad	div	rot

* A similar table appears in the Introduction (p. 12) to *Le Calcul Vectoriel* by Guiot (Paris, 1912).

SHORT COURSE

The student who wishes to take a short course only in the *theory* of advanced vector analysis is recommended to read the following Arts. :

1–11, 13–17, 19–20, (22–25), 26, 53–64, 83–87 .

CHAPTER I.

THE DIFFERENTIAL OPERATORS.

1. Vector function of several independent variables. The vector functions considered in our elementary volume * were functions of only one independent variable. But vector quantities which depend on the values of several independent variables are very common. The Cartesian coordinates x, y, z of a point, and the time variable t, form the set that we have most frequently to deal with.

Let $\mathbf{F}$ be a vector function of *any* set of independent variables which we shall denote by $x, y, \ldots$; and let $\mathbf{F}(x, y, \ldots)$ represent the value of the function for the values of the variables indicated within the brackets. Suppose that the value of the first variable increases from x to $x + \delta x$, while those of the other variables remain unaltered. Let $\delta\mathbf{F}$ be the corresponding increment in the function. Then the limiting value of the quotient $\delta\mathbf{F}/\delta x$ as δx tends to zero is called the *partial derivative* of $\mathbf{F}$ with respect to x and is written

$$\frac{\partial \mathbf{F}}{\partial x} = \underset{\delta x \to 0}{\mathrm{Lt}} \frac{\delta \mathbf{F}}{\delta x}.$$

Similarly we may define partial derivatives with respect to the other variables.

These derivatives, being themselves functions of the same set of variables, may be again differentiated partially, yielding second order partial derivatives. We denote the derivatives of $\frac{\partial \mathbf{F}}{\partial x}$ with respect to x and y by $\frac{\partial^2 \mathbf{F}}{\partial x^2}$ and $\frac{\partial^2 \mathbf{F}}{\partial x \partial y}$ respectively. Further differentiation leads to derivatives of the third and higher orders.

Suppose next that the values of the variables increase from $x, y, z, \ldots$ to $x + \delta x$, $y + \delta y$, $z + \delta z, \ldots$ The consequent increment $\delta\mathbf{F}$ in the function is given by

$$\delta\mathbf{F} = \mathbf{F}(x + \delta x, y + \delta y, \ldots) - \mathbf{F}(x, y, \ldots),$$

* *Elementary Vector Analysis, with Application to Geometry and Physics*, by the Author (G. Bell & Sons).

which may be written

$$\delta\mathbf{F} = \frac{\mathbf{F}(x+\delta x,\ y+\delta y,\ .\ .\ .) - \mathbf{F}(x,\ y+\delta y,\ .\ .\ .)}{\delta x}\delta x$$
$$+\frac{\mathbf{F}(x,\ y+\delta y,\ z+\delta z,\ .\ .\ .) - \mathbf{F}(x,\ y,\ z+\delta z,\ .\ .\ .)}{\delta y}\delta y$$
$$+\ .\ .\ .$$

If now the increments δx, δy, . . . all tend to the limit zero, so also in general will $\delta\mathbf{F}$; and the coefficients of δx, δy, . . . in the above expression tend to the limiting values *

$$\frac{\partial\mathbf{F}(x,\ y,\ .\ .\ .)}{\partial x},\ \frac{\partial\mathbf{F}(x,\ y,\ .\ .\ .)}{\partial y},\ .\ .\ .$$

Using the notation of *differentials*, let $d\mathbf{F}$, dx, dy, . . . denote small quantities whose quotients are equal to the limiting values of the quotients of $\delta\mathbf{F}$, δx, δy, . . . Then the above equation becomes in the limit

$$d\mathbf{F} = \frac{\partial\mathbf{F}}{\partial x}dx + \frac{\partial\mathbf{F}}{\partial y}dy + \quad .\quad .\quad . \quad (1)$$

the terms of the second member being called the *partial differentials* of the function $\mathbf{F}$ and their sum $d\mathbf{F}$ the *total differential*.

If the variables x, y, . . . were expressed in terms of several new variables, s, t, . . . the function $\mathbf{F}$ would become a function of those variables. Then the partial derivatives of $\mathbf{F}$ with respect to s, t, . . . follow from the equation (1) as in the scalar calculus, their values being given by

$$\frac{\partial\mathbf{F}}{\partial s} = \frac{\partial\mathbf{F}}{\partial x}\frac{\partial x}{\partial s} + \frac{\partial\mathbf{F}}{\partial y}\frac{\partial y}{\partial s} + \quad .\quad .\quad . \quad (2)$$

and similar equations. These are the formulæ for changing from one set of independent variables to another.

2. Scalar and vector point-functions. A quantity which assumes one or more definite values at each point of a region of space is said to be a function of position, or a *point-function* in that region. If it has only one value at each point the function is said to be *uniform* or single-valued. In Physics we meet with both scalar and vector point-functions. As examples of the former may be mentioned the density of a body, its temperature at any instant, and the potential due to a distribution of matter or electricity. Vector point-functions are illustrated by the velocity of a moving fluid at any instant, and the gravitational or electrical intensity of force.

We shall begin by considering *scalar* point-functions, and shall be concerned only with real functions. Denote such a function by

* This introductory Art. is by way of *explanation*, not *proof*.

and its value at the point P by V_P. The function is said to be *continuous* at the point P provided that, corresponding to any positive real number ϵ however small, it is possible to find another η such that $V_Q \sim V_P < \epsilon$ for all points Q within a sphere with centre at P and radius less than η.

If V is a uniform continuous point-function, then through any point P of the region considered we can draw a surface such that at each point on it the function has the same value as at P. Such a surface is called a *level-surface* of the function, or an iso-V. No two level-surfaces corresponding to different values of the function can intersect; for then there would be two different values of the function for each point of intersection, which is contrary to the assumption that the function is uniform. Isothermal surfaces and equipotential surfaces are level-surfaces for the temperature and potential respectively.

A point-function V is a function of the Cartesian coordinates x, y, z of the point, the coordinate axes being not necessarily rectangular. The partial derivative $\dfrac{\partial V}{\partial x}$ gives the rate of increase or *directional derivative* of V along the x-axis; and, as the coordinate axes may be chosen arbitrarily, a similar statement may be made for any direction.

3. Gradient of a scalar point-function. Let V be a uniform point-function which is continuous at P, having there the value V, and at a neighbouring point P' the value $V + \delta V$. Then δV tends to zero with the distance δs from P to P'. The limiting value of the quotient $\delta V/\delta s$, as δs tends to zero, is finite in general, and is called the *directional derivative* of V at P for the direction P to P'.

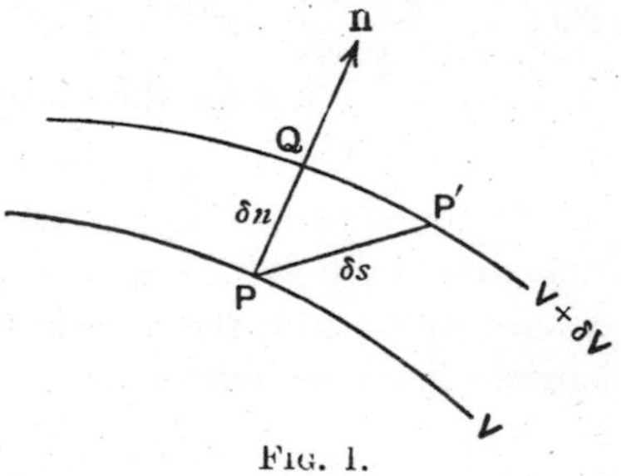

FIG. 1.

It is denoted by $\dfrac{\partial V}{\partial s}$, in which the variable s measures distance* in the direction PP'; and the notation of partial differentiation is employed because V is a function of three such variables as s.

Consider the level-surfaces of the function through P, P' with values V, $V + \delta V$ respectively. Let Q be the point at which the second surface is cut by the normal at P to the first, and let δn be

* After reading Art. 11 the student will see that s may be regarded as one of a system of (curvilinear) coordinates, the coordinate axis of s at the point P being in the limiting direction PP' as $P' \to P$.

the length of PQ. Then the limiting value of $\delta V/\delta n$ as δn tends to zero is the derivative of V in the direction normal to the level-surface at P, and is written $\frac{\partial V}{\partial n}$. This derivative is greater than that for any other direction. For if θ is the angle $P'PQ$ between the normal direction and that originally considered, taking limiting values as the two level-surfaces tend to coincidence, we have

$$\frac{\partial V}{\partial s} = \text{Lt}\,\frac{\delta V}{\delta n}\,\frac{\delta n}{\delta s} = \frac{\partial V}{\partial n}\cos\theta \quad . \quad . \quad . \quad (3)$$

which proves the statement. If then $\mathbf{n}$ is the unit vector normal to the level-surface at P and having the sense P to Q, the vector $\frac{\partial V}{\partial n}\mathbf{n}$ gives both the direction and the magnitude of the maximum rate of increase of the function at P. This vector is called the *gradient* or *slope* of the function V, and is denoted by grad V or ∇V (pronounced *del* V). It is a sort of vector derivative. And from the equation (3) it follows that the directional derivative $\frac{\partial V}{\partial s}$ for any direction is the (scalar) resolute of ∇V in that direction.

From its definition it is clear that the gradient of a scalar point-function is independent of any choice of coordinate axes. But it is frequently convenient to introduce fixed rectangular axes of reference, relative to which x, y, z are the coordinates of a current point. Then $\frac{\partial V}{\partial x}, \frac{\partial V}{\partial y}, \frac{\partial V}{\partial z}$ are the resolutes of ∇V in the directions of these axes; and if $\mathbf{i}, \mathbf{j}, \mathbf{k}$ are the unit vectors in these directions,

$$\nabla V = \frac{\partial V}{\partial x}\mathbf{i} + \frac{\partial V}{\partial y}\mathbf{j} + \frac{\partial V}{\partial z}\mathbf{k} \quad . \quad . \quad . \quad (4)$$

This expression for the gradient, as the vector sum of the rates of change of V along the coordinate axes, is a very useful one. The equation may be written

$$\nabla V = \left(\mathbf{i}\frac{\partial}{\partial x} + \mathbf{j}\frac{\partial}{\partial y} + \mathbf{k}\frac{\partial}{\partial z}\right)V$$

if we interpret the right-hand side according to the distributive law, and regard

$$\nabla \equiv \mathbf{i}\frac{\partial}{\partial x} + \mathbf{j}\frac{\partial}{\partial y} + \mathbf{k}\frac{\partial}{\partial z}$$

as a sort of vector operator, the result of whose operation on a scalar function is a vector.

Further, if $\mathbf{r}$ is the position vector of P and $\mathbf{r} + \delta\mathbf{r}$ that of P', relative to a definite origin O, the increment δV corresponding to the displacement $\delta\mathbf{r}$ may be written

$$\delta V = \frac{\delta V}{\delta n}\delta n = \frac{\delta V}{\delta n}\frac{\delta n}{\delta s}\delta s.$$

If now P' moves to coincidence with P, this relation becomes in the notation of differentials

$$\begin{aligned} dV &= \frac{\partial V}{\partial n}\cos\theta ds = \frac{\partial V}{\partial n}\mathbf{n}\cdot d\mathbf{r} \\ &= d\mathbf{r}\cdot\nabla V \qquad . \quad . \quad . \quad . \quad . \quad . \quad (5) \end{aligned}$$

This result is very useful, and is sometimes employed to define the gradient ∇V. With the ordinary notation

$$\mathbf{r} = x\mathbf{i} + y\mathbf{j} + z\mathbf{k}$$

it is easily seen that (5) is equivalent to

$$dV = \frac{\partial V}{\partial x}dx + \frac{\partial V}{\partial y}dy + \frac{\partial V}{\partial z}dz.$$

4. We have seen that the **directional derivative** of V in the direction of the unit vector $\hat{\mathbf{a}}$ is $\hat{\mathbf{a}}\cdot\nabla V$. If l, m, n are the direction cosines of $\hat{\mathbf{a}}$ relative to the coordinate axes, this may be expanded

$$\begin{aligned} \hat{\mathbf{a}}\cdot\nabla V &= (l\mathbf{i} + m\mathbf{j} + n\mathbf{k})\cdot\left(\frac{\partial V}{\partial x}\mathbf{i} + \frac{\partial V}{\partial y}\mathbf{j} + \frac{\partial V}{\partial z}\mathbf{k}\right) \\ &= l\frac{\partial V}{\partial x} + m\frac{\partial V}{\partial y} + n\frac{\partial V}{\partial z} \qquad . \quad . \quad . \quad . \quad (6) \end{aligned}$$

This may be written

$$\hat{\mathbf{a}}\cdot\nabla V = \left(l\frac{\partial}{\partial x} + m\frac{\partial}{\partial y} + n\frac{\partial}{\partial z}\right)V \quad . \quad . \quad . \quad (6')$$

the operator in brackets being interpreted according to the distributive law. This operator is the formal scalar product of $\hat{\mathbf{a}}$ and ∇, and is frequently written $\hat{\mathbf{a}}\cdot\nabla$. The equation (6′) then becomes

$$\hat{\mathbf{a}}\cdot(\nabla V) = (\hat{\mathbf{a}}\cdot\nabla)V.$$

The brackets are therefore unnecessary, and the expression is written simply $\hat{\mathbf{a}}\cdot\nabla V$. Similarly for any vector $\mathbf{a} = a\hat{\mathbf{a}}$, which may be written

$$\mathbf{a} = a_1\mathbf{i} + a_2\mathbf{j} + a_3\mathbf{k},$$

we have

$$\begin{aligned} \mathbf{a}\cdot\nabla V &= a\hat{\mathbf{a}}\cdot\nabla V \\ &= a\left(l\frac{\partial}{\partial x} + m\frac{\partial}{\partial y} + n\frac{\partial}{\partial z}\right)V \\ &= \left(a_1\frac{\partial}{\partial x} + a_2\frac{\partial}{\partial y} + a_3\frac{\partial}{\partial z}\right)V \\ &= (\mathbf{a}\cdot\nabla)V \qquad . \quad . \quad . \quad . \quad . \quad (6'') \end{aligned}$$

The *gradient of a sum or product* of point-functions is found by the ordinary rules of differentiation. Thus if there are several functions V_1, V_2, . . . the gradient of their sum is

$$\begin{aligned}\nabla\Sigma V &= \mathbf{i}\frac{\partial}{\partial x}\Sigma V + \mathbf{j}\frac{\partial}{\partial y}\Sigma V + \mathbf{k}\frac{\partial}{\partial z}\Sigma V \\ &= \Sigma\mathbf{i}\frac{\partial V}{\partial x} + \Sigma\mathbf{j}\frac{\partial V}{\partial y} + \Sigma\mathbf{k}\frac{\partial V}{\partial z} \\ &= \Sigma\nabla V.\end{aligned}$$

Thus the gradient of the sum of any number of scalar point-functions is equal to the vector sum of their gradients.

Similarly the gradient of the product of two functions U, V is

$$\begin{aligned}\nabla(UV) &= \mathbf{i}\frac{\partial}{\partial x}(UV) + \mathbf{j}\frac{\partial}{\partial y}(UV) + \mathbf{k}\frac{\partial}{\partial z}(UV) \\ &= U\left(\mathbf{i}\frac{\partial V}{\partial x} + \mathbf{j}\frac{\partial V}{\partial y} + \ . \ . \ . \right) + \left(\mathbf{i}\frac{\partial U}{\partial x} + \mathbf{j}\frac{\partial U}{\partial y} + \ . \ . \ . \right)V \\ &= U\nabla V + V\nabla U \qquad . \quad . \quad . \quad . \quad . \quad . \qquad (7)\end{aligned}$$

Thus the gradient of a product of scalar functions is formed according to the same rule as the derivatives of algebraic products. The gradient of a scalar function of the form $\mathbf{F}\cdot\mathbf{G}$, where $\mathbf{F}$ and $\mathbf{G}$ are vector point-functions, will be considered in Art. 8.

The application of the gradient function to physical quantities will be abundantly illustrated in the following pages. It is unnecessary here to anticipate the contents of later chapters by giving examples.

5. Gradient of r^m. As a useful example in the calculation of ∇V consider the function $V \equiv r^m$, where m is a real number, and r the distance of a variable point P from a fixed origin O. The level-surfaces of this function are concentric spheres with centre at O; and the unit normal $\mathbf{n}$ to a level-surface at any point is parallel to the position vector $\mathbf{r}$ of that point relative to O. Thus since $\mathbf{r} = r\hat{\mathbf{r}}$ we have

$$\begin{aligned}\nabla r^m &= \frac{\partial r^m}{\partial n}\mathbf{n} = \frac{\partial r^m}{\partial r}\hat{\mathbf{r}} \\ &= mr^{m-1}\hat{\mathbf{r}} = mr^{m-2}\mathbf{r} \qquad . \quad . \quad . \qquad (8)\end{aligned}$$

For the particular values ± 1 of m,

$$\nabla r = \hat{\mathbf{r}}$$

and

$$\nabla\left(\frac{1}{r}\right) = -\frac{1}{r^2}\hat{\mathbf{r}} = -\frac{1}{r^3}\mathbf{r}.$$

If V is *any* scalar real function of r, the level surfaces are still concentric spheres, and

$$\nabla V = \frac{\partial V}{\partial n}\mathbf{n} = \frac{\partial V}{\partial r}\hat{\mathbf{r}} \quad . \quad . \quad . \quad . \quad (9)$$

6. Vector point-function. Examples of vector point-functions were mentioned in Art. 2; and the gradient of any scalar function is a vector point-function. Any such function $\mathbf{F}$ may be resolved into components parallel to the coordinate axes, and expressed as

$$\mathbf{F} = F_1\mathbf{i} + F_2\mathbf{j} + F_3\mathbf{k}$$

where F_1, F_2, F_3 are scalar point-functions.

The *condition of continuity* of the vector function $\mathbf{F}$ at the point P is that, corresponding to any positive real number ϵ however small, it is possible to find another η such that mod. $(\mathbf{F}_Q - \mathbf{F}_P) < \epsilon$ for all points Q within a sphere with centre at P and radius $< \eta$.

If, for a displacement of length δs in any direction, $\delta\mathbf{F}$ is the corresponding increment in the function, the derivative of $\mathbf{F}$ in this direction is

$$\begin{aligned} \text{Lt}\,\frac{\delta \mathbf{F}}{\delta s} &= \frac{\partial \mathbf{F}}{\partial s} \\ &= \frac{\partial \mathbf{F}}{\partial x}\,\frac{\partial x}{\partial s} + \frac{\partial \mathbf{F}}{\partial y}\,\frac{\partial y}{\partial s} + \frac{\partial \mathbf{F}}{\partial z}\,\frac{\partial z}{\partial s} \end{aligned}$$

by equation (2). If l, m, n are the cosines of the angles which this direction makes with the coordinate axes, and $\hat{\mathbf{a}}$ is the unit vector in this direction, the above expression may be written

$$l\frac{\partial \mathbf{F}}{\partial x} + m\frac{\partial \mathbf{F}}{\partial y} + n\frac{\partial \mathbf{F}}{\partial z} = (\hat{\mathbf{a}}\cdot\nabla)\mathbf{F} \quad . \quad . \quad . \quad (10)$$

Thus $\hat{\mathbf{a}}\cdot\nabla$ operating on either a scalar or a vector point-function gives the *directional derivative* of the function parallel to $\hat{\mathbf{a}}$. There is no need for the brackets in the last equation, for the expression $\hat{\mathbf{a}}\cdot\nabla\mathbf{F}$ can have only one interpretation, no meaning having yet been assigned to $\nabla\mathbf{F}$.

7. Divergence and curl of a vector. From a vector function $\mathbf{F}$ may be derived two other point-functions, the one a scalar and the other a vector, which occupy a very important place in vector analysis. The former of these is called the *divergence* of $\mathbf{F}$ and is denoted by div $\mathbf{F}$. It is defined by the equation

$$\text{div}\,\mathbf{F} = \mathbf{i}\cdot\frac{\partial \mathbf{F}}{\partial x} + \mathbf{j}\cdot\frac{\partial \mathbf{F}}{\partial y} + \mathbf{k}\cdot\frac{\partial \mathbf{F}}{\partial z} \quad . \quad . \quad . \quad (11)$$

The other is called the *curl* or *rotation* of $\mathbf{F}$ and is written briefly curl $\mathbf{F}$ or rot $\mathbf{F}$. It is similarly defined by the equation

$$\text{curl } \mathbf{F} = \mathbf{i}\times\frac{\partial \mathbf{F}}{\partial x} + \mathbf{j}\times\frac{\partial \mathbf{F}}{\partial y} + \mathbf{k}\times\frac{\partial \mathbf{F}}{\partial z} \quad . \quad . \quad . \quad (12)$$

These functions are also denoted by $\nabla\cdot\mathbf{F}$ and $\nabla\times\mathbf{F}$ (pronounced *del dot* **F** and *del cross* **F**) respectively. To justify this notation we have only to expand these formal products according to the distributive law. Then

$$\nabla\cdot\mathbf{F} = \left(\mathbf{i}\frac{\partial}{\partial x} + \mathbf{j}\frac{\partial}{\partial y} + \mathbf{k}\frac{\partial}{\partial z}\right)\cdot\mathbf{F} = \mathbf{i}\cdot\frac{\partial \mathbf{F}}{\partial x} + \mathbf{j}\cdot\frac{\partial \mathbf{F}}{\partial y} + \ldots$$
$$= \text{div } \mathbf{F}$$

and similarly for $\nabla\times\mathbf{F}$.

Express the function $\mathbf{F}$ as the sum of three resolutes

$$\mathbf{F} = F_1\mathbf{i} + F_2\mathbf{j} + F_3\mathbf{k}.$$

Substitution of this form in the above equations gives for the values of the divergence and curl

$$\text{div } \mathbf{F} = \frac{\partial F_1}{\partial x} + \frac{\partial F_2}{\partial y} + \frac{\partial F_3}{\partial z} \quad . \quad . \quad . \quad . \quad . \quad (13)$$

and

$$\text{curl } \mathbf{F} = \left(\frac{\partial F_3}{\partial y} - \frac{\partial F_2}{\partial z}\right)\mathbf{i} + \left(\frac{\partial F_1}{\partial z} - \frac{\partial F_3}{\partial x}\right)\mathbf{j} + \left(\frac{\partial F_2}{\partial x} - \frac{\partial F_1}{\partial y}\right)\mathbf{k} \quad (14)$$

This value of the curl may also be put in the determinantal form

$$\text{curl } \mathbf{F} = \begin{vmatrix} \frac{\partial}{\partial x} & \frac{\partial}{\partial y} & \frac{\partial}{\partial z} \\ F_1 & F_2 & F_3 \\ \mathbf{i} & \mathbf{j} & \mathbf{k} \end{vmatrix} \quad . \quad . \quad . \quad . \quad (14')$$

which is sometimes an aid to memory.

Since the result of the operation of ∇ on a scalar function is invariant with respect to the choice of rectangular axes, we should expect the functions $\nabla\cdot\mathbf{F}$ and $\nabla\times\mathbf{F}$ also to be invariant. That such is the case may be verified by transforming from one set of rectangular axes to any other. We leave this as an exercise for the student.* The invariant property of these functions will be established in the following chapter in connection with the transformation of certain integrals; and it will then be seen how the divergence and curl of a vector function may be defined independently of coordinate axes. The physical meanings of the divergence and curl of certain vector quantities will also appear in subsequent chapters.

It should perhaps be remarked that the operators $\nabla\cdot$ and $\nabla\times$

* *Cf.* Ex. 16 at the end of the present chapter.

applied to the sum of several vector functions $\mathbf{F}_1$, $\mathbf{F}_2$, . ., are distributive. For

$$\begin{aligned}\nabla\cdot\Sigma\mathbf{F} &= \mathbf{i}\cdot\frac{\partial}{\partial x}\Sigma\mathbf{F} + \mathbf{j}\cdot\frac{\partial}{\partial y}\Sigma\mathbf{F} + \mathbf{k}\cdot\frac{\partial}{\partial z}\Sigma\mathbf{F} \\ &= \Sigma\left(\mathbf{i}\cdot\frac{\partial\mathbf{F}}{\partial x} + \mathbf{j}\cdot\frac{\partial\mathbf{F}}{\partial y} + \mathbf{k}\cdot\frac{\partial\mathbf{F}}{\partial z}\right) \\ &= \Sigma\nabla\cdot\mathbf{F},\end{aligned}$$

which proves the statement for this operator; and similarly for the other. Thus the divergence of the sum of several vectors is equal to the sum of their divergences; and a similar statement is true for the curl.

It is also worth noticing that, if

$$\mathbf{r} = x\mathbf{i} + y\mathbf{j} + z\mathbf{k}$$

is the position vector of a variable point with respect to a fixed origin, div $\mathbf{r} = 3$ and curl $\mathbf{r} = 0$.

8. Formulæ of expansion. In our analysis we frequently meet with the curl and divergence of vector functions of the form $u\mathbf{v}$ or $\mathbf{u}\times\mathbf{v}$, where u, $\mathbf{u}$, $\mathbf{v}$ are themselves point-functions, the first a scalar and the other two vectors. It is convenient to know their expansions in terms of the differential functions of u, $\mathbf{u}$, and $\mathbf{v}$. Similarly the gradient of the scalar product $\mathbf{u}\cdot\mathbf{v}$ presents itself. The following formulæ of expansion will be found very useful:

$$\text{div}\,(u\mathbf{v}) = \nabla u\cdot\mathbf{v} + u\,\text{div}\,\mathbf{v} \quad . \quad . \quad . \quad . \quad . \quad (15)$$

$$\text{curl}\,(u\mathbf{v}) = \nabla u\times\mathbf{v} + u\,\text{curl}\,\mathbf{v}. \quad . \quad . \quad . \quad . \quad (16)$$

$$\text{div}\,(\mathbf{u}\times\mathbf{v}) = \mathbf{v}\cdot\,\text{curl}\,\mathbf{u} - \mathbf{u}\cdot\,\text{curl}\,\mathbf{v} \quad . \quad . \quad . \quad . \quad (17)$$

$$\text{curl}\,(\mathbf{u}\times\mathbf{v}) = \mathbf{v}\cdot\nabla\mathbf{u} - \mathbf{u}\cdot\nabla\mathbf{v} + \mathbf{u}\,\text{div}\,\mathbf{v} - \mathbf{v}\,\text{div}\,\mathbf{u} \quad . \quad . \quad (18)$$

$$\text{grad}\,(\mathbf{u}\cdot\mathbf{v}) = \mathbf{v}\cdot\nabla\mathbf{u} + \mathbf{u}\cdot\nabla\mathbf{v} + \mathbf{v}\times\text{curl}\,\mathbf{u} + \mathbf{u}\times\text{curl}\,\mathbf{v} \quad . \quad (19)$$

in which, as explained above, $\mathbf{v}\cdot\nabla\mathbf{u}$ is to be interpreted as $(\mathbf{v}\cdot\nabla)\mathbf{u}$. The proofs of these formulæ are all obtained along the same lines, using the relations

$$\nabla u = \Sigma\mathbf{i}\frac{\partial u}{\partial x}, \quad \text{div}\,\mathbf{u} = \Sigma\mathbf{i}\cdot\frac{\partial\mathbf{u}}{\partial x}, \quad \text{curl}\,\mathbf{u} = \Sigma\mathbf{i}\times\frac{\partial\mathbf{u}}{\partial x}.$$

Take for instance the first formula. We have

$$\begin{aligned}\text{div}\,(u\mathbf{v}) &= \Sigma\mathbf{i}\cdot\frac{\partial}{\partial x}(u\mathbf{v}) \\ &= \Sigma\mathbf{i}\cdot\left(\frac{\partial u}{\partial x}\mathbf{v} + u\frac{\partial\mathbf{v}}{\partial x}\right) \\ &= \left(\Sigma\mathbf{i}\frac{\partial u}{\partial x}\right)\cdot\mathbf{v} + u\left(\Sigma\mathbf{i}\cdot\frac{\partial\mathbf{v}}{\partial x}\right) \\ &= \nabla u\cdot\mathbf{v} + u\,\text{div}\,\mathbf{v},\end{aligned}$$

which proves (15); and (16) may be shown in a similar manner.

In the case of (18) we may proceed :

$$\operatorname{curl}(\mathbf{u}\times\mathbf{v}) = \Sigma\mathbf{i}\times\frac{\partial}{\partial x}(\mathbf{u}\times\mathbf{v})$$
$$= \Sigma\mathbf{i}\times\left(\frac{\partial\mathbf{u}}{\partial x}\times\mathbf{v} + \mathbf{u}\times\frac{\partial\mathbf{v}}{\partial x}\right)$$
$$= \Sigma\left(\mathbf{i}\cdot\mathbf{v}\frac{\partial\mathbf{u}}{\partial x} - \mathbf{i}\cdot\frac{\partial\mathbf{u}}{\partial x}\mathbf{v} + \mathbf{i}\cdot\frac{\partial\mathbf{v}}{\partial x}\mathbf{u} - \mathbf{i}\cdot\mathbf{u}\frac{\partial\mathbf{v}}{\partial x}\right)$$
$$= \mathbf{v}\cdot\nabla\mathbf{u} - \mathbf{v}\operatorname{div}\mathbf{u} + \mathbf{u}\operatorname{div}\mathbf{v} - \mathbf{u}\cdot\nabla\mathbf{v},$$

which is the required result. A similar proof applies to (17).

To demonstrate (19) we write

$$\nabla(\mathbf{u}\cdot\mathbf{v}) = \Sigma\mathbf{i}\,\frac{\partial}{\partial x}(\mathbf{u}\cdot\mathbf{v})$$
$$= \Sigma\mathbf{i}\,\frac{\partial\mathbf{u}}{\partial x}\cdot\mathbf{v} + \Sigma\mathbf{i}\,\mathbf{u}\cdot\frac{\partial\mathbf{v}}{\partial x} \quad . \quad . \quad . \quad \text{i}$$

Again $\mathbf{v}\times\operatorname{curl}\mathbf{u} = \mathbf{v}\times\left(\Sigma\mathbf{i}\times\frac{\partial\mathbf{u}}{\partial x}\right) = \Sigma\mathbf{v}\cdot\frac{\partial\mathbf{u}}{\partial x}\mathbf{i} - \Sigma\mathbf{v}\cdot\mathbf{i}\,\frac{\partial\mathbf{u}}{\partial x}$,

which is equivalent to

$$\Sigma\mathbf{v}\cdot\frac{\partial\mathbf{u}}{\partial x}\mathbf{i} = \mathbf{v}\times\operatorname{curl}\mathbf{u} + \mathbf{v}\cdot\nabla\mathbf{u} \quad . \quad . \quad . \quad \text{ii}$$

Similarly $\Sigma\mathbf{u}\cdot\frac{\partial\mathbf{v}}{\partial x}\mathbf{i} = \mathbf{u}\times\operatorname{curl}\mathbf{v} + \mathbf{u}\cdot\nabla\mathbf{v} \quad . \quad . \quad . \quad \text{iii}$

Substituting in i from ii and iii we obtain the required formula (19).

9. Second order differential functions. If V and $\mathbf{F}$ are point-functions, ∇V, $\nabla\cdot\mathbf{F}$, and $\nabla\times\mathbf{F}$ are also point-functions. The first and third possess divergence and curl, and the second a gradient. Consider then the functions

$$\left.\begin{aligned} \operatorname{div}\operatorname{grad} V &\equiv \nabla\cdot\nabla V \\ \operatorname{curl}\operatorname{grad} V &\equiv \nabla\times\nabla V \\ \operatorname{div}\operatorname{curl}\mathbf{F} &\equiv \nabla\cdot\nabla\times\mathbf{F} \\ \operatorname{curl}\operatorname{curl}\mathbf{F} &\equiv \nabla\times\nabla\times\mathbf{F} \\ \operatorname{grad}\operatorname{div}\mathbf{F} &\equiv \nabla\nabla\cdot\mathbf{F} \end{aligned}\right\} \quad . \quad . \quad . \quad \text{iv}$$

which are independent of coordinate axes, since ∇, $\nabla\cdot$, and $\nabla\times$ are invariant operators. The second and third of these vanish identically. For

$$\operatorname{curl}\operatorname{grad} V = \operatorname{curl}\left(\frac{\partial V}{\partial x}\mathbf{i} + \frac{\partial V}{\partial y}\mathbf{j} + \frac{\partial V}{\partial z}\mathbf{k}\right)$$
$$= \left(\frac{\partial^2 V}{\partial y\partial z} - \frac{\partial^2 V}{\partial z\partial y}\right)\mathbf{i} + \ldots + \ldots = 0,$$

and similarly

$$\operatorname{div}\operatorname{curl}\mathbf{F} = \operatorname{div}\left\{\left(\frac{\partial F_3}{\partial y} - \frac{\partial F_2}{\partial z}\right)\mathbf{i} + \ldots + \ldots\right\}$$
$$= \frac{\partial}{\partial x}\left(\frac{\partial F_3}{\partial y} - \frac{\partial F_2}{\partial z}\right) + \ldots + \ldots = 0.$$

These two identities,

$$\left.\begin{aligned}\text{curl grad } V &\equiv 0\\ \text{div curl } \mathbf{F} &\equiv 0\end{aligned}\right\} \qquad . \quad . \quad . \quad . \quad (20)$$

are very important, and should be remembered. It may help the student to do so if he notices that, when written formally $\nabla\times\nabla V$ and $\nabla\cdot\nabla\times\mathbf{F}$, the first *appears* as a vector product of like vector operators with a scalar coefficient V, while the second has the form of a scalar triple product with a repeated factor. We should therefore expect them to have the value zero. Conversely, it will be proved in the next chapter that a vector function whose curl vanishes identically is the gradient of some scalar function; while one whose divergence vanishes identically is the curl of some vector function.

The first of the functions iv may be expanded

$$\begin{aligned}\text{div grad } V &= \text{div}\left(\frac{\partial V}{\partial x}\mathbf{i} + \frac{\partial V}{\partial y}\mathbf{j} + \frac{\partial V}{\partial z}\mathbf{k}\right)\\ &= \frac{\partial^2 V}{\partial x^2} + \frac{\partial^2 V}{\partial y^2} + \frac{\partial^2 V}{\partial z^2} \qquad . \quad . \quad . \quad (21)\end{aligned}$$

This function, whose symbolic representation is $\nabla\cdot\nabla V$, is generally written $\nabla^2 V$ in harmony with the notation for a scalar product. The operator

$$\nabla^2 \equiv \frac{\partial^2}{\partial x^2} + \frac{\partial^2}{\partial y^2} + \frac{\partial^2}{\partial z^2}$$

is called *Laplace's operator*, and is invariant with respect to rectangular axes. The equation $\nabla^2 V = 0$ is called Laplace's equation, and is of frequent occurrence in mathematical physics. The operator ∇^2 may be applied to a vector function, provided we interpret the result according to the formula

$$\nabla^2\mathbf{F} = \frac{\partial^2\mathbf{F}}{\partial x^2} + \frac{\partial^2\mathbf{F}}{\partial y^2} + \frac{\partial^2\mathbf{F}}{\partial z^2} \qquad . \quad . \quad . \quad (21')$$

for $\nabla\cdot(\nabla\mathbf{F})$ has not yet been given a meaning.

The fourth of the functions iv has an alternative expression which will be found useful. Thus

$$\begin{aligned}\text{curl curl } \mathbf{F} &= \Sigma\mathbf{i}\times\frac{\partial}{\partial x}\left(\mathbf{i}\times\frac{\partial\mathbf{F}}{\partial x} + \mathbf{j}\times\frac{\partial\mathbf{F}}{\partial y} + \mathbf{k}\times\frac{\partial\mathbf{F}}{\partial z}\right)\\ &= \Sigma\frac{\partial}{\partial x}\left(\mathbf{i}\frac{\partial F_1}{\partial x} + \mathbf{j}\frac{\partial F_1}{\partial y} + \mathbf{k}\frac{\partial F_1}{\partial z}\right) - \Sigma\frac{\partial^2\mathbf{F}}{\partial x^2}\\ &= \Sigma\mathbf{i}\frac{\partial}{\partial x}\left(\frac{\partial F_1}{\partial x} + \frac{\partial F_2}{\partial y} + \frac{\partial F_3}{\partial z}\right) - \nabla^2\mathbf{F}\\ &= \text{grad div } \mathbf{F} - \nabla^2\mathbf{F} \qquad . \quad . \quad . \quad . \quad (22)\end{aligned}$$

This formula should be remembered. Written symbolically it is

$$\nabla\times\nabla\times\mathbf{F} = \nabla\nabla\cdot\mathbf{F} - \nabla^2\mathbf{F}.$$

This can be easily remembered by writing down the formal expansion of $\nabla\times(\nabla\times\mathbf{F})$ as a vector triple product.

10. The function r^m. Let $\mathbf{r}$ be the position vector of a current point with respect to a fixed origin, and $r = \text{mod } \mathbf{r}$. Then r^m is a scalar point-function, and by Art. 5

$$\nabla r^m = mr^{m-2}\mathbf{r}.$$

Hence

$$\begin{aligned}\nabla^2 r^m &= \nabla\cdot\nabla r^m = m \text{ div } (r^{m-2}\mathbf{r})\\ &= m(\nabla r^{m-2}\cdot\mathbf{r} + r^{m-2} \text{ div } \mathbf{r})\end{aligned}$$

in virtue of (15). Then since $\text{div } \mathbf{r} = 3$, the equation reduces to

$$\begin{aligned}\nabla^2 r^m &= m\{(m-2)r^{m-4}\mathbf{r}^2 + 3r^{m-2}\}\\ &= m(m+1)r^{m-2} \quad . \quad . \quad . \quad . \quad (23)\end{aligned}$$

This expression vanishes for the values 0 and -1 of m. The former makes r^m merely a constant. Taking the latter value for m, we have

$$\nabla^2\left(\frac{1}{r}\right) = 0,$$

showing that $\frac{1}{r}$ is a solution of Laplace's equation.

More generally, if u is a scalar function of r, and u', u'' denote its first and second derivatives with respect to r, then by Art. 5

$$\begin{aligned}\nabla^2 u &= \text{div } (u'\hat{\mathbf{r}}) = \text{div } \left(\frac{u'}{r}\mathbf{r}\right)\\ &= \nabla\left(\frac{u'}{r}\right)\cdot\mathbf{r} + \frac{3u'}{r} \text{ by (15)}\\ &= \left(\frac{u''}{r} - \frac{u'}{r^2}\right)\hat{\mathbf{r}}\cdot\mathbf{r} + \frac{3u'}{r}\\ &= u'' + \frac{2u'}{r} \quad . \quad . \quad . \quad . \quad . \quad (24)\end{aligned}$$

11. Orthogonal curvilinear coordinates. Consider three uniform point-functions u, v, w. Each of these has a level-surface passing through an arbitrary point P. Let the functions be such that these three level-surfaces do not coincide or intersect in a common curve. Then the values of u, v, w on these surfaces determine the point P, and may be considered as coordinates of P. The three surfaces are called the coordinate surfaces through P, their three lines of intersection the coordinate lines, and the tangents at P to the coordinate lines are the coordinate axes. The directions of the axes vary from point to point. A great simplification is introduced by choosing coordinates u, v, w such that at every point the coordinate axes are mutually perpendicular. The functions are then said to constitute an orthogonal system of curvilinear coordinates.

Take as the positive directions of the orthogonal coordinate axes of u, v, w at P those forming a right-handed system, and let **a**, **b**, **c** be *unit* vectors in these directions. These of course are not constant vectors, as their directions vary from point to point. Consider also the neighbouring level-surfaces corresponding to the values $u + du$, $v + dv$, $w + dw$. These, with the coordinate surfaces at P, bound an infinitesimal curvilinear figure $PAFBDCEP'$, the lengths of whose edges are

$$PA = h_1 du$$
$$PB = h_2 dv$$
$$PC = h_3 dw$$

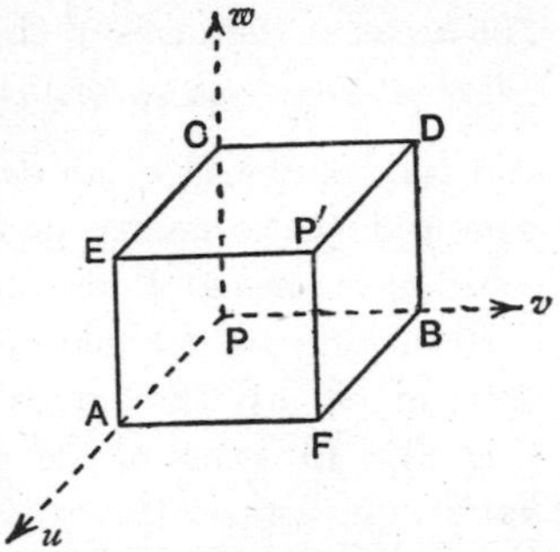

FIG. 2.

where the parameters h_1, h_2, h_3 are functions of u, v, w. The areas of the faces of the figure are $h_2 h_3 dv dw$, $h_3 h_1 dw du$, $h_1 h_2 du dv$, and its volume is $h_1 h_2 h_3 du dv dw$.

As an example of such a system may be mentioned the spherical polar coordinates r, θ, ϕ of a point P. These are its distance OP from a fixed point O, the angle of inclination θ of OP to a fixed direction OZ, and the angle ϕ which the meridian plane POZ makes with a fixed meridian plane XOZ. The level-surfaces of r are concentric spheres with centre O; those of θ are right circular cones with OZ as axis; and those of ϕ are meridian planes through OZ. These intersect in orthogonal lines, the coordinate lines through P being the radial line OP, the meridian circle through P, and the parallel of latitude through the point.

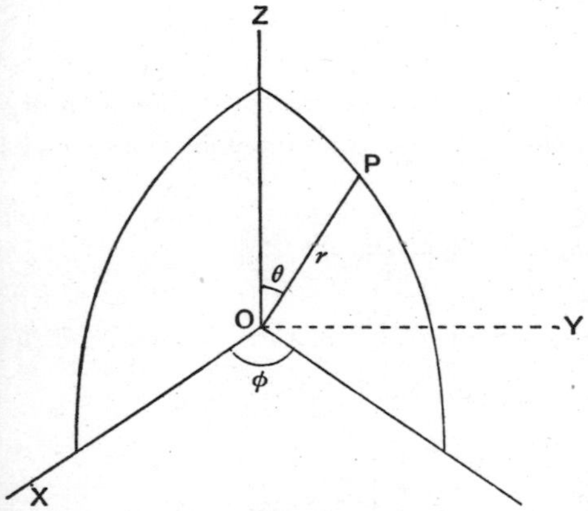

FIG. 3.

We take as positive directions for the axes through P those corresponding to r, θ, ϕ increasing; and these form a right-handed system. The level-surfaces for the values $r + dr$, $\theta + d\theta$, $\phi + d\phi$, and the coordinate surfaces through P bound a curvilinear figure, the lengths of whose edges are

$$dr, \quad rd\theta, \quad r \sin \theta \, d\phi.$$

Hence for this system the parameters have the values

$$h_1 = 1, \quad h_2 = r, \quad h_3 = r \sin \theta.$$

The areas of the faces of the infinitesimal curvilinear figures are

$$r^2 \sin \theta \, d\theta d\phi, \quad r \sin \theta \, drd\phi, \quad rdrd\theta,$$

and its volume is $r^2 \sin \theta drd\theta d\phi$. If Z be regarded as the North pole and O the centre of the earth, the positive directions of the coordinate axes at P are up, South and East.

Returning to the general case, consider the elementary vectors determined by the edges of the infinitesimal curvilinear figure (Fig. 2). In terms of the unit vectors **a**, **b**, **c** introduced above, we have

$$\overrightarrow{PA} = h_1 du \, \mathbf{a}$$

$$\overrightarrow{BF} = h_1 du \, \mathbf{a} + \frac{\partial}{\partial v}(h_1 du \, \mathbf{a}) dv,$$

while

$$\overrightarrow{PB} = h_2 dv \, \mathbf{b}$$

$$\overrightarrow{AF} = h_2 dv \, \mathbf{b} + \frac{\partial}{\partial u}(h_2 dv \, \mathbf{b}) du.$$

Then since the sum of the vectors determined by the sides of the closed figure $PAFBP$ is zero, we have the relation

$$\frac{\partial}{\partial u}(h_2 \mathbf{b}) = \frac{\partial}{\partial v}(h_1 \mathbf{a}) \quad . \quad . \quad . \quad . \quad \text{i}$$

while two similar relations may be written down by cyclic permutation of the symbols. Form the scalar product of each member with the vector **b**. Then

$$\mathbf{b} \cdot \left(\frac{\partial h_2}{\partial u} \mathbf{b} + h_2 \frac{\partial \mathbf{b}}{\partial u} \right) = \mathbf{b} \cdot \left(\frac{\partial h_1}{\partial v} \mathbf{a} + h_1 \frac{\partial \mathbf{a}}{\partial v} \right).$$

But $\mathbf{b} \cdot \frac{\partial \mathbf{b}}{\partial u}$ is zero because **b** is a vector of constant length, and $\mathbf{b} \cdot \mathbf{a}$ is zero because the axes are orthogonal. Hence the relation

$$\frac{\partial h_2}{\partial u} = h_1 \mathbf{b} \cdot \frac{\partial \mathbf{a}}{\partial v}$$

and similarly

$$\frac{\partial h_3}{\partial u} = h_1 \mathbf{c} \cdot \frac{\partial \mathbf{a}}{\partial w} \quad . \quad . \quad . \quad . \quad \text{ii}$$

Four similar equations may be written down by cyclic permutation of the variables.

12. Curvilinear expressions for grad, div, curl, and ∇^2. Since the functions obtained by operating with ∇, $\nabla\cdot$, $\nabla\times$, and ∇^2 are independent of coordinate axes, we may take the axes of x, y, z as coincident with the axes of the curvilinear coordinates at P. By doing so we make at this point

$$dx = h_1 du, \quad dy = h_2 dv, \quad dz = h_3 dw,$$

and if V is a scalar point-function,

$$\frac{\partial V}{\partial x} = \frac{1}{h_1}\frac{\partial V}{\partial u}, \quad \frac{\partial V}{\partial y} = \frac{1}{h_2}\frac{\partial V}{\partial v}, \quad \frac{\partial V}{\partial z} = \frac{1}{h_3}\frac{\partial V}{\partial w}.$$

Therefore, since **i**, **j**, **k** now coincide with the unit vectors **a**, **b**, **c** for the point P, we have

$$\begin{aligned} \nabla V &= \mathbf{i}\frac{\partial V}{\partial x} + \mathbf{j}\frac{\partial V}{\partial y} + \mathbf{k}\frac{\partial V}{\partial z} \\ &= \frac{\mathbf{a}}{h_1}\frac{\partial V}{\partial u} + \frac{\mathbf{b}}{h_2}\frac{\partial V}{\partial v} + \frac{\mathbf{c}}{h_3}\frac{\partial V}{\partial w} \quad . \quad . \quad . \quad (25) \end{aligned}$$

which is the required expression for ∇V in curvilinear coordinates. The coefficients of **a**, **b**, **c** are the rates of increase of V in the directions of the coordinate axes. The *directional derivative* of V in the direction of the unit vector

$$\mathbf{A} = A_1\mathbf{a} + A_2\mathbf{b} + A_3\mathbf{c}$$

is

$$\mathbf{A}\cdot\nabla V = \frac{A_1}{h_1}\frac{\partial V}{du} + \frac{A_2}{h_2}\frac{\partial V}{\partial v} + \frac{A_3}{h_3}\frac{\partial V}{\partial w} \quad . \quad . \quad (25')$$

The curvilinear expression for the divergence of the point-function $\mathbf{F} = F_1\mathbf{a} + F_2\mathbf{b} + F_3\mathbf{c}$ may be found thus:

$$\begin{aligned} \operatorname{div}\mathbf{F} &= \mathbf{i}\cdot\frac{\partial\mathbf{F}}{\partial x} + \mathbf{j}\cdot\frac{\partial\mathbf{F}}{\partial y} + \mathbf{k}\cdot\frac{\partial\mathbf{F}}{\partial z} \\ &= \frac{\mathbf{a}}{h_1}\cdot\frac{\partial}{\partial u}(F_1\mathbf{a} + F_2\mathbf{b} + F_3\mathbf{c}) + \frac{\mathbf{b}}{h_2}\cdot\frac{\partial}{\partial v}(F_1\mathbf{a} + \ldots + \ldots) + \ldots \end{aligned}$$

Remembering that $\mathbf{a}\cdot\frac{\partial\mathbf{a}}{\partial u}$ is zero, and that **a**, **b**, **c** are orthogonal, we find for the terms involving F_1

$$\frac{1}{h_1}\frac{\partial F_1}{\partial u} + \frac{F_1}{h_2}\mathbf{b}\cdot\frac{\partial\mathbf{a}}{\partial v} + \frac{F_1}{h_3}\mathbf{c}\cdot\frac{\partial\mathbf{a}}{\partial w},$$

which, in virtue of ii, may be written

$$\begin{aligned} &\frac{1}{h_1}\frac{\partial F_1}{\partial u} + \frac{F_1}{h_1h_2}\frac{\partial h_2}{\partial u} + \frac{F_1}{h_1h_3}\frac{\partial h_3}{\partial u} \\ &= \frac{1}{h_1h_2h_3}\frac{\partial}{\partial u}(h_2h_3F_1). \end{aligned}$$

The terms in F_2 and F_3 may be written down by symmetry, leading to the result

$$\operatorname{div} \mathbf{F} = \frac{1}{h_1 h_2 h_3}\left[\frac{\partial}{\partial u}(h_2 h_3 F_1) + \frac{\partial}{\partial v}(h_3 h_1 F_2) + \frac{\partial}{\partial w}(h_1 h_2 F_3)\right] \quad (26)$$

To find the expression for $\nabla^2 V$ we have only to combine the results (25) and (26). Thus

$$\nabla^2 V = \nabla\cdot\nabla V = \operatorname{div}\left(\frac{\mathbf{a}}{h_1}\frac{\partial V}{\partial u} + \frac{\mathbf{b}}{h_2}\frac{\partial V}{\partial v} + \frac{\mathbf{c}}{h_3}\frac{\partial V}{\partial w}\right)$$

$$= \frac{1}{h_1 h_2 h_3}\left[\frac{\partial}{\partial u}\left(\frac{h_2 h_3}{h_1}\frac{\partial V}{\partial u}\right) + \frac{\partial}{\partial v}\left(\frac{h_3 h_1}{h_2}\frac{\partial V}{\partial v}\right) + \frac{\partial}{\partial w}\left(\frac{h_1 h_2}{h_3}\frac{\partial V}{\partial w}\right)\right] \quad (27)$$

Similarly the curvilinear expression for curl **F** may be found from the formula

$$\operatorname{curl} \mathbf{F} = \Sigma\frac{\mathbf{a}}{h_1}\times\frac{\partial}{\partial u}(F_1\mathbf{a} + F_2\mathbf{b} + F_3\mathbf{c}),$$

leading to the result

$$\operatorname{curl} \mathbf{F} = \frac{\mathbf{a}}{h_2 h_3}\left\{\frac{\partial}{\partial v}(h_3 F_3) - \frac{\partial}{\partial w}(h_2 F_2)\right\}$$
$$+ \frac{\mathbf{b}}{h_3 h_1}\left\{\frac{\partial}{\partial w}(h_1 F_1) - \frac{\partial}{\partial u}(h_3 F_3)\right\} + \quad . \quad . \quad (28)$$

We shall not give the details of the transformation, as both formulæ (26) and (28) are most easily obtained, as in the following chapter, from the values of certain definite integrals.

EXERCISES ON CHAPTER I.

1. If **r** and r have their usual meanings, show that

$$\operatorname{div} \mathbf{r} = 3, \qquad \operatorname{curl} \mathbf{r} = 0,$$
$$\operatorname{div} r^n\mathbf{r} = (n+3)r^n, \qquad \operatorname{curl} r^n\mathbf{r} = 0.$$

2. If **a** is a constant vector,

$$\nabla(\mathbf{a}\cdot\mathbf{u}) = \mathbf{a}\cdot\nabla\mathbf{u} + \mathbf{a}\times\operatorname{curl}\mathbf{u}$$
$$\nabla\cdot(\mathbf{a}\times\mathbf{u}) = -\mathbf{a}\cdot\operatorname{curl}\mathbf{u}$$
$$\nabla\times(\mathbf{a}\times\mathbf{u}) = \mathbf{a}\operatorname{div}\mathbf{u} - \mathbf{a}\cdot\nabla\mathbf{u}.$$

3. Show that

$$\mathbf{u}\cdot\nabla\mathbf{r} = \mathbf{u},$$

and that if **a** is constant,

$$\nabla(\mathbf{a}\cdot\mathbf{r}) = \mathbf{a}, \quad \nabla\cdot(\mathbf{a}\times\mathbf{r}) = 0,$$
$$\nabla\times(\mathbf{a}\times\mathbf{r}) = 2\mathbf{a}.$$

4. Prove that

$$\mathbf{v}\cdot\nabla\mathbf{v} = \tfrac{1}{2}\nabla\mathbf{v}^2 - \mathbf{v}\times\operatorname{curl}\mathbf{v}.$$

5. If **v** is the velocity of a particle of a rigid body whose angular velocity is **A**, show that

$$\operatorname{curl}\mathbf{v} = 2\mathbf{A}.$$

6. Given that

$$\rho \mathbf{F} = \nabla p$$

where ρ, p, $\mathbf{F}$ are point-functions, prove that

$$\mathbf{F} \cdot \text{curl}\, \mathbf{F} = 0.$$

7. Prove that

$$f(u)\nabla u = \nabla \int f(u)du.$$

8. If $f = f(u, v, \ldots)$ is a function of several point-functions, show that

$$\nabla f = \frac{\partial f}{\partial u}\nabla u + \frac{\partial f}{\partial v}\nabla v + \ldots$$

9. Prove that $\mathbf{a}\cdot\{\nabla(\mathbf{v}\cdot\mathbf{a}) - \nabla\times(\mathbf{v}\times\mathbf{a})\} = \text{div}\, \mathbf{v}$

where $\mathbf{a}$ is a constant *unit* vector.

10. If $\mathbf{v} = v_1\mathbf{i} + v_2\mathbf{j} + v_3\mathbf{k}$, show that

$$\nabla\cdot\mathbf{v} = \nabla v_1\cdot\mathbf{i} + \nabla v_2\cdot\mathbf{j} + \nabla v_3\cdot\mathbf{k}$$
$$\nabla\times\mathbf{v} = \nabla v_1\times\mathbf{i} + \nabla v_2\times\mathbf{j} + \nabla v_3\times\mathbf{k}.$$

11. By means of formula (7) show that, if $\mathbf{a}$, $\mathbf{b}$, $\mathbf{c}$ are constant,

$$\nabla(\mathbf{a}\cdot\mathbf{r}\ \mathbf{b}\cdot\mathbf{r}\ \mathbf{c}\cdot\mathbf{r}) = \mathbf{b}\cdot\mathbf{r}\ \mathbf{c}\cdot\mathbf{r}\ \mathbf{a} + \mathbf{a}\cdot\mathbf{r}\ \mathbf{c}\cdot\mathbf{r}\ \mathbf{b} + \mathbf{a}\cdot\mathbf{r}\ \mathbf{b}\cdot\mathbf{r}\ \mathbf{c}.$$

12. Prove that $\mathbf{a}\cdot\nabla\left(\mathbf{b}\cdot\nabla\frac{1}{r}\right) = \frac{3\mathbf{a}\cdot\mathbf{r}\ \mathbf{b}\cdot\mathbf{r}}{r^5} - \frac{\mathbf{a}\cdot\mathbf{b}}{r^3}$

where $\mathbf{a}$ and $\mathbf{b}$ are constant.

13. If $\mathbf{F}$ is a solenoidal vector (*i.e.* one whose divergence vanishes identically), show that

$$\text{curl curl curl curl}\, \mathbf{F} = \nabla^2\nabla^2\mathbf{F} = \nabla^4\mathbf{F}.$$

14. If $\mathbf{F}$ and f are point-functions, prove that the components of the former tangential and normal to the level-surface $f = 0$ are

$$\frac{\nabla f\times(\mathbf{F}\times\nabla f)}{(\nabla f)^2} \quad \text{and} \quad \frac{(\mathbf{F}\cdot\nabla f)\nabla f}{(\nabla f)^2}.$$

15. From the equations

$$\text{div}\, \mathbf{D} = \rho, \qquad \text{div}\, \mathbf{H} = 0,$$
$$\text{curl}\, \mathbf{H} = \frac{1}{c}\left(\frac{\partial \mathbf{D}}{\partial t} + \rho\mathbf{v}\right), \quad \text{curl}\, \mathbf{D} = -\frac{1}{c}\frac{\partial \mathbf{H}}{\partial t},$$

in which t is the time variable, c a constant, and the other symbols denote point-functions, prove that

$$\nabla^2\mathbf{D} - \frac{1}{c^2}\frac{\partial^2\mathbf{D}}{\partial t^2} = \nabla\rho + \frac{1}{c^2}\frac{\partial}{\partial t}(\rho\mathbf{v})$$
$$\nabla^2\mathbf{H} - \frac{1}{c^2}\frac{\partial^2\mathbf{H}}{\partial t^2} = -\frac{1}{c}\,\text{curl}\,(\rho\mathbf{v}).$$

16. Prove that the values of div $\mathbf{F}$ and curl $\mathbf{F}$ are independent of the choice of rectangular axes.

If the mutual direction cosines of two sets of axes are those in the table, and (x, y, z), (x', y', z') are the corresponding coordinates,

	$\mathbf{i}$	$\mathbf{j}$	$\mathbf{k}$
$\mathbf{i}'$	l_1	m_1	n_1
$\mathbf{j}'$	l_2	m_2	n_2
$\mathbf{k}'$	l_3	m_3	n_3

$$\mathbf{i}' = l_1\mathbf{i} + m_1\mathbf{j} + n_1\mathbf{k},$$
$$x' = l_1x + m_1y + n_1z, \text{ etc.}$$

and
$$\Sigma\mathbf{i}'\cdot\frac{\partial\mathbf{F}}{\partial x'} = \Sigma(l_1\mathbf{i} + m_1\mathbf{j} + n_1\mathbf{k})\cdot\left(l_1\frac{\partial\mathbf{F}}{\partial x} + m_1\frac{\partial\mathbf{F}}{\partial y} + n_1\frac{\partial\mathbf{F}}{\partial z}\right)$$
$$= \Sigma\mathbf{i}\cdot\frac{\partial\mathbf{F}}{\partial x}.$$

Similarly
$$\Sigma\mathbf{i}'\times\frac{\partial\mathbf{F}}{\partial x'} = \Sigma\mathbf{i}\times\frac{\partial\mathbf{F}}{\partial x},$$

which proves the invariance of the functions.

17. In curvilinear coordinates the expression for curl $\mathbf{F}$ may be written

$$\text{curl } \mathbf{F} = \begin{vmatrix} \dfrac{\mathbf{a}}{h_2h_3} & \dfrac{\mathbf{b}}{h_3h_1} & \dfrac{\mathbf{c}}{h_1h_2} \\ \dfrac{\partial}{\partial u} & \dfrac{\partial}{\partial v} & \dfrac{\partial}{\partial w} \\ h_1F_1 & h_2F_2 & h_3F_3 \end{vmatrix}$$

18. From the formulæ (25)–(28) deduce that in terms of spherical polar coordinates, for which $h_1 = 1$, $h_2 = r$, $h_3 = r \sin\theta$,

$$\nabla V = \mathbf{a}\frac{\partial V}{\partial r} + \frac{\mathbf{b}}{r}\frac{\partial V}{\partial \theta} + \frac{\mathbf{c}}{r\sin\theta}\frac{\partial V}{\partial\phi}$$
$$\nabla\cdot\mathbf{F} = \frac{1}{r^2}\frac{\partial}{\partial r}(r^2F_1) + \frac{1}{r\sin\theta}\frac{\partial}{\partial\theta}(\sin\theta F_2) + \frac{1}{r\sin\theta}\frac{\partial F_3}{\partial\phi}$$
$$\nabla^2 V = \frac{1}{r^2}\frac{\partial}{\partial r}\left(r^2\frac{\partial V}{\partial r}\right) + \frac{1}{r^2\sin\theta}\frac{\partial}{\partial\theta}\left(\sin\theta\frac{\partial V}{\partial\theta}\right) + \frac{1}{r^2\sin^2\theta}\frac{\partial^2 V}{\partial\phi^2}$$
$$\nabla\times\mathbf{F} = \frac{\mathbf{a}}{r\sin\theta}\left\{\frac{\partial}{\partial\theta}(F_3\sin\theta) - \frac{\partial F_2}{\partial\phi}\right\} + \frac{\mathbf{b}}{r}\left\{\frac{1}{\sin\theta}\frac{\partial F_1}{\partial\phi} - \frac{\partial}{\partial r}(rF_3)\right\}$$
$$+ \frac{\mathbf{c}}{r}\left\{\frac{\partial}{\partial r}(rF_2) - \frac{\partial F_1}{\partial\theta}\right\}.$$

19. In the case of cylindrical (*i.e.* semi-polar) coordinates r, ϕ, z show that $h_1 = 1$, $h_2 = r$, $h_3 = 1$, and that

$$\nabla V = \mathbf{a}\frac{\partial V}{\partial r} + \frac{\mathbf{b}}{r}\frac{\partial V}{\partial\phi} + \mathbf{c}\frac{\partial V}{\partial z}$$
$$\nabla\cdot\mathbf{F} = \frac{1}{r}\frac{\partial}{\partial r}(rF_1) + \frac{1}{r}\frac{\partial F_2}{\partial\phi} + \frac{\partial F_3}{\partial z}$$
$$\nabla^2 V = \frac{1}{r}\frac{\partial}{\partial r}\left(r\frac{\partial V}{\partial r}\right) + \frac{1}{r^2}\frac{\partial^2 V}{\partial\phi^2} + \frac{\partial^2 V}{\partial z^2}$$
$$\nabla\times\mathbf{F} = \mathbf{a}\left\{\frac{1}{r}\frac{\partial F_3}{\partial\phi} - \frac{\partial F_2}{\partial z}\right\} + \mathbf{b}\left\{\frac{\partial F_1}{\partial z} - \frac{\partial F_3}{\partial r}\right\}$$
$$+ \mathbf{c}\left\{\frac{\partial F_2}{\partial r} - \frac{1}{r}\frac{\partial F_1}{\partial\phi}\right\}$$

CHAPTER II.

LINE, SURFACE, AND SPACE INTEGRALS.

13. Tangential line integral of ∇V. The tangential line integral of a vector function **F** along a curve C from A to B is * the definite integral of the scalar resolute of **F** in the direction of the tangent to the curve, the variable of integration being the arc-length s of the curve measured from a fixed point in the sense A to B, and the limits of integration being the values of s corresponding to the points A and B. If **t** is the unit tangent at the point P, and **F** the value of the function there, the integral has the value

$$\int_A^B \mathbf{F}\cdot\mathbf{t}ds = \int_A^B \mathbf{F}\cdot d\mathbf{r}$$

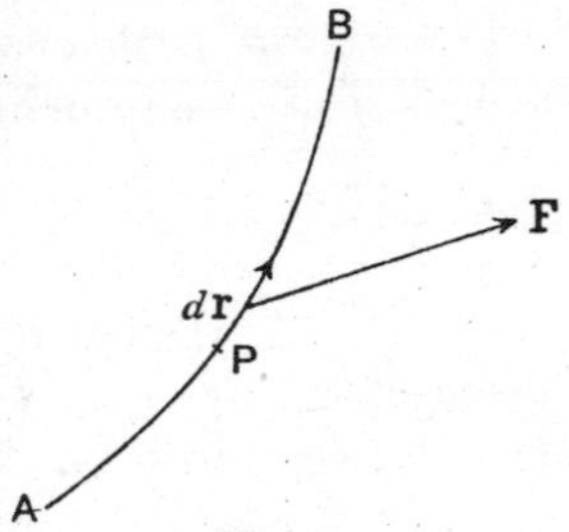

FIG. 4.

where $d\mathbf{r}$ is the infinitesimal vector $\mathbf{t}ds$ determined by the element of arc at P. It is clear that the line integral from A to B is the negative of that from B to A. For in changing from one to the other the sign of every elementary vector $d\mathbf{r}$ is reversed. Thus

$$\int_A^B \mathbf{F}\cdot d\mathbf{r} = -\int_B^A \mathbf{F}\cdot d\mathbf{r}.$$

Suppose now that the function **F** is the gradient of a scalar point-function V. Then

$$\int_A^B \mathbf{F}\cdot d\mathbf{r} = \int_A^B \nabla V\cdot d\mathbf{r} = \int_A^B dV$$

by formula (5) of the previous chapter. The last integral is equal to $V_B - V_A$, where the suffix denotes the point for which the value of V is to be taken. Hence the result

$$\int_A^B \nabla V\cdot d\mathbf{r} = V_B - V_A \qquad (1)$$

* Cf. *Elem. Vector Anal.*, Art.

If the function V is single-valued, and the integral is taken round a closed curve, the initial and final points coincide, and $V_B = V_A$ because the function is uniform. When the path of integration is a closed curve, we denote the fact by a small circle at the foot of the integral sign. Thus for a uniform function

$$\int_0 \nabla V \cdot d\mathbf{r} = 0 \quad . \quad . \quad . \quad . \quad (1')$$

Conversely, if the tangential line integral of $\mathbf{F}$ vanishes for *every* closed curve, $\mathbf{F}$ is the gradient of some scalar function V. Consider any closed curve $APRQ$. Since the integral taken right round it is zero, the integral along APR must be equal to that along AQR, and similarly to that along any curve joining A and R. Let A be a fixed point and R a variable one. Then the value of the tangential line integral from A to R, being independent of the path chosen, is a scalar point-function which we may denote by V; or

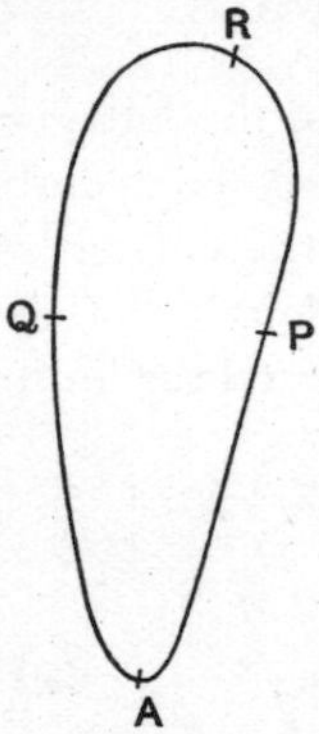

FIG. 5.

$$\int_A^R \mathbf{F} \cdot d\mathbf{r} = V.$$

Hence if dV is the increment in V due to a small displacement $d\mathbf{r}$ of R, $dV = \mathbf{F} \cdot d\mathbf{r}$. But we have already seen that $dV = \nabla V \cdot d\mathbf{r}$; so that

$$\mathbf{F} \cdot d\mathbf{r} = \nabla V \cdot d\mathbf{r}$$

for all values of $d\mathbf{r}$. Hence the result

$$\mathbf{F} = \nabla V$$

as stated above.

14. Gauss's Divergence Theorem. Consider the region bounded by a closed surface, or by an outer surface and one or more inner surfaces, the latter being enclosed by the former. In either case we shall denote the complete bounding surface by S. Let $\mathbf{n}$ be the unit normal at a point of the boundary, directed always *outward* from the region. Consider also a vector point-function $\mathbf{F}$ which, together with its derivative in any direction, is uniform, finite and continuous. The normal surface integral of $\mathbf{F}$ over the boundary is * the surface integral of the scalar resolute of $\mathbf{F}$ in the direction of the normal. We write it †

$$\int \mathbf{F} \cdot \mathbf{n} dS = \int \mathbf{F} \cdot d\mathbf{S}$$

* Cf. *Elem. Vector Anal.*, Art. 64.

† We shall use only one integral sign for surface and space integrals, the variable of integration, S or v, being sufficient to indicate its nature.

where dS is the area of an element of the bounding surface, and $d\mathbf{S} = \mathbf{n}dS$ the vector area * of the element.

There is a very important theorem, due to Gauss, which states that *the normal surface integral of the function* **F** *over the boundary of a closed region is equal to the space integral of the divergence of* **F** *taken throughout the enclosed space.* If dv is the volume of an element of the region, we may express the theorem by the equation

$$\int \mathbf{F}\cdot\mathbf{n}dS = \int \text{div } \mathbf{F}\, dv \quad . \quad . \quad . \quad . \quad (2)$$

It is commonly called Gauss's *Divergence Theorem,* and it should be remembered by the student, as its applications are very numerous.

To prove the theorem, take rectangular coordinate axes parallel to the unit vectors **i**, **j**, **k**, and let

$$\mathbf{F} = U\mathbf{i} + V\mathbf{j} + W\mathbf{k}$$

where U, V, W and their derivatives in any direction are assumed to be uniform, finite and continuous. Consider the volume integral

$$I = \iiint \frac{\partial U}{\partial x} dxdydz \quad . \quad . \quad . \quad \text{i}$$

where we have written $dxdydz$ for the volume element dv. For fixed values of y, z take the rectangular prism parallel to the x axis, bounded by the planes y, $y + dy$, z, $z + dz$, the area of its normal section being $dydz$. Such a prism cuts the boundary an even

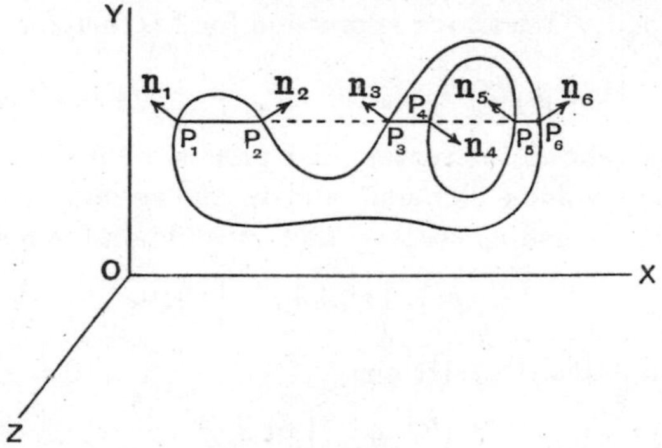

FIG. 6.

number of times at the points P_1, P_2, . . ., P_{2n}, since the bounding surface is closed. If a point moves along the prism in the direction of x increasing, it enters the region at P_1, P_3, . . . , P_{2n-1} and leaves it at P_2, P_4, . . . , P_{2n}.

Taking then the integral I and integrating with respect to x (*i.e.* summing for all the volume elements in the above prism), we

* Cf. *Elem. Vector Anal.*, Art. 23.

have

$$I = \iint(-U_1 + U_2 - U_3 + \ \ldots \ - U_{2n-1} + U_{2n})dydz$$

where U_r is the value of U at the point P_r. Let dS_r be the area of the element of the boundary intercepted by the prism at the point

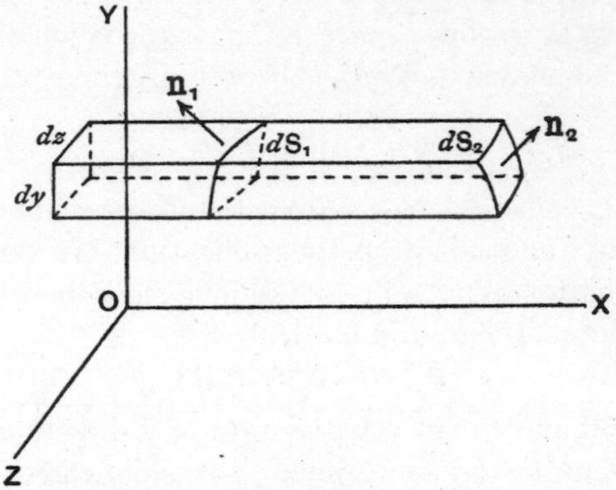

FIG. 7.

P_r. Then, since $dydz$ is the area of the projection of this element on the YZ plane, we have

$$dydz = -\,\mathbf{i}\cdot\mathbf{n}_r dS_r, \text{ for } r \text{ odd,}$$
$$= \ \mathbf{i}\cdot\mathbf{n}_r dS_r, \text{ for } r \text{ even,}$$

because the angle $\mathbf{n}_r$ makes with $\mathbf{i}$ is acute or obtuse according as r is even or odd. The above expression for I is therefore equivalent to

$$I = \int \mathbf{i}\cdot(U_1\mathbf{n}_1 dS_1 + U_2\mathbf{n}_2 dS_2 + \ \ldots \ + U_{2n}\mathbf{n}_{2n} dS_{2n}).$$

Summing then for all the rectangular prisms, we include in the first member every volume element, and in the second member every element of the bounding surface, and thus obtain the result *

$$\int \frac{\partial U}{\partial x} dv = \int U\mathbf{i}\cdot\mathbf{n} dS = \int U\mathbf{i}\cdot d\mathbf{S} \quad . \quad . \quad . \quad (3)$$

Similarly we prove the relations

$$\int \frac{\partial V}{\partial y} dv = \int V\mathbf{j}\cdot\mathbf{n} dS \quad . \quad . \quad . \quad . \quad (3')$$

$$\int \frac{\partial W}{\partial z} dv = \int W\mathbf{k}\cdot\mathbf{n} dS \quad . \quad . \quad . \quad (3'')$$

and from these three results by addition we have

$$\int \left(\frac{\partial U}{\partial x} + \frac{\partial V}{\partial y} + \frac{\partial W}{\partial z}\right) dv = \int (U\mathbf{i} + V\mathbf{j} + W\mathbf{k})\cdot\mathbf{n} dS,$$

* The argument leading from i to (3) is equally true of a vector function **U**. Hence another proof of (2) may be obtained. *Cf.* Art. 87.

which is identical with the equation (2) as required. Gauss's divergence theorem is thus established.

If we apply the theorem to an infinitesimal closed surface, and the enclosed element of space whose volume is dv, we obtain

$$\text{div } \mathbf{F}dv = \int \mathbf{F}\cdot\mathbf{n}dS$$

or

$$\text{div } \mathbf{F} = \frac{1}{dv}\int \mathbf{F}\cdot\mathbf{n}dS \quad . \quad . \quad . \quad (4)$$

That is to say, the divergence of a vector function is the limit to which the average value of the normal surface integral, per unit of enclosed volume, tends as the bounding surface converges to a point. Since this is independent of coordinate axes, it follows that the function div $\mathbf{F}$ is *invariant*, as stated in the preceding chapter. The equation (4) is sometimes used to define the divergence of a vector; and the original definition may be deduced from this, as in Art. 18 below.

15. Theorems deducible from the Divergence Theorem. We may mention here two other theorems easily deducible from the above. These are not of the same importance as Gauss's theorem, but they will be found useful. In the equations (3), (3′), (3″) put $U = W = V$. Then on multiplying * the equations by $\mathbf{i}$, $\mathbf{j}$, $\mathbf{k}$ respectively, and adding, we have

$$\int\left(\frac{\partial V}{\partial x}\mathbf{i} + \frac{\partial V}{\partial y}\mathbf{j} + \frac{\partial V}{\partial z}\mathbf{k}\right)dv = \int V(\mathbf{i}\cdot\mathbf{n}\,\mathbf{i} + \mathbf{j}\cdot\mathbf{n}\,\mathbf{j} + \mathbf{k}\cdot\mathbf{n}\,\mathbf{k})dS,$$

that is,

$$\int \nabla V dv = \int V\mathbf{n}dS \quad . \quad . \quad . \quad . \quad (5)$$

Thus the volume integral of the gradient of a scalar function may be expressed in terms of the values assumed by the function at the boundary of the region. This is one of the theorems sought.

The other theorem referred to is expressed by the equation

$$\int \text{curl } \mathbf{F}dv = \int \mathbf{n}\times\mathbf{F}dS \quad . \quad . \quad . \quad (6)$$

The student may deduce this from the equations (3)–(3″) by a method similar to that just employed.† But for the purpose of illustrating a different method we proceed thus. In the divergence theorem (2) put $\mathbf{F} = \mathbf{V}\times\mathbf{d}$ where $\mathbf{V}$ is a vector point-function and $\mathbf{d}$ a constant vector. Then

$$\text{div }(\mathbf{V}\times\mathbf{d}) = \mathbf{d}\cdot \text{ curl } \mathbf{V}, \quad \text{by (17) Art. 8,}$$

* Strictly speaking, we *multiply* the vector by the number.

† *Cf.* also another proof in Art. 87.

and the theorem leads to

$$\mathbf{d}\cdot\int \text{curl } \mathbf{V}\, dv = \int \mathbf{V}\times\mathbf{d}\cdot\mathbf{n}dS = \mathbf{d}\cdot\int \mathbf{n}\times\mathbf{V}dS.$$

And since this is true for all values of **d**, we must have

$$\int \text{curl } \mathbf{V}\, dv = \int \mathbf{n}\times\mathbf{V}dS,$$

which is the required result (6).

If we apply the theorem to an infinitesimal closed surface, and the enclosed element of space of volume dv, we obtain

$$\text{curl } \mathbf{F}dv = \int \mathbf{n}\times\mathbf{F}dS,$$

or

$$\text{curl } \mathbf{F} = \frac{1}{dv}\int \mathbf{n}\times\mathbf{F}dS. \quad . \quad . \quad . \quad (7)$$

This leads to an alternative definition of curl **F** corresponding to the definition of div **F** by (4) ; and, as in that case, since the value of the integral (7) is independent of coordinate axes, it follows that curl **F** is *invariant* with respect to the choice of these.

The theorems of this Art. and the preceding are all variations of the one transformation. This is also apparent from their symbolic representation

$$\left.\begin{aligned} \int \nabla V dv &= \int \mathbf{n} V dS \\ \int \nabla\cdot\mathbf{F}dv &= \int \mathbf{n}\cdot\mathbf{F}dS \\ \int \nabla\times\mathbf{F}dv &= \int \mathbf{n}\times\mathbf{F}dS \end{aligned}\right\}. \quad . \quad . \quad . \quad (8)$$

It will be proved in Chapter VII. that these transformations hold for other meanings of V and **F** than those here adopted.

16. Stokes's Theorem. Consider a closed curve C and an open surface S bounded by that curve. Let **n** be the unit normal at a point P of the surface, in the sense which is positive relative to that in which the boundary C is supposed to be described. Stokes's theorem states that *for a vector function* **F**, *which is uniform, finite and continuous along with its derivative in any direction, the tangential line integral of* **F** *round the closed curve C is equal to the normal surface integral of curl* **F** *over S* ; that is

$$\int_0 \mathbf{F}\cdot d\mathbf{r} = \int \mathbf{n}\cdot\text{curl } \mathbf{F}dS \quad . \quad . \quad . \quad . \quad (9)$$

Take the level-surfaces of two scalar point-functions u, v. The intersections of these with the surface S are level lines of u, v respectively on that surface. Choose these functions so that their level lines are orthogonal. Then the values of u, v constitute a system of orthogonal curvilinear coordinates for points on S. Let P be the point u, v, and R the point $u + du$, $v + dv$. The level lines through P, R bound a curvilinear rectangular figure $PQRT$ the lengths of whose sides are

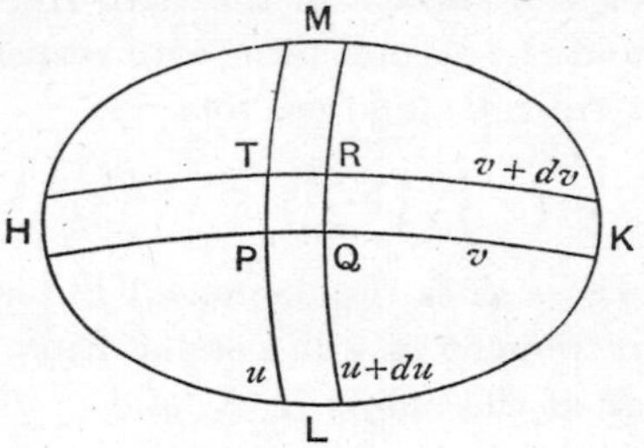

FIG. 8.

$$ds_1 = h_1 du,$$
$$ds_2 = h_2 dv,$$

h_1, h_2 being the variable parameters of the system of coordinates. The area of this element of surface is

$$dS = h_1 h_2 du dv.$$

Let $\mathbf{l}$, $\mathbf{m}$ be the unit vectors parallel to the axes of curvilinear coordinates at P, so that $\mathbf{l}$, $\mathbf{m}$, and $\mathbf{n} = \mathbf{l} \times \mathbf{m}$ form a right-handed system. Since the first two are the unit tangents to the coordinate lines at P, if $\mathbf{r}$ is the position vector of this point, we have

$$\mathbf{l} = \frac{\partial \mathbf{r}}{\partial s_1} = \frac{1}{h_1} \frac{\partial \mathbf{r}}{\partial u}$$
$$\mathbf{m} = \frac{\partial \mathbf{r}}{\partial s_2} = \frac{1}{h_2} \frac{\partial \mathbf{r}}{\partial v}.$$

Now, by the definition of curl $\mathbf{F}$ in Art. 7,

$$\text{curl } \mathbf{F} = \mathbf{l} \times \frac{\partial \mathbf{F}}{\partial s_1} + \mathbf{m} \times \frac{\partial \mathbf{F}}{\partial s_2} + \mathbf{n} \times \frac{\partial \mathbf{F}}{\partial n},$$

and therefore

$$\mathbf{n} \cdot \text{curl } \mathbf{F} = \mathbf{n} \times \mathbf{l} \cdot \frac{\partial \mathbf{F}}{\partial s_1} + \mathbf{n} \times \mathbf{m} \cdot \frac{\partial \mathbf{F}}{\partial s_2}$$
$$= \mathbf{m} \cdot \frac{\partial \mathbf{F}}{h_1 \partial u} - \mathbf{l} \cdot \frac{\partial \mathbf{F}}{h_2 \partial v} \quad . \quad . \quad . \quad \text{i}$$

The normal surface integral of curl $\mathbf{F}$ over S is then

$$I = \int \mathbf{n} \cdot \text{curl } \mathbf{F} dS = \iint \left(h_2 \mathbf{m} \cdot \frac{\partial \mathbf{F}}{\partial u} - h_1 \mathbf{l} \cdot \frac{\partial \mathbf{F}}{\partial v} \right) du dv$$
$$= \iint \left(\frac{\partial \mathbf{F}}{\partial u} \cdot \frac{\partial \mathbf{r}}{\partial v} - \frac{\partial \mathbf{F}}{\partial v} \cdot \frac{\partial \mathbf{r}}{\partial u} \right) du dv$$
$$= \iint \left\{ \frac{\partial}{\partial u} \left(\mathbf{F} \cdot \frac{\partial \mathbf{r}}{\partial v} \right) - \frac{\partial}{\partial v} \left(\mathbf{F} \cdot \frac{\partial \mathbf{r}}{\partial u} \right) \right\} du dv.$$

Integrate the first term with respect to u (*i.e.* sum for all elements of the surface in the strip HK between the level lines v, $v + dv$), and the second term with respect to v (*i.e.* sum for elements in the strip LM), and we obtain

$$I = \int\left\{\left(\mathbf{F}\cdot\frac{\partial\mathbf{r}}{\partial v}\right)_K - \left(\mathbf{F}\cdot\frac{\partial\mathbf{r}}{\partial v}\right)_H\right\}dv - \int\left\{\left(\mathbf{F}\cdot\frac{\partial\mathbf{r}}{\partial u}\right)_M - \left(\mathbf{F}\cdot\frac{\partial\mathbf{r}}{\partial u}\right)_L\right\}du$$

where dv is the increment in v in passing from P to T, and du the increment in u in passing from P to Q. If, however, we assign to dv at the points H, K, and to du at L, M, the values corresponding to the passage round C in the sense in which the curve was supposed to be described, the equation becomes

$$I = \int\left\{\left(\mathbf{F}\cdot\frac{\partial\mathbf{r}}{\partial v}\right)_K + \left(\mathbf{F}\cdot\frac{\partial\mathbf{r}}{\partial v}\right)_H\right\}dv + \int\left\{\left(\mathbf{F}\cdot\frac{\partial\mathbf{r}}{\partial u}\right)_M + \left(\mathbf{F}\cdot\frac{\partial\mathbf{r}}{\partial u}\right)_L\right\}du.$$

In the integration with respect to v we include every element of the bounding curve once; and similarly in the integration with respect to u. Thus

$$I = \int_0\left(\mathbf{F}\cdot\frac{\partial\mathbf{r}}{\partial v}dv + \mathbf{F}\cdot\frac{\partial\mathbf{r}}{\partial u}du\right)$$

$$= \int_0 \mathbf{F}\cdot\left(\frac{\partial\mathbf{r}}{\partial v}dv + \frac{\partial\mathbf{r}}{\partial u}du\right) = \int_0 \mathbf{F}\cdot d\mathbf{r} \quad . \quad . \quad \text{ii}$$

which proves the theorem. The formula (9) is of very great importance, and the student should commit it to memory.

Conversely, if the normal surface integral of $\mathbf{V}$ over the open surface S is equal to the tangential line integral of $\mathbf{F}$ round the bounding curve C, for every such curve drawn in the field

$$\mathbf{V} \equiv \text{curl } \mathbf{F}.$$

For, by the theorem of Stokes, the surface integrals of $\mathbf{V}$ and curl $\mathbf{F}$ are equal; and therefore the equation

$$\int \mathbf{n}\cdot(\mathbf{V} - \text{curl } \mathbf{F})dS = 0$$

holds for every open surface. Thus for every element of surface

$$\mathbf{n}\cdot(\mathbf{V} - \text{curl } \mathbf{F})dS \equiv 0,$$

which shows that ($\mathbf{V}$ − curl $\mathbf{F}$) vanishes identically. Hence this converse of Stokes's theorem is true.

17. Certain deductions from the preceding theorems. The transformation of the preceding Art. may also be used to prove the formula

$$\int \mathbf{n}\times\nabla V dS = \int_0 V d\mathbf{r} \quad . \quad . \quad . \quad . \quad (10)$$

where V is a scalar point-function, and the other symbols have the same meaning as above. For

$$\mathbf{n}\times\nabla V = \mathbf{n}\times\left(\mathbf{l}\frac{1}{h_1}\frac{\partial V}{\partial u} + \mathbf{m}\frac{1}{h_2}\frac{\partial V}{\partial v} + \mathbf{n}\frac{\partial V}{\partial n}\right)$$
$$= \mathbf{m}\frac{1}{h_1}\frac{\partial V}{\partial u} - \mathbf{l}\frac{1}{h_2}\frac{\partial V}{\partial v},$$

which corresponds to i of the preceding Art. From there onward the steps of the argument are exactly the same. We have only to replace **F** by V and omit the dot for the scalar products, and the formula (10) results. The student may also prove the theorem by putting $\mathbf{F} = V\mathbf{d}$ in Stokes's theorem, **d** being a constant vector. We leave this as an exercise. It will be proved in Chapter VII. that the formulæ (9) and (10) hold for other meanings of **F** and V than those here adopted.

The identities

$$\left.\begin{array}{r}\text{curl grad } V = 0\\ \text{div curl } \mathbf{F} = 0\end{array}\right\} \quad . \quad . \quad . \quad . \quad (11)$$

already proved in Art. 9, may be deduced from the theorems of Stokes and Gauss, and their converses established. If, for instance, we apply Stokes's theorem to the function ∇V, we find

$$\int \mathbf{n}\cdot \text{curl grad } V dS = \int_0 \nabla V\cdot d\mathbf{r}$$
$$= 0 \quad \text{by } (1').$$

And since this is true for every open surface S, the function $\nabla\times\nabla V$ must be identically zero. Conversely, if curl **F** is identically zero, **F** is expressible as the gradient of a scalar function V. For then the tangential line integral of **F** round any closed curve is

$$\int_0 \mathbf{F}\cdot d\mathbf{r} = \int \mathbf{n}\cdot \text{curl } \mathbf{F} dS = 0.$$

And, this being true for every closed curve, it follows from Art. 13 that **F** is the gradient of some function V. The level-surfaces of V divide the region into shells or laminæ ; and the function **F** whose curl vanishes identically is called a *lamellar* or *irrotational* function.

Again, applying the divergence theorem to the function curl **F**, we have

$$\int \text{div curl } \mathbf{F} dv = \int \mathbf{n}\cdot \text{curl } \mathbf{F} dS$$

for the region bounded by any *closed* surface S. But it is easily shown that the surface integral is zero, by dividing the surface S into two parts, S_1 and S_2, by any closed curve C drawn on it. The parts of the surface integrals over S_1 and S_2 have equal and opposite values, by Stokes's theorem, being equal to the tangential line integrals of **F** round C in opposite directions. Thus the volume integral of div curl **F** vanishes for the region bounded by any closed surface, showing that the integrand is identically zero. Conversely, if the divergence of a vector **V** vanishes identically, the vector is expressible as the curl of another vector function. Such a vector **V** is called a *solenoidal* vector.

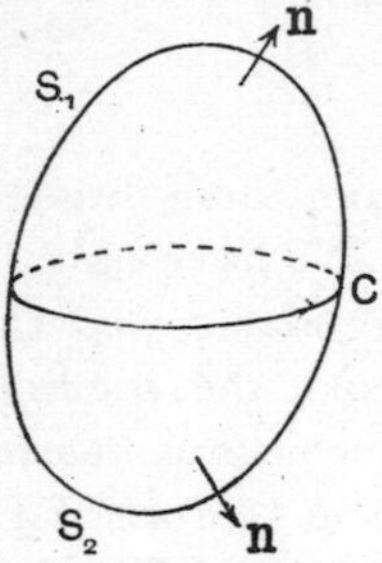

FIG. 9.

18. Curvilinear coordinates. From the theorems of Gauss and Stokes we may easily deduce expressions for div **F** and curl **F** in orthogonal curvilinear coordinates. Using the notation of Arts. 11–12, apply the divergence theorem to the elementary figure bounded by the level-surfaces $u, u + du, v, v + dv, w, w + dw$ (Fig. 2). The lengths of the edges are h_1du, h_2dv, h_3dw, and its volume is

$$dv = h_1h_2h_3dudvdw.$$

The volume integral of the divergence differs from

$$h_1h_2h_3dudvdw \text{ div } \mathbf{F} \qquad \text{i}$$

by a quantity of higher order than the third.

With the previous notation we have

$$\mathbf{F} = F_1\mathbf{a} + F_2\mathbf{b} + F_3\mathbf{c}$$

where **a**, **b**, **c** are unit vectors parallel to the coordinate axes. The value of the normal surface integral over the face $PBDC$ is *

$$-\mathbf{a}\cdot\mathbf{F}\, h_2h_3dvdw = -F_1h_2h_3dvdw,$$

and that over the face $AFP'E$ is therefore

$$F_1h_2h_3dvdw + \frac{\partial}{\partial u}(F_1h_2h_3dvdw)du.$$

These two faces therefore contribute to the integral the amount

$$\frac{\partial}{\partial u}(F_1h_2h_3)dudvdw \qquad \text{ii}$$

* If the approximation were carried further we should write for the contribution of the face $PBDC$

$$-f = -\left[F_1h_2h_3dvdw + \theta\frac{\partial}{\partial v}(F_1h_2h_3dvdw)dv + \varphi\frac{\partial}{\partial w}(\ \ldots\ )dw\right]$$

where θ, φ are proper fractions. The contribution of $AFP'E$ is then

$$f + \frac{\partial f}{\partial u}du.$$

The pair of faces therefore contribute an amount which differs from ii by a quantity of higher order than the third.

In the same way we find for the contributions of the other pairs of faces

$$\frac{\partial}{dv}(F_2h_3h_1)dudvdw$$

and

$$\frac{\partial}{\partial w}(F_3h_1h_2)dudvdw$$

respectively. Equating the sum of these to the value of the volume integral given by i, we have

$$\text{div } \mathbf{F} = \frac{1}{h_1h_2h_3}\left[\frac{\partial}{\partial u}(h_2h_3F_1) + \frac{\partial}{\partial v}(h_3h_1F_2) + \frac{\partial}{\partial w}(h_1h_2F_3)\right] \qquad (12)$$

as found in Art. 12 by a different method.

To find the corresponding expression for curl **F** apply Stokes's theorem to the elementary circuit *PBDC* described in this sense, and the element of the coordinate surface bounded by it. The normal to this surface at *P* is **a** ; and the value of the normal surface integral of curl **F** differs from

$$\mathbf{a}\cdot\text{curl } \mathbf{F}h_2h_3dvdw \quad . \quad . \quad . \quad . \quad \text{iii}$$

by a quantity of higher order than the second. As for the tangential line integral of **F**, the portion *PB* contributes *

$$\mathbf{b}\cdot\mathbf{F}h_2dv = F_2h_2dv,$$

and the portion *DC*, therefore the amount

$$-\left[F_2h_2dv + \frac{\partial}{\partial w}(F_2h_2dv)dw\right].$$

The two sides together therefore contribute

$$-\frac{\partial}{\partial w}(F_2h_2)dvdw \quad . \quad . \quad . \quad . \quad \text{iv}$$

Similarly the contribution of the other two sides is

$$\frac{\partial}{\partial v}(F_3h_3)dvdw.$$

Equating then the whole of the line integral to the value of the surface integral given by iii, we have

$$\mathbf{a}\cdot \text{curl } \mathbf{F} = \frac{1}{h_2h_3}\left[\frac{\partial}{\partial v}(h_3F_3) - \frac{\partial}{\partial w}(h_2F_2)\right].$$

* More accurately the contribution of *PB* is

$$f = \left[F_2h_2 + \theta\frac{\partial}{\partial v}(F_2h_2)dv\right]dv$$

and that of *DC* is then $-\left(f + \frac{\partial f}{\partial w}dw\right)$. The sum of these differs from iv by a quantity of higher order than the second.

This is the scalar resolute of curl **F** in the direction of **a**. The resolutes in the directions of **b** and **c** may be written down by permutation of the symbols, giving for the whole vector the value

$$\begin{aligned}\text{curl }\mathbf{F} = \frac{\mathbf{a}}{h_2h_3}\left[\frac{\partial}{\partial v}(h_3F_3) - \frac{\partial}{\partial w}(h_2F_2)\right] \\ + \frac{\mathbf{b}}{h_3h_1}\left[\frac{\partial}{\partial w}(h_1F_1) - \frac{\partial}{\partial u}(h_3F_3)\right] \\ + \frac{\mathbf{c}}{h_1h_2}\left[\frac{\partial}{\partial u}(h_2F_2) - \frac{\partial}{\partial v}(h_1F_1)\right] \quad . \quad (13)\end{aligned}$$

as already stated in Art. 12.

19. Green's Theorem. Let U, V be scalar point-functions which, together with their derivatives in any direction, are uniform and continuous within the region bounded by a closed surface S. Apply the divergence theorem for this region to the vector function $U\nabla V$. Then since by (15) of Art. 8

$$\text{div }(U\nabla V) = \nabla U\cdot\nabla V + U\nabla^2 V,$$

Gauss's theorem gives

$$\int U\nabla V\cdot\mathbf{n}dS = \int(\nabla U\cdot\nabla V + U\nabla^2 V)dv.$$

Transposing terms, and writing down a similar equation got by interchanging U and V, we have

$$\int\nabla U\cdot\nabla V dv = \int U\mathbf{n}\cdot\nabla V dS - \int U\nabla^2 V dv \quad . \quad . \quad (14)$$

$$= \int V\mathbf{n}\cdot\nabla U dS - \int V\nabla^2 U dv \quad . \quad . \quad (14')$$

These results are known as *Green's theorem*, which is of great importance in mathematical physics.

Equating the second members of (14) and (14′), we have the symmetrical relation

$$\int(U\nabla V - V\nabla U)\cdot\mathbf{n}dS = \int(U\nabla^2 V - V\nabla^2 U)dv \quad (15)$$

which is also sometimes referred to as Green's theorem. The first member of this equation may also be written

$$\int\left(U\frac{\partial V}{\partial n} - V\frac{\partial U}{\partial n}\right)dS$$

where $\frac{\partial V}{\partial n}$ denotes the derivative of V in the direction of the *outward* normal to the surface of the region.

A point-function U satisfying Laplace's equation $\nabla^2 U = 0$ is called a *harmonic function* for the region considered. If, then, U is harmonic the equation (14′) becomes

$$\int \nabla U \cdot \nabla V dv = \int V \mathbf{n} \cdot \nabla U dS \quad . \quad . \quad . \ (14'')$$

while if both U and V are harmonic (15) gives

$$\int \left(U \frac{\partial V}{\partial n} - V \frac{\partial U}{\partial n} \right) dS = 0 \quad . \quad . \quad . \ (15')$$

20. Green's Formula. If P is a fixed point, and r the distance from P to a variable point of the region, $\frac{1}{r}$ is a scalar point-function. When P is *outside the region* considered, $\frac{1}{r}$ and its derivative in any direction are uniform, finite, and continuous, and we may put $U = \frac{1}{r}$ in the formulæ of the preceding Art. For example, (15) then leads to

$$\int \left\{ V \frac{\partial}{\partial n}\left(\frac{1}{r}\right) - \frac{1}{r} \frac{\partial V}{\partial n} \right\} dS + \int \frac{1}{r} \nabla^2 V dv = 0 \quad . \quad . \ (16)$$

since $\frac{1}{r}$ is harmonic, as shown in Art. 10.

If, however, P is *within the region* bounded by S, $\frac{1}{r}$ becomes infinite at P, and the preceding theorems no longer apply to this function. But if we surround P by a small closed surface Σ, we can apply the theorems to the function $\frac{1}{r}$ provided the region taken is that lying between S and Σ. The surface integrals must now be taken over the complete boundary S and Σ, and the volume integral only throughout the region lying between them.

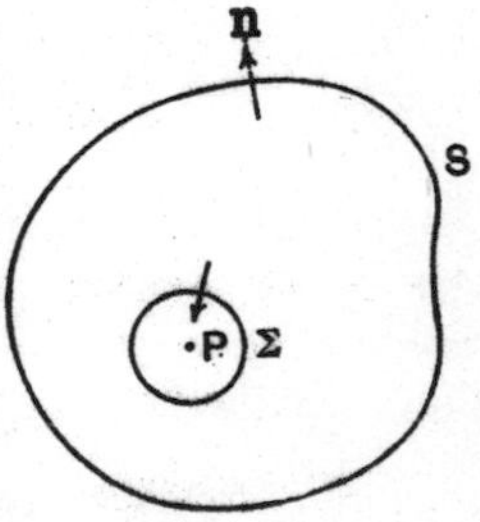

FIG. 10.

Take for the surface Σ a small sphere with centre P and radius ϵ. Then at this surface the direction of the normal drawn outward from the region is toward P, and the value of $\frac{\partial U}{\partial n}$ on Σ is

$$\left[-\frac{\partial}{\partial r}\left(\frac{1}{r}\right) \right]_{r=\epsilon} = \frac{1}{\epsilon^2}.$$

Applying the formula (15) for this modified region to the function $U = \frac{1}{r}$ we obtain

$$\int_\Sigma \left\{ \frac{1}{r} \frac{\partial V}{\partial n} - V \frac{\partial}{\partial n}\left(\frac{1}{r}\right) \right\} d\Sigma = \int_S \left\{ V \frac{\partial}{\partial n}\left(\frac{1}{r}\right) - \frac{1}{r} \frac{\partial V}{\partial n} \right\} dS + \int \frac{1}{r} \nabla^2 V dv.$$

Over Σ the function $\frac{1}{r}$ has everywhere the same value $\frac{1}{\epsilon}$, and $\frac{\partial}{\partial n}\left(\frac{1}{r}\right)$ the value $\frac{1}{\epsilon^2}$. Suppose now that we make the radius ϵ of the sphere decrease indefinitely. Then since V and $\frac{\partial V}{\partial n}$ remain finite over Σ, the first term on the left-hand side tends to the value

$$\operatorname*{Lt}_{\epsilon\to 0} \frac{1}{\epsilon}\left[\frac{\partial V}{\partial n}\right]_P 4\pi\epsilon^2 = 0$$

and the second term to the value

$$\operatorname*{Lt}_{\epsilon\to 0} -[V]_P\frac{1}{\epsilon^2}4\pi\epsilon^2 = -4\pi V_P.$$

The surface integral on the right-hand side is independent of Σ. The volume integral applies only to the region between Σ and S; but on proceeding to the limit we may ignore the difference, and take the whole region bounded by S. For the infinitesimal volume of the sphere contributes only the amount $\frac{1}{\epsilon}[\nabla^2 V]_P\frac{4}{3}\pi\epsilon^3$, which tends to zero with ϵ. On substituting the limiting values of the terms in the above formula we obtain the result

$$4\pi V_P = \iint\left[\frac{1}{r}\frac{\partial V}{\partial n} - V\frac{\partial}{\partial n}\left(\frac{1}{r}\right)\right]dS - \int\frac{1}{r}\nabla^2 V dv \quad . \quad . \quad (17)$$

which is sometimes called *Green's formula*. It gives the value of a function V at any point P within the region in terms of the values of V and $\frac{\partial V}{\partial n}$ over the boundary, and the value of $\nabla^2 V$ throughout the region. If the function V is *harmonic* within the region bounded by S, the volume integral vanishes and the formula becomes

$$4\pi V_P = \iint\left[\frac{1}{r}\frac{\partial V}{\partial n} - V\frac{\partial}{\partial n}\left(\frac{1}{r}\right)\right]dS. \quad . \quad . \quad (17')$$

Lastly, if in (17) we put V equal to unity, $\nabla^2 V$ and $\frac{\partial V}{\partial n}$ both vanish, and the formula leads to

$$\left.\begin{aligned} 4\pi &= -\int\frac{\partial}{\partial n}\left(\frac{1}{r}\right)dS \\ &= -\int \mathbf{n}\cdot\nabla\left(\frac{1}{r}\right)dS \end{aligned}\right\} . \quad . \quad . \quad . \quad (18)$$

This result is due to Gauss, and the integral on the right-hand side is called *Gauss's integral*. The point P is here supposed to be within the region bounded by S. If, however, P is outside the region the equation (16) holds, and on putting V equal to unity we obtain

$$\int \frac{\partial}{\partial n}\left(\frac{1}{r}\right) dS = 0 \quad . \quad . \quad . \quad . \quad (18')$$

Thus Gauss's integral has the value 4π or zero according as the pole P is within or without the region considered.

The geometrical significance of Gauss's integral may be seen as follows. We may write

$$-\mathbf{n}\cdot\nabla\left(\frac{1}{r}\right)dS = \frac{1}{r^2}\mathbf{n}\cdot\hat{\mathbf{r}}dS = \frac{1}{r^2}\cos\theta\, dS,$$

where θ is the angle between the direction of $\mathbf{n}$ and that from P to the element of surface. Now $\cos\theta\, dS$ is the area of the projection of this element on a plane perpendicular to $\mathbf{r}$; and $\frac{1}{r^2}\cos\theta\, dS$ is the area intercepted on a unit sphere with centre at P, by the elementary cone whose vertex is at P and whose generating lines pass through the boundary of the element of surface. This is called the *solid angle* subtended at P by the element, and is positive or negative according as θ is acute or obtuse. Suppose first that P is within the closed surface S. Then when we sum for all the elements, the integral takes in the whole of the surface of the unit sphere whose area is 4π. Thus the solid angle subtended by a closed surface at an enclosed point is equal to 4π. If, however, P is external to the surface, each elementary cone cuts the surface twice,* and the solid angles subtended by the two elements included in the cone are equal and opposite, $\cos\theta$ having opposite signs at the two points. The solid angle subtended by the whole surface at an external point is therefore zero.

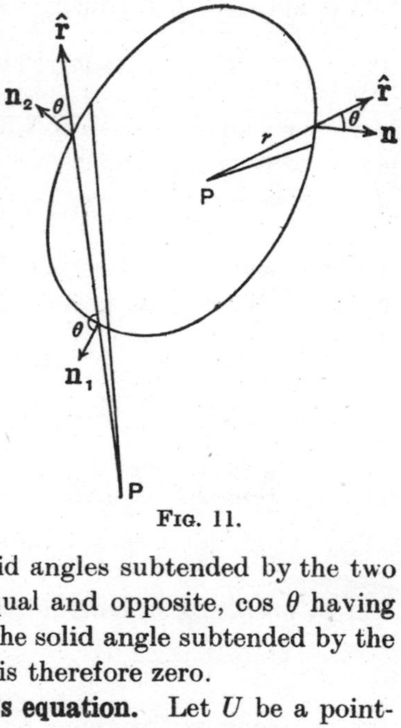

FIG. 11.

21. Green's Function for Laplace's equation. Let U be a point-function, harmonic within the region bounded by S, and having at a point of the surface the value $\frac{1}{r}$, where r is the distance measured from a fixed point P within the region. Then the function

$$G = \frac{1}{r} - U \quad . \quad . \quad . \quad . \quad (19)$$

* More correctly, for an internal point the elementary cone cuts the surface an *odd* number of times; for an external point an *even* number.

vanishes at all points of the boundary, and satisfies Laplace's equation throughout the enclosed space, except at the point P, where it becomes infinite like $\frac{1}{r}$. This function G is called the *Green's function* for the given region, with *pole* at P and vanishing over the boundary.*

If V is another function, which is uniform and continuous along with its derivative in any direction, it follows from (15), since U is harmonic, that

$$\int\left(U\frac{\partial V}{\partial n} - V\frac{\partial U}{\partial n}\right)dS - \int U\nabla^2 V dv = 0.$$

From this equation and the formula (17) we obtain by subtraction

$$4\pi V_P = \int\left[\left(\frac{1}{r} - U\right)\frac{\partial V}{\partial n} - V\frac{\partial}{\partial n}\left(\frac{1}{r} - U\right)\right]dS - \int\left(\frac{1}{r} - U\right)\nabla^2 V dv,$$

that is, since $\frac{1}{r} - U$ is equal to G, which vanishes over the boundary,

$$-4\pi V_P = \int V\frac{\partial G}{\partial n}dS + \int G\nabla^2 V dv \quad . \quad . \quad (20)$$

If then we know the Green's function for the region, this formula gives the value of a function V at any point, in terms of its values at the boundary of the region and the value of $\nabla^2 V$ throughout the region.

In particular for a function V which vanishes over the boundary surface S, the first integral in (20) is zero, and we have

$$-4\pi V_P = \int G\nabla^2 V dv \quad . \quad . \quad . \quad (20')$$

Suppose further that $\nabla^2 V$ is a continuous point-function, and write

$$\nabla^2 V = f \quad . \quad . \quad . \quad . \quad . \quad (21)$$

The equation (20′) is then

$$-4\pi V_P = \int G f dv \quad . \quad . \quad . \quad . \quad (20'')$$

and by operating on both sides with ∇^2 we obtain the relation

$$-4\pi f = \nabla^2\int G f dv \quad . \quad . \quad . \quad . \quad (22)$$

We may express the above result by stating that a solution of the differential equation (21), which vanishes over the boundary of the region, is given by (20″), where G is the Green's function for Laplace's equation vanishing over the boundary.

Symmetry of the Green's Function. The function G possesses an

* There are, of course, Green's functions for other partial differential equations, and other boundary conditions than the vanishing of the function as here defined.

important property of symmetry, according to which the value $G(P, Q)$ at the point P, of the Green's function whose pole is at Q, is equal to the value $G(Q, P)$ at the point Q of the function whose pole is at P. To prove this apply formula (15), putting $U = G(P, Q)$ and $V = G(Q, P)$. In order to do this we must isolate the poles P, Q with (say) small spherical surfaces Σ_1, Σ_2 with these points as centres, extending then the surface integrals over S, Σ_1, and Σ_2, and the volume integral over the region bounded by these surfaces. Thus if T denote a current point on these boundary surfaces and R another in the enclosed space, the formula (15) becomes

$$\int_{S+\Sigma_1+\Sigma_2}\left[G(T, Q)\frac{\partial}{\partial n}G(T, P) - G(T, P)\frac{\partial}{\partial n}G(T, Q)\right]dS$$
$$= \int[G(R, Q)\nabla^2 G(R, P) - G(R, P)\nabla^2 G(R, Q)]dv.$$

Now the surface integral over S is zero because both the Green's functions vanish at the boundary. Also the volume integral vanishes, because these functions are harmonic throughout the region. We have therefore only to consider the surface integrals over Σ_1 and Σ_2. Let ϵ_1, ϵ_2 be the radii of these two spheres, their centres being P, Q respectively. If now we make ϵ_1 and ϵ_2 both tend to zero, the function $G(T, P)$ for points on Σ_1 becomes infinite like $\dfrac{1}{\epsilon_1}$ and $\dfrac{\partial}{\partial n} G(T, P)$ like $\dfrac{1}{\epsilon_1{}^2}$; while $G(T, Q)$ and $\dfrac{\partial}{\partial n} G(T, Q)$ remain finite on Σ_1. Similarly for points on Σ_2 the function $G(T, Q)$ becomes infinite like $\dfrac{1}{\epsilon_2}$ and $\dfrac{\partial}{\partial n} G(T, Q)$ like $\dfrac{1}{\epsilon_2{}^2}$; while $G(T, P)$ and $\dfrac{\partial}{\partial n} G(T, P)$ remain finite. On proceeding to the limit, only the integral of the first term over Σ_1 and the integral of the second over Σ_2 survive, giving the result

$$G(P, Q) = G(Q, P) \quad . \quad . \quad . \qquad (23)$$

The symmetrical property is thus established.

EXERCISES ON CHAPTER II.

1. Prove that
$$\int_0 \mathbf{r}\cdot d\mathbf{r} = 0$$
independently of the origin of $\mathbf{r}$; and that
$$\int_0 \mathbf{r}\times d\mathbf{r}$$
represents twice the vector area of an open surface bounded by the closed curve.

2. Prove that

$$\tfrac{1}{3}\int \mathbf{r}\cdot\mathbf{n}dS$$

is the volume of the space enclosed by the surface S.

3. For a closed surface S, and point-functions $\mathbf{F}$, V, prove that the integrals

$$\int \mathbf{n}\cdot \text{curl } \mathbf{F}dS \quad \text{and} \quad \int \mathbf{n}\times\nabla V dS$$

vanish identically.

4. For integration along a curve from A to B show that

$$\int_A^B \mathbf{v}\cdot(\mathbf{t}\cdot\nabla)\mathbf{v}ds = \tfrac{1}{2}(\mathbf{v}_B{}^2 - \mathbf{v}_A{}^2),$$

where $\mathbf{t}$ is the unit tangent to the curve.

5. From the divergence theorem deduce that

$$\int \mathbf{V}\cdot\nabla p dv = \int p\mathbf{V}\cdot\mathbf{n}dS - \int p \text{ div } \mathbf{V}dv$$

and

$$\int \mathbf{V}\cdot \text{curl } \mathbf{U}dv = \int \mathbf{U}\times\mathbf{V}\cdot\mathbf{n}dS + \int \mathbf{U}\cdot \text{curl } \mathbf{V}dv.$$

6. If $\mathbf{V} = \nabla\phi$ and $\nabla^2\phi = 0$, show that, for S closed,

$$\int \mathbf{V}^2 dv = \int \phi\mathbf{V}\cdot\mathbf{n}dS.$$

7. If $\mathbf{F} = \nabla V$ and $\nabla^2 V = -4\pi\rho$, show that

$$\int \mathbf{F}\cdot\mathbf{n}dS = -4\pi\int \rho dv.$$

8. By putting $\mathbf{F} = V\mathbf{d}$ in the divergence theorem, $\mathbf{d}$ being a constant vector, deduce (5) of Art. 15; and by the same substitution deduce from Stokes's theorem the formula (10) of Art. 17.

9. Modify the proof of Gauss's theorem given in Art. 14 by using curvilinear coordinates, and find the result in terms of these.

10. Find the value of Gauss's integral (18) of Art. 20, independently of Green's formula.

11. If $c\rho\dfrac{\partial V}{\partial t} = \text{div }(k\nabla V)$, and V is zero over the closed surface S, show that

$$\int c\rho V\frac{\partial V}{\partial t}dv = -\int k(\nabla V)^2 dv.$$

12. If $\mathbf{W} = \tfrac{1}{2}$ curl $\mathbf{V}$, and $\mathbf{V} =$ curl $\mathbf{U}$, show that

$$\tfrac{1}{2}\int \mathbf{V}^2 dv = \tfrac{1}{2}\int \mathbf{U}\times\mathbf{V}\cdot\mathbf{n}dS + \int \mathbf{U}\cdot\mathbf{W}dv.$$

13. Using (7) of Art. 4 and (1′) of Art. 13, show that

$$\int_0 U\nabla V\cdot d\mathbf{r} = -\int_0 V\nabla U\cdot d\mathbf{r}.$$

14. From (16) of Art. 8 and Stokes's theorem deduce the relation

$$\int u\mathbf{n}\cdot \text{curl } \mathbf{v}dS = \int_0 u\mathbf{v}\cdot d\mathbf{r} - \int \nabla u\times\mathbf{v}\cdot\mathbf{n}dS.$$

Putting $\mathbf{v} = \nabla v$ in this result, prove that

$$\int \nabla u\times\nabla v\cdot\mathbf{n}dS = \int_0 u\nabla v\cdot d\mathbf{r} = -\int_0 v\nabla u\cdot d\mathbf{r}.$$

15. Expanding div $(\nabla u\times\mathbf{v})$ by (17) of Art. 8, and using the divergence theorem, show that

$$-\int \nabla u\times\mathbf{v}\cdot\mathbf{n}dS = \int \nabla u\cdot\nabla\times\mathbf{v}dv.$$

16. Prove Kelvin's generalisation of Green's theorem

$$\int W\nabla U\cdot\nabla V dv = \int UW\nabla V\cdot\mathbf{n}dS - \int U\nabla\cdot(W\nabla V)dv$$

$$= \int VW\nabla U\cdot\mathbf{n}dS - \int V\nabla\cdot(W\nabla U)dv$$

CHAPTER III.

ELEMENTS OF THE POTENTIAL THEORY. EQUATION OF THERMAL CONDUCTION.

I. Newtonian Potential.

22. Potential due to gravitating particles. Consider two particles at Q, P of masses m, m' respectively. Then, according to the Newtonian law of gravitation, there is a force of attraction between them jointly proportional to their masses, and inversely proportional to the square of their distance r apart ; or

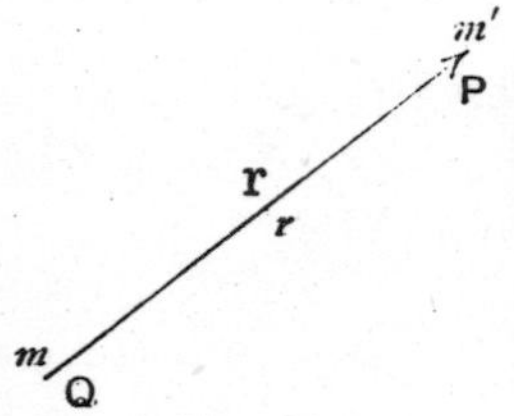

Fig. 12.

$$F \propto \frac{mm'}{r^2}.$$

If we choose the unit of mass as that of a particle which, placed at unit distance from one of equal mass, attracts it with unit force, the equation becomes simply

$$F = \frac{mm'}{r^2}.$$

Denoting the vector $\overrightarrow{QP}$ by $\mathbf{r}$, we may express the force per unit mass at P due to the attracting particle at Q by

$$\mathbf{F} = -\frac{m\hat{\mathbf{r}}}{r^2} = \nabla\left(\frac{m}{r}\right),$$

which is called the *intensity of force*, or briefly the *intensity*, at the point P.

Suppose now that the particle m is stationary at Q, and that another of unit mass moves under the attraction of the former from infinity up to P along any path. The work done by the force of attraction during an infinitesimal displacement $d\mathbf{r}$ of the unit mass is $\mathbf{F}\cdot d\mathbf{r}$: and the total work done while the unit particle moves from infinity up to P is

$$\int_\infty^P \mathbf{F}\cdot d\mathbf{r} = \int_\infty^P \nabla\left(\frac{m}{r}\right)\cdot d\mathbf{r} = \left[\frac{m}{r}\right]_\infty^P = \frac{m}{r}$$

by Art. 13. This is independent of the path by which the particle comes to P, and is called the *potential* at P due to the particle of mass m at Q. Denoting it by V we have

$$V = \frac{m}{r} \quad . \quad . \quad . \quad . \quad (1)$$

while the intensity of force at P due to it is

$$\mathbf{F} = \nabla\left(\frac{m}{r}\right) = \nabla V \quad . \quad . \quad . \quad . \quad (2)$$

The intensity at any point is thus equal to the gradient of the potential.

Suppose next that there are several particles of masses $m_1, m_2, \ldots$ at the points $Q_1, Q_2, \ldots$ relative to which P has position vectors $\mathbf{r}_1, \mathbf{r}_2, \ldots$ respectively. Then the force of attraction per unit mass at P due to the system of particles is the vector sum of the intensities due to each; that is,

$$\mathbf{F} = \nabla\left(\frac{m_1}{r_1}\right) + \nabla\left(\frac{m_2}{r_2}\right) + \ldots = \nabla\Sigma\frac{m}{r} \quad . \quad . \quad (2')$$

Then, by the same argument as before, the work done by the attracting forces on a particle of unit mass while it moves from infinity up to P is

$$\int_{\infty}^{P} \mathbf{F}\cdot d\mathbf{r} = \Sigma\frac{m}{r} = V \quad \text{(say)} \quad . \quad . \quad . \quad (1')$$

Thus the potential at P due to the system of particles is the sum of the potentials due to each. This potential V is a scalar point-function, having a definite value at each point. And, except at each of the points Q, it satisfies Laplace's equation. For

$$\nabla^2 V = \nabla^2\Sigma\frac{m}{r} = \Sigma\nabla^2\left(\frac{m}{r}\right) = 0 \quad . \quad . \quad . \quad (3)$$

for each of the terms $\frac{m}{r}$ is harmonic, as already proved in Art. 10.

23. Continuous distribution of matter. Suppose now that the attracting matter forms a continuous body, filling the space bounded by the closed surface S. If dm is the mass and dv the volume of an element of the body round the point Q, the density ρ of the body at that point is $\frac{dm}{dv}$. We divide the body into an infinite number of particles, the mass of the particle at Q being $dm = \rho dv$. The

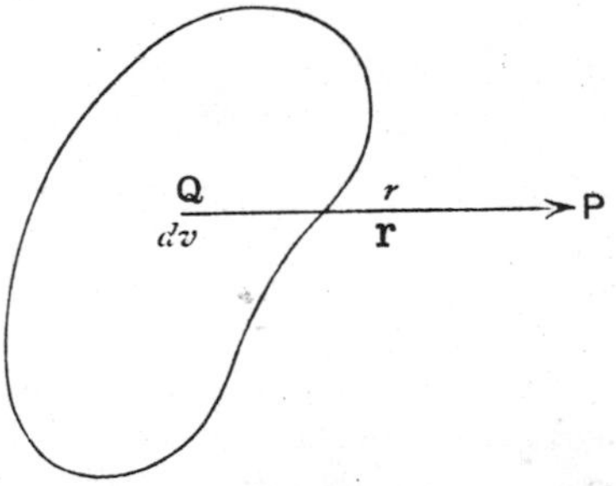

Fig. 13.

potential at a point P due to this is $\rho dv/r$; and, if this point is *outside the body*, the potential V there due to the whole body is

$$V = \int \frac{\rho dv}{r} \quad . \quad . \quad . \quad . \quad . \quad (4)$$

Similarly the intensity at P due to the body is the vector sum of the intensities due to all the particles, and is therefore given by

$$\mathbf{F} = \int \nabla\left(\frac{\rho dv}{r}\right) = \nabla \int \frac{\rho dv}{r} = \nabla V \quad . \quad . \quad . \quad (5)$$

ρ and dv being constant with respect to the operator ∇.

At a point P *inside the body*—that is, a point occupied by the attracting matter—the integrand in (4) becomes infinite. We define the potential at this point in the following manner. Surround the point by a closed spherical surface Σ, and consider the potential

$$V' = \int_\Sigma^S \frac{\rho dv}{r}$$

due to the matter in the space between Σ and S. The integrand in this case is finite everywhere, since P is outside the region. Now let the surface Σ decrease indefinitely, converging to the point P as a limit. Then since the volume of Σ is of the same order as ϵ^3, where ϵ is its radius, while the integrand becomes infinite only like $\frac{1}{\epsilon}$ if ρ is finite, the value of the integral V' tends to a definite finite limit V, which is called the potential at P due to the whole body. The potential at a point inside the body is thus defined by the equation

$$V = \operatorname*{Lt}_{\Sigma \to 0} \int_\Sigma^S \frac{\rho dv}{r}.$$

Similarly we define the intensity $\mathbf{F}$ at the point P within the body. The function

$$\mathbf{F}' = \int_\Sigma^S - \rho \frac{\hat{\mathbf{r}}}{r^2} dv = \int_\Sigma^S \rho \nabla\left(\frac{1}{r}\right) dv$$

is the intensity at P due to the matter in the region between Σ and S. The limiting value of $\mathbf{F}'$ as Σ converges to the point P is what we mean by the intensity at P due to the whole body. This limit $\mathbf{F}$ is finite since the integrand becomes infinite only like $\frac{1}{\epsilon^2}$, while the volume of Σ is of the same order as ϵ^3.

The functions V and $\mathbf{F}$, thus defined as the limiting values of certain integrals, are not only finite but also continuous; and the derivative of $\mathbf{F}$ in any direction is continuous at points where the density ρ is continuous. The proofs of these properties are rather lengthy, and would be out of place here. We refer the reader to Poincaré's *Potentiel Newtonien*, Arts. 35–37, where it is also shown that the functions are still connected by the relation $\mathbf{F} = \nabla V$. In terms of the tendency of ϵ to the limit zero, this equation means that the result obtained by differentiating and then proceeding to the limit is identical with that obtained by proceeding to the limit and then differentiating.

At points outside the body no difficulty presents itself. The integrand is everywhere finite in both the integrals V and $\mathbf{F}$. The potential then satisfies Laplace's equation, being equal to the sum of the potentials due to the individual particles, each of which satisfies that equation. Hence at points where $\rho = 0$,

$$\nabla^2 V = 0 \quad . \quad . \quad . \quad . \quad (3')$$

If the point P is *at an infinite distance* R from the c.m. of the body, the potential there vanishes like M/R and the intensity like $-M\hat{\mathbf{r}}/R^2$, M being the total mass of the body and $\hat{\mathbf{r}}$ the unit vector in the direction from the c.m. to P. For if r is the distance of P from a particle of the body, and r_1, r_2 the least and greatest values of r, we have

$$\int \frac{\rho dv}{r_1} \geqslant \int \frac{\rho dv}{r} \geqslant \int \frac{\rho dv}{r_2}.$$

Hence if V is the potential at P,

$$\frac{M}{r_1} \geqslant V \geqslant \frac{M}{r_2}.$$

On multiplying throughout by R, and observing that

$$\underset{r \to \infty}{\mathrm{Lt}} \frac{R}{r_1} = 1 = \underset{r \to \infty}{\mathrm{Lt}} \frac{R}{r_2},$$

we find, on proceeding to the limit, that $RV = M$. Thus at infinity the potential has the value M/R and therefore vanishes to the first order.

Similarly the intensity at the point P is

$$\mathbf{F} = -\int \frac{\rho \hat{\mathbf{r}} dv}{r^2} = -\hat{\mathbf{r}} \int \frac{\rho dv}{r^2},$$

since the direction $\hat{\mathbf{r}}$ from the body to an infinite point P is the same for all particles of the body. But, with the same notation as above,

$$\int \frac{\rho dv}{{r_1}^2} \geqslant \int \frac{\rho dv}{r^2} \geqslant \int \frac{\rho dv}{{r_2}^2},$$

or, if F is the module of $\mathbf{F}$,

$$\frac{M}{{r_1}^2} \geqslant F \geqslant \frac{M}{r}$$

Multiplying by R^2 and proceeding to the limit we have the result $R^2F = M$.

Thus at an infinite distance the intensity has the value $-M\hat{\mathbf{r}}/R^2$, and therefore vanishes to the second order.

24. Theorem of total normal intensity. We shall now prove that *the normal surface integral of the intensity over a closed surface drawn in the field is equal to* -4π *times the total mass enclosed by the surface.* This theorem, also due to Gauss, is called the theorem of *total normal intensity.*

Let S be the closed surface, and m the mass of a particle at P. At a point Q of the surface the intensity due to this particle is

$$\mathbf{F} = -\frac{m\hat{\mathbf{r}}}{r^2} = m\nabla\left(\frac{1}{r}\right),$$

where $r = PQ$ and $r\hat{\mathbf{r}} = \overrightarrow{PQ}$. The normal resolute of this intensity is then

$$m\mathbf{n}\cdot\nabla\left(\frac{1}{r}\right) = -\frac{m}{r^2}\cos\theta,$$

θ being the angle between the vectors $\hat{\mathbf{r}}$ and $\mathbf{n}$. The total normal intensity, or the normal surface integral of $\mathbf{F}$, is therefore

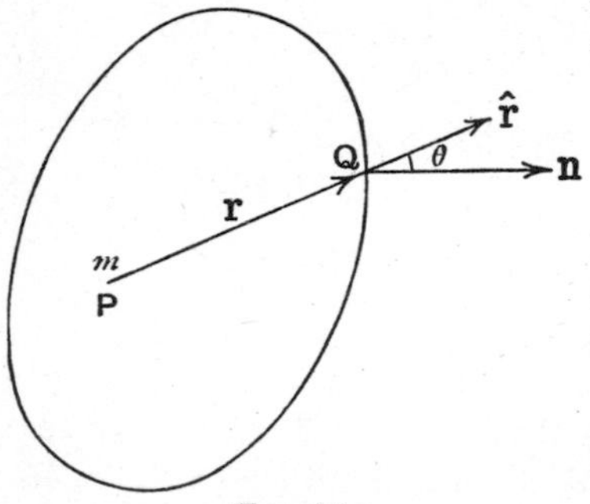

FIG. 14.

$$m\int\mathbf{n}\cdot\nabla\left(\frac{1}{r}\right)dS = -m\int\frac{\cos\theta dS}{r^2}.$$

But we saw in Art. 20 that the coefficient of $-m$ in this expression is the solid angle subtended at P by the surface S, and has the value 4π or zero according as P is inside or outside the surface Hence the total normal intensity due to the particle m is equal to $-4\pi m$ or zero, according as the particle is inside or outside the surface S.

If the field is that due to any number of particles at different points, the intensity at any point is the vector sum of the intensities due to the separate particles. Hence the normal intensity at any point of the surface is the sum of the normal intensities due to the separate particles. The particles outside S contribute nothing to the total normal intensity, whose value is therefore -4π times the sum of the masses of the enclosed particles.

If the distribution of matter within S is of finite density ρ, the intensity at the point Q on the surface is

$$\mathbf{F} = -\int \frac{\rho \hat{\mathbf{r}}}{r^2} dv,$$

where the integral is extended over all the attracting matter. The total normal intensity is therefore

$$\int \mathbf{n}\cdot\mathbf{F} dS = \int \rho \left[\int \mathbf{n}\cdot\nabla\left(\frac{1}{r}\right) dS \right] dv.$$

In this expression r is the distance from the particle of mass ρdv to the element of surface dS. For particles outside S the surface integral is zero; while for a particle inside it has the value -4π (Art. 20). The expression for the total normal intensity is therefore equal to $\int -4\pi\rho dv$, where the integration is extended only over the region inside S. The value of this expression is clearly equal to -4π times the mass enclosed by S, and the theorem is thus established.

25. Poisson's Equation. According to Art. 23, the potential and the intensity are finite and continuous throughout space where the density ρ is finite, and are connected by the equation $\mathbf{F} = \nabla V$. The derivatives of the intensity are also finite and continuous where ρ is finite and continuous. We may therefore apply the divergence theorem to transform the result of the preceding Art. If S is any closed surface drawn within the region for which ρ is continuous, the theorem of total normal intensity gives

$$\int \mathbf{n}\cdot\nabla V dS = -4\pi \int \rho dv \quad . \quad . \quad . \quad (6)$$

where the volume integral is extended throughout the space enclosed by S. Transforming the first member by the divergence theorem we have

$$\int \nabla\cdot\nabla V dv = -4\pi \int \rho dv.$$

And since this is true for the region bounded by any closed surface S within which ρ is continuous, it follows that the integrands are identically equal, or

$$\nabla^2 V = -4\pi\rho \quad . \quad . \quad . \quad . \quad (7)$$

This relation is known as *Poisson's equation.* At points not occupied by matter $\rho = 0$, and the potential there satisfies Laplace's equation, as already shown.

Conversely, given the differential equation (7), where ρ is a point function vanishing outside a finite region of space, we may take for a solution of the equation the function

$$V = \int \frac{\rho dv}{r} \quad . \quad . \quad . \quad . \quad (8)$$

where the integration is extended over the region in which ρ does not vanish, or over the whole of space since ρ is zero elsewhere. The function V defined by (8) is often spoken of as the potential of the scalar function ρ.

We define a *vector potential* by means of a similar integral. If $\mathbf{U}$ is a vector point-function which is everywhere finite, and vanishes outside a finite region of space, then

$$\mathbf{V} = \int \frac{\mathbf{U}dv}{r} \quad . \quad . \quad . \quad . \quad . \quad (9)$$

is called the vector potential of the function $\mathbf{U}$. If we write

$$\mathbf{U} = U_1\mathbf{i} + U_2\mathbf{j} + U_3\mathbf{k},$$

the vector potential is

$$\mathbf{V} = \mathbf{i}\int \frac{U_1 dv}{r} + \mathbf{j}\int \frac{U_2 dv}{r} + \mathbf{k}\int \frac{U_3 dv}{r}.$$

This function $\mathbf{V}$ is thus a vector whose resolutes are the potentials of the resolutes of $\mathbf{U}$. Each of the scalar potentials represented by the integrals in the last equation satisfies Poisson's equation. Hence

$$\begin{aligned} \nabla^2\mathbf{V} &= -4\pi(U_1\mathbf{i} + U_2\mathbf{j} + U_3\mathbf{k}) \\ &= -4\pi\mathbf{U} \quad . \quad . \quad . \quad . \quad . \quad (7') \end{aligned}$$

Thus $\mathbf{V}$ also satisfies Poisson's equation. And conversely, a solution of the differential equation (7′), in which $\mathbf{U}$ has the properties stated above, is given by the integral (9), where the integration is extended throughout the whole of space, or through the region in which $\mathbf{U}$ does not vanish.

26. Expression of a vector function as the sum of lamellar and solenoidal components. Let $\mathbf{F}$ be a vector point-function which, along with its derivatives, is uniform, finite and continuous, and vanishes at infinity or outside a finite region. It was shown by Helmholtz that such a function can be expressed as the sum of two others, one lamellar and the other solenoidal, in the form

$$\mathbf{F} = \nabla\phi + \nabla\times\mathbf{H} \quad . \quad . \quad . \quad . \quad (10)$$

where ϕ, $\mathbf{H}$ are point-functions.

To determine ϕ take the divergence of both members in (10). Then, since div curl $\mathbf{H}$ is identically zero, we obtain

$$\text{div}\,\mathbf{F} = \nabla^2\phi \quad . \quad . \quad . \quad . \quad \text{i}$$

a solution of which, by the preceding Art., is

$$\phi = -\frac{1}{4\pi}\int \frac{\text{div}\,\mathbf{F}}{r}dv \quad . \quad . \quad . \quad . \quad (11)$$

the integration being extended throughout the whole of space, or the region in which **F** is not zero. The function ϕ determined from i is indefinite to the extent of an harmonic function; but since **F** vanishes at infinity the equation (11) gives the required value of ϕ. For this integral, being of the nature of a potential, has already been shown to vanish at infinity; while the only harmonic function satisfying this condition is identically zero (Art. 28).*

To find **H** take the curl of both members in (10). Then

$$\text{curl } \mathbf{F} = \text{curl curl } \mathbf{H} = \nabla \text{ div } \mathbf{H} - \nabla^2 \mathbf{H}.$$

We now restrict the vector **H** desired by the condition that it is to be solenoidal, that is, div **H** = 0. Then the last equation becomes

$$\text{curl } \mathbf{F} = -\nabla^2 \mathbf{H} \quad . \quad . \quad . \quad . \quad \text{ii}$$

and, as before, the solution of this equation vanishing at infinity is

$$\mathbf{H} = \frac{1}{4\pi}\int \frac{\text{curl } \mathbf{F}}{r} dv \quad . \quad . \quad . \quad . \quad (12)$$

the integration extending through the whole of space.†

The functions ϕ and **H** are thus determined from the values of div **F** and curl **F** respectively, and the required resolution of **F** is then given by (10), which may be written

$$\mathbf{F} = -\frac{1}{4\pi} \text{ grad} \int \frac{\text{div } \mathbf{F}}{r} dv + \frac{1}{4\pi} \text{ curl} \int \frac{\text{curl } \mathbf{F}}{r} dv. \quad . \quad (10')$$

If **F** is solenoidal, the first integral is zero, and **F** is then the curl of a vector, as stated at the end of Art. 17. If **F** is lamellar, the second term vanishes identically, and **F** is the gradient of a scalar function.

27. Surface distribution of matter. Suppose that the matter is distributed over a surface S, not necessarily closed, in such a way that if δm is the mass on an element of surface of area δS the quotient $\delta m/\delta S$ tends to a definite finite limit σ as δS tends to zero. The quantity σ is called the *surface density* of the distribution at that point; and the matter is said to constitute a *simple stratum*. The mass on an element of area dS is σdS; and the potential due to it at a point P distant r from the element is $\sigma dS/r$. Summing for all the elements of surface, we have for the potential due to the whole stratum at a point P not on the surface

$$V = \int \frac{\sigma dS}{r} \quad . \quad . \quad . \quad . \quad (13)$$

and the value of the integral is finite and continuous.

* The theorems in Art. 28 are deduced from Green's formulæ, and are independent of the argument in this chapter.

† We leave it as an exercise for the student to verify that this value of **H** satisfies the condition div **H**=0. *Cf.* Ex. 16 at end of this chapter.

At a point P' *on the surface* the potential is defined as follows: Surround the point by a small closed curve C drawn on the surface, say a small circle of radius ϵ. Calculate the potential V' at the point due to the portion of the stratum not enclosed by C. This potential is finite, since there is now no attracting matter at the point P'. The limiting value of V' as ϵ tends to zero is what we mean by the potential at P' due to the whole stratum. This limiting value is finite and equal to the potential V at the consecutive point P just off the surface. For though the integrand becomes infinite like $\frac{1}{\epsilon}$, the area dS enclosed by C becomes infinitesimal like ϵ^2. The potential due to the simple stratum is therefore finite and continuous at any point P, and remains so as P passes through the stratum.

The intensity, however, is discontinuous at the stratum, the normal intensity

$$\mathbf{n}\cdot\nabla V = \frac{\partial V}{\partial n}$$

experiencing there a discontinuity of $4\pi\sigma$. To prove this, apply the theorem of total normal intensity to a small surface enclosing an element of the stratum. Take this surface as cylindrical, with plane ends PQ, RS parallel to the tangent plane to the surface at the element, one just on either side of the tangent plane, their distance apart being negligible compared with the linear dimensions of the element of surface enclosed. The area of the curved part of this cylindrical surface is therefore negligible compared with that of the plane faces, and the theorem of total normal intensity gives

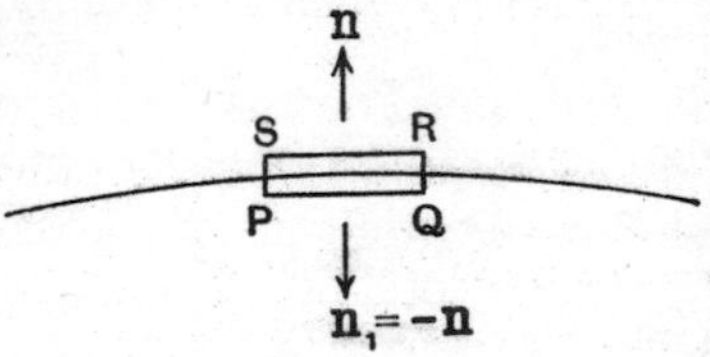

FIG. 15.

$$\mathbf{F}\cdot\mathbf{n}dS + \mathbf{F}_1\cdot\mathbf{n}_1 dS = -4\pi\sigma dS,$$

where $\mathbf{F}$, $\mathbf{F}_1$ are the values of the intensity ∇V on either side of the element, and $\mathbf{n}$, $\mathbf{n}_1$ the unit normals drawn *from* the surface on each side. Then, since $\mathbf{n}_1 = -\mathbf{n}$, we deduce the formula

$$(\mathbf{n}\cdot\nabla V)_e - (\mathbf{n}\cdot\nabla V)_i = -4\pi\sigma,$$

or

$$\left(\frac{\partial V}{\partial n}\right)_e - \left(\frac{\partial V}{\partial n}\right)_i = -4\pi\sigma \quad . \quad . \quad . \quad (14)$$

the suffixes e, i indicating the different sides of the surface, the former referring to that side for which $\mathbf{n}$ is directed from the surface.

28. Theorems on harmonic functions. The potential V due to any finite distribution of matter is harmonic in free space, that is to say, in space not occupied by this matter. Such harmonic point-functions possess certain properties easily deducible from Green's formulæ. Take a surface S enclosing a region which contains none of the attracting matter. Then the potential V satisfies $\nabla^2 V = 0$ at all points within this region. If then in Green's theorem (14) (Art. 19) we take V as this potential, and put U equal to unity, the formula becomes simply

$$\int \mathbf{n} \cdot \nabla V dS = 0 \quad . \quad . \quad . \quad . \quad (15)$$

whose interpretation is, of course, that *the total normal intensity is zero over a closed surface containing none of the attracting matter.* Or, quite generally, the surface integral of the normal derivative of an harmonic function is zero for any closed surface within which the function is regular.

In the same formula put both functions equal to the above potential V. Then we obtain the result

$$\int V \frac{\partial V}{\partial n} dS = \int (\nabla V)^2 dv \quad . \quad . \quad . \quad (16)$$

The integral on the right-hand side represents the sum of a number of positive terms. Hence also the first member of (16) is an *essentially positive* function.

Suppose now that the potential V is constant over the surface S. The last equation may then be written

$$V \int \frac{\partial V}{\partial n} dS = \int (\nabla V)^2 dv.$$

But the first member vanishes by (15). Hence the second is also zero; and as this is the sum of a number of positive terms, these must all be zero. Thus the function ∇V vanishes identically, showing that V is constant throughout the region. Hence *an harmonic function which is constant over the surface enclosing a region in which it is regular, is constant throughout that region.* In particular if the function vanishes over the boundary of the region it vanishes throughout. Thus if two harmonic functions have equal values at all points of the boundary, they are identical throughout the enclosed region.

Similarly if the normal derivative $\frac{\partial V}{\partial n}$ of the potential vanishes over the whole surface, the equation (16) becomes

$$0 = \int (\nabla V)^2 dv,$$

showing as before that V is constant throughout the region. If, then, two harmonic functions have the same normal derivative at all points of the boundary, their difference has zero normal derivative and is therefore constant throughout the region. Or, *for given values of the normal derivative at the boundary, the value of the harmonic function throughout the region is determined to an additive constant.*

Next take S as a spherical surface of centre P and radius R. Then if r is the distance from P, $\frac{1}{r}$ is constant over the surface, and so also is $\frac{\partial}{\partial n}\left(\frac{1}{r}\right)$, which has the value $-1/R^2$. Applying Green's formula (17) of Art. 20 to this region and the potential V, we have

$$4\pi V_P = \frac{1}{R}\int \frac{\partial V}{\partial n} dS + \frac{1}{R^2}\int V dS.$$

But the first integral vanishes by (15). Hence

$$V_P = \frac{1}{4\pi R^2}\int V dS.$$

That is to say, *the value of the potential at the centre of the sphere is the mean value of the potential over the surface of the sphere.* This is true for any spherical surface which does not enclose attracting matter. It follows that *the potential cannot have a maximum or minimum value at a point in free space.* For if the potential were a maximum (or minimum) at P, its value at this point would be greater (or less) than the values at all points on a small spherical surface with P as centre, and could not then be the mean of such values.

II. Equation of Thermal Conduction.

29. Fourier's law for isotropic bodies. Consider the flow of heat by conduction through the material of a body. The temperature V within the body is a finite and continuous point-function. Through any point of the body passes a level-surface of the temperature, called an *isothermal* surface; and at each point the temperature possesses a gradient ∇V in the direction normal to the isothermal surface at that point. This temperature gradient is a finite and continuous point-function.

The fundamental assumption in the mathematical theory of thermal conduction for an isotropic body is that the direction of the flow of heat at any point P is normal to the isothermal surface at that point, and that the rate of flow of heat per unit area across that surface is proportional to the temperature gradient at that point. We express this by the equation

$$\mathbf{F} = -k\nabla V \quad . \quad . \quad . \quad . \quad (17)$$

where $\mathbf{F}$ is the *flux* of heat at the point P, having the direction of the flow, and magnitude equal to the quantity of heat per unit area per unit time crossing the isothermal at P. The scalar k measures the *conductivity* of the body at P, and may be either constant or a point-function; while the negative sign indicates that the heat is passing from points at higher to others at lower temperatures. The assumption embodied in the equation (17) is called *Fourier's law*.

30. Differential equation of conduction. Let ρ denote the density of the body at P, and c the specific heat, that is to say, the amount of heat absorbed by the matter round this point per unit mass per unit rise in temperature. If then dv is the volume of an element of the body at P, a rise in temperature of dV at this point corresponds to an absorption of heat equal to $c\rho dv dV$ by the element Besides the conduction of heat from one point to another of the body, there may be a generation of heat in it due, for example, to the passage of a current of electricity through the body. Let M denote the rate of generation of heat per unit volume at the point P. Then Mdv is the rate of generation of heat within the above element.

Let S be a closed surface drawn entirely within the body, and $\mathbf{n}$ the unit outward normal to it. The rate per unit area at which heat is flowing outward across this surface is the normal resolute of the flux, and is therefore given by $\mathbf{n}\cdot\mathbf{F} = -k\nabla V\cdot\mathbf{n}$. Hence the rate at which heat is leaving that portion of the body enclosed by S is

$$-\int k\nabla V\cdot\mathbf{n}dS = -\int \text{div}\,(k\nabla V)dv$$

by the divergence theorem. At the same time, the generation of heat at a rate M per unit volume produces within this region a quantity $\int Mdv$ per unit time. Thus the total rate at which this portion is *gaining* heat from the two causes is

$$\int[\text{div}\,(k\nabla V) + M]dv.$$

This gain of heat brings about a rise of temperature throughout the region. If $\frac{\partial V}{\partial t}$ is the rate of rise of temperature at P, then $c\rho\frac{\partial V}{\partial t}dv$ is the rate of absorption of heat by the element of the body there, and $\int c\rho\frac{\partial V}{\partial t}dv$ is the rate of absorption of heat by the matter within S.

This must be equal to the rate of gain of heat just found ; so that

$$\int c\rho\frac{\partial V}{\partial t}dv = \int[\text{div}\ (k\nabla V) + M]dv.$$

And since the surface S is arbitrary, this relation holds for every element of the body. Thus the integrands must be equal, giving

$$c\rho\frac{\partial V}{\partial t} = \text{div}\ (k\nabla V) + M \quad . \quad . \quad . \quad (18)$$

This is the required differential equation of heat conduction.

If the body is *homogeneous* k is constant, and the equation assumes the simpler form

$$c\rho\frac{\partial V}{\partial t} = k\nabla^2 V + M \quad . \quad . \quad . \quad . \quad (18')$$

More frequently than not there is no internal generation of heat, that is to say, M is zero. In this case the equation for a homogeneous body becomes simply

$$\frac{\partial V}{\partial t} = \kappa\nabla^2 V \quad . \quad . \quad . \quad . \quad (18'')$$

where

$$\kappa = \frac{k}{c\rho}$$

is a quantity called the *diffusivity* or the *thermometric conductivity*.

31. A problem in heat conduction. Consider a body bounded by a surface S. Suppose that the temperature of each point of the body is known at some instant, which we may take as the initial instant ($t = 0$). Denote this point-function by V_0. Suppose also that the temperature U at the surface of the body is known everywhere and at every subsequent instant. Thus U is both a point-function and a function of t. The problem of heat conduction then requires the determination of the temperature V at any instant and for any point of the body. This temperature will be a function of t satisfying the *initial condition*

$$\underset{t \to 0}{\text{Lt}}\ V = V_0,$$

and also a function of the point P satisfying the *boundary condition* that, as P moves up to coincidence with a point T on the surface, the function V tends to coincidence with U ; or

$$\underset{P \to T}{\text{Lt}}\ V_P = U_T.$$

The temperature V will also satisfy the differential equation (18) of heat conduction, in which the function M is supposed given.

It is easy to show, in the case of no internal generation of heat ($M = 0$), that the solution of the problem is unique. For if V_1 and

V_2 are two different solutions, their difference

$$V = V_1 - V_2$$

vanishes identically over the boundary, and for $t = 0$ vanishes throughout the body ; while it satisfies the differential equation

$$c\rho \frac{\partial V}{\partial t} = \text{div } (k\nabla V) \quad . \quad . \quad . \quad (19)$$

Considering, then, the integral

$$J = \tfrac{1}{2}\int c\rho V^2 dv,$$

we have on differentiating with respect to t

$$\frac{\partial J}{\partial t} = \int c\rho V \frac{\partial V}{\partial t} dv,$$

ρ and c being independent of t. In virtue of (19) this may be written

$$\begin{aligned} \frac{\partial J}{\partial t} &= \int V \text{ div } (k\nabla V) dv \\ &= \int [\text{div } (kV\nabla V) - k(\nabla V)^2] dv. \end{aligned}$$

The volume integral due to the first term in this expression is equal to the surface integral

$$\int kV\nabla V \cdot \mathbf{n} dS,$$

which is zero because V vanishes over the boundary. Hence

$$\frac{\partial J}{\partial t} = -\int k(\nabla V)^2 dv.$$

Now since k is essentially positive, the value of this integral is positive, and therefore $\frac{\partial J}{\partial t}$ is negative. But J vanishes when $t = 0$, because V is initially zero. Hence J is negative after the initial instant. But the integral J is essentially positive, because the integrand is always positive. The assumption of different solutions to the problem thus leads to an absurdity, showing that the solution is unique.

32.* Solution of the problem. We shall assume that the body is *homogeneous*, so that k is constant. Then, in the more general case in which M is not zero, we require a solution of the equation

$$c\rho \frac{\partial V}{\partial t} = k\nabla^2 V + M \quad . \quad . \quad . \quad (18')$$

which takes the boundary value U and the initial value V_0.

* This Art. is not essential to the argument of the book.

Omitting the term containing $\frac{\partial V}{\partial t}$, we first find a solution of the differential equation

$$k\nabla^2 V + M = 0 \quad . \quad . \quad . \quad . \quad (20)$$

assuming the boundary value U. This solution is obtained at once from (20) of Art. 21, in the form

$$V = \frac{1}{4\pi}\int G\frac{M}{k}dv - \frac{1}{4\pi}\int U\frac{\partial G}{\partial n}dS \quad . \quad . \quad . \quad (21)$$

where G is the Green's function for Laplace's equation vanishing over the surface of the body, U being the value of V at the boundary, and $-M/k$ the value of $\nabla^2 V$ throughout the body.

Our next step is to find a solution of the equation

$$\frac{\partial V}{\partial t} = \kappa\nabla^2 V \quad . \quad . \quad . \quad . \quad (18'')$$

vanishing over the boundary, and taking a prescribed initial value W. For this purpose assume that V is of the form

$$V = e^{-\lambda t}\psi$$

where ψ is a point-function independent of t, and λ a constant whose value is to be determined. On substituting this value of V in (18″) we obtain for ψ the equation

$$-\lambda\psi = \kappa\nabla^2\psi \quad . \quad . \quad . \quad . \quad (22)$$

In virtue of formula (22), Art. 21, such a function ψ must satisfy the relation

$$\psi = \frac{\lambda}{4\pi\kappa}\int G\psi dv \quad . \quad . \quad . \quad . \quad (23)$$

G being the same Green's function as before ; and ψ then vanishes over the boundary because G does so. This equation (23) from which ψ is to be determined, is called a homogeneous *integral equation* with ψ as unknown and G as *kernel*. According to the theory * of such equations, (23) admits a non-zero solution only if $\frac{\lambda}{4\pi\kappa}$ is equal to one of an infinite series of real numbers, called the *characteristic numbers* of the kernel. In the present instance these numbers are all positive. For if in Green's theorem (14) of Art. 19 we put both functions equal to ψ, which vanishes over the boundary, we find in virtue of (22) that

$$\int(\nabla\psi)^2 dv = \frac{\lambda}{\kappa}\int\psi^2 dv.$$

* For the theory of integral equations the student is referred to one of the following : Bôcher, *An Introduction to the Study of Integral Equations* (Cambridge Tract, 1914) ; Heywood and Fréchet, *L'Equation de Fredholm*, etc. (Paris, 1912) ; Lalesco, *Introduction à la théorie des equations intégrales* (Paris 1912) ; Whittaker and Watson, *Modern Analysis* (3rd ed.), chapter xi.

And since both integrands and κ are essentially positive, it follows that the values of λ for which a solution ψ exists are all positive. Denote them by

$$\lambda_1, \lambda_2, \lambda_3, \ldots, \lambda_n, \ldots,$$

and the corresponding solutions of (23) by

$$\psi_1, \psi_2, \psi_3, \ldots, \psi_n, \ldots$$

There may be several solutions ψ for the same characteristic number; but in all cases these solutions can be chosen so as to satisfy the orthogonal relations.*

$$\int \psi_m \psi_n dv = \begin{matrix} 1 \text{ if } m = n \\ 0 \text{ if } m \neq n \end{matrix} \quad . \quad . \quad . \quad (24)$$

and are then called the principal system of characteristic functions. The function W gives the prescribed initial temperature, and by hypothesis vanishes over the boundary. If the derivatives of W of the first and second orders are also continuous,† the function may be expanded in an absolutely and uniformly convergent series † of the characteristic functions, in the form

$$W = A_1\psi_1 + A_2\psi_2 + \ldots + A_n\psi_n + \ldots$$

The coefficient A_n in this Fourier series are found by multiplying both members by ψ_n and integrating throughout the region. Then, in virtue of the above orthogonal relations satisfied by the characteristic functions, it follows that

$$A_n = \int W\psi_n dv.$$

The required solution of the equation (18″) vanishing over the boundary is then

$$V = \sum_{n=1}^{\infty} A_n \psi_n e^{-\lambda_n t} \quad . \quad . \quad . \quad . \quad (25)$$

for this assumes the value W when $t = 0$, and also vanishes at the boundary because each of the functions ψ does so.

Having obtained the solutions (21) and (25) of the subsidiary problems, we may deduce that of the general problem corresponding to the differential equation (18′), the boundary value U and the initial value V_0. We first find a solution V' of the equation (20) answering to the assigned boundary value U; then, as just shown,

* *Cf.* Bôcher, *loc. cit.*, Art. 12: Heywood, *loc. cit.*, Art. 35.

† Any function W may be so expanded which satisfies the same boundary condition as G, and is continuous along with its first derivatives, while its second and third derivatives are piecemeal continuous (that is to say, continuous throughout each of a finite number of subregions into which the whole region may be divided).

determine a solution V'' of (18″) vanishing over the boundary and assuming the initial value

$$W = V_0 - [V']_{t=0}.$$

The required solution of the whole problem is then

$$V = V' + V'',$$

which clearly satisfies (18′), and assumes the boundary value U and the initial value V_0.

NOTE.—*The greater part of Chapter IX. is independent of the theory of dyadics, and can be read at this stage if desired.*

EXERCISES ON CHAPTER III.

1. Show that the intensity, due to a thin uniform circular disc of surface density σ, at a point P on the axis of the disc, is $2\pi\sigma (1 - \cos\theta)$ toward the centre, 2θ being the angle subtended at P by a diameter of the disc.

2. Show that the potential due to a solid sphere of mass M and uniform density, at an *external* point distant r from the centre, is $\frac{M}{r}$; and hence that the intensity is $\frac{M}{r^2}$ toward the centre.

3. A homogeneous spherical shell has mass M and radii a and b ($<a$). Show that the potential due to it, at a point distant r from the centre, is $\frac{M}{r}$ for an *external* point, and $2\pi\rho\,(a^2 - b^2)$ at an *internal* point, where the value of the density ρ is easily written down in terms of M, a and b.

Hence show that the intensity is zero inside the shell; and that, outside the shell, it is the same as if the whole of the matter were concentrated at the centre.

4. From the results of the previous exercise, or otherwise, show that the potential *inside* the solid uniform sphere of exercise 2 is $2\pi\rho\left(a^2 - \frac{r^2}{3}\right)$ at a point distant r from the centre. Hence the intensity is $\frac{4}{3}\pi\rho r$ toward the centre.

Also verify that the potential satisfies Poisson's equation.

5. Show that two uniform spherical bodies attract each other with the same force as two particles at their centres, with masses equal to those of the two bodies.

6. Show that the equipotential surfaces and the lines of force in the field due to a uniform rod are ellipsoids and hyperbolas with the ends of the rod as foci.

7. If $\mathbf{r}$ is the position vector of a point relative to P, show that the potential at P due to a body is represented by

$$V = \tfrac{1}{2}\int \hat{\mathbf{r}}\cdot\mathbf{n}\rho dS - \tfrac{1}{2}\int \hat{\mathbf{r}}\cdot\nabla\rho dv,$$

the surface integral extending over the surface of the body and the volume integral throughout the body.

8. Hence if the body is of uniform density, and Poisson's formula

$$-4\pi\rho = \nabla^2 V = \nabla\cdot\mathbf{F}$$

holds, the potential at P is

$$V = -\frac{1}{8\pi}\int \hat{\mathbf{r}}\cdot\mathbf{n}\nabla^2 V dS = -\frac{1}{8\pi}\int \hat{\mathbf{r}}\cdot\mathbf{n} \text{ div } \mathbf{F} dS.$$

Thus the value of the potential may be calculated if that of the intensity is known at all points of the surface of the body.

9. If the intensity $\mathbf{F}$ is everywhere parallel to a given plane, and is constant along any line perpendicular to that plane, show that curl $\mathbf{F}$ is perpendicular to the plane.

10. If the potential at a distance r from the origin is e^{-r^2}, show that the density is

$$\rho = 2e^{-r^2}(2r^2 - 3).$$

[Use Poisson's theorem, and (24) of Art. 10.]

11. The equilibrium of a free isolated particle attracted by fixed bodies cannot be stable for all displacements or unstable for all, but must be stable with respect to some and unstable with respect to others.

12. If two different bodies have the same equipotential surfaces throughout any empty space, their potentials throughout that space are connected by a linear relation.

13. If two finite bodies have the same external equipotential surfaces and have equal masses, their intensities are equal at all external points.

14. If W is a point-function, and V_1, V_2 are two solutions of the differential equation

$$\text{div }(W\nabla V) = 0,$$

which have equal values at all points of a closed surface S, show that $V_1 = V_2$ throughout the enclosed space (*cf.* Ex. 16, Chap. II.).

Similarly if the normal derivatives of V_1 and V_2 are equal at all points of S, the functions are equal throughout the enclosed space.

15. Deduce Poisson's theorem by applying Green's formula (17) of Art. 20 to the region bounded by a sphere of infinite radius, showing that the surface integrals vanish over the surface of this sphere.

16. Verify that the value of $\mathbf{H}$ given by formula (12) of Art. 26 satisfies the condition div $\mathbf{H} = 0$.

The formula (12) gives the value of **H** at a point P, dv being the volume of an element at another point Q, and r being the distance between these points. If ∇ refers to variation of the point P, and ∇' to variation of the point Q,

$$\nabla\left(\frac{1}{r}\right) = -\frac{1}{r^3}\overrightarrow{QP} = \frac{1}{r^3}\overrightarrow{PQ} = -\nabla'\left(\frac{1}{r}\right).$$

Hence writing $\mathbf{W} \equiv \text{curl } \mathbf{F}$ we have

$$4\pi\nabla\cdot\mathbf{H} = \nabla\cdot\int\frac{\mathbf{W}}{r}dv = \int\mathbf{W}\cdot\nabla\left(\frac{1}{r}\right)dv$$

by (15) of Art. 8, **W** being constant relative for variation of the point P. Then, in virtue of the above result, we may write this

$$4\pi\nabla\cdot\mathbf{H} = -\int\mathbf{W}\cdot\nabla'\left(\frac{1}{r}\right)dv$$
$$= -\int\left[\nabla'\cdot\left(\frac{\mathbf{W}}{r}\right) - \frac{1}{r}\nabla'\cdot\mathbf{W}\right]dv.$$

The last term vanishes identically because **W** is a solenoidal function. Transforming the remaining integral by the divergence theorem we obtain

$$4\pi \text{ div } \mathbf{H} = -\int\frac{\mathbf{W}\cdot\mathbf{n}}{r}dS.$$

And this surface integral has the value zero, because **F** vanishes identically at infinity, or outside a finite region of space. Hence the vector **H** is solenoidal.

17. Use Green's formula of Art. 20 to prove that, if S is an equipotential surface of an attracting system, the potential outside S is the same as that due to a simple stratum over S of surface density,

$$\sigma = \frac{1}{4\pi}\mathbf{F}\cdot\mathbf{n} = \frac{1}{4\pi}\frac{\partial V}{\partial n},$$

and that the total mass of the stratum is equal to the mass of that portion of the attracting system which is inside S. Such a stratum is called an *equipotential layer* for the system. (This theorem is due to Chasles and Gauss.)

18. Show that the equation (18) of thermal conduction, when expressed in curvilinear coördinates, is

$$h_1h_2h_3c\rho\frac{\partial V}{\partial t} = \frac{\partial}{\partial u}\left(\frac{h_2h_3}{h_1}k\frac{\partial V}{\partial u}\right) + \frac{\partial}{\partial v}\left(\frac{h_3h_1}{h_2}k\frac{\partial V}{\partial v}\right) + \frac{\partial}{\partial w}\left(\frac{h_1h_2}{h_3}k\frac{\partial V}{\partial w}\right).$$

In particular write the equation in spherical polar coordinates and in cylindrical coordinates.

19. The inner and outer surfaces of a conducting shell are concentric spheres of radii r_1, r_2, and are maintained at constant temperatures v_1, v_2 respectively. If the conductivity of the substance is a linear function $f(v)$ of the temperature, show that the quantity of heat transmitted through the shell in unit time is the same as if the conductivity had the uniform values $f\left(\frac{v_1 + v_2}{2}\right)$.

CHAPTER IV.

MOTION OF FRICTIONLESS FLUIDS.

33. Pressure at a point. Consider any surface passing through the point P within the fluid. There is a mutual action between the portions of the fluid on either side of this surface; and the *intensity of stress* across the surface at the point P is defined as the force per unit area. That is to say, if δS is the area of the element of surface around P, and δF the total stress across that element, the intensity of stress is given by

$$\operatorname*{Lt}_{\delta S \to 0} \frac{\delta F}{\delta S}.$$

For frictionless fluids the intensity of stress across the surface is everywhere normal to the surface, and is therefore represented by $p\mathbf{n}$, where $\mathbf{n}$ is the unit normal at the point considered and p the scalar intensity of stress.

Now the value of p at a definite point P in a frictionless fluid is independent of $\mathbf{n}$, that is to say, is the same for all surfaces passing through P. To prove this, consider the equation of motion of the fluid within the elementary tetrahedron $PLMN$, whose edges through P are mutually perpendicular, and parallel to the unit vectors $\mathbf{i}$, $\mathbf{j}$, $\mathbf{k}$. The unit normal to the face LMN drawn outward from the tetrahedron is expressible as

$$\mathbf{n} = l\mathbf{i} + m\mathbf{j} + n\mathbf{k}.$$

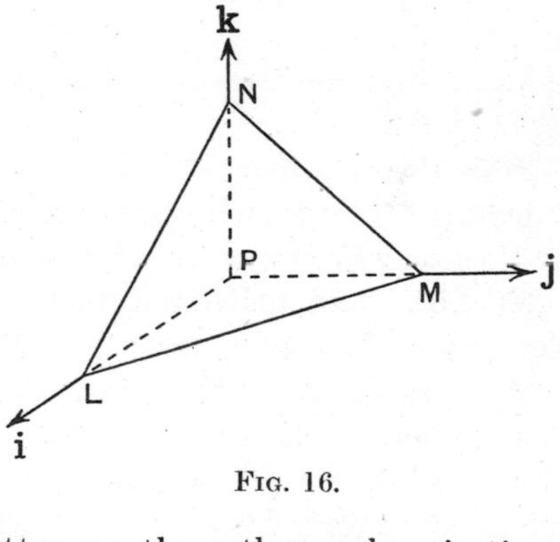

FIG. 16.

Let A be the area of this face, and A_1, A_2, A_3 those of the faces perpendicular to $\mathbf{i}$, $\mathbf{j}$, $\mathbf{k}$ respectively. Then, since the latter are the orthogonal projections of the face LMN upon their respective planes, it follows that

$$A_1 = lA, \quad A_2 = mA, \quad A_3 = nA.$$

If now $\bar{p}$ is the average intensity of stress across the face LMN, and $\bar{p}_1, \bar{p}_2, \bar{p}_3$ those across the other three faces, the total forces across the four faces, acting on the fluid within the tetrahedron, are given by

$$-\bar{p}A\mathbf{n}, \quad \bar{p}_1A_1\mathbf{i}, \quad \bar{p}_2A_2\mathbf{j}, \quad \bar{p}_3A_3\mathbf{k}.$$

The volume of the tetrahedron is $\frac{1}{3}hA$, where h is the perpendicular distance of P from the face LMN. Hence if ρ is the average density of the fluid within the tetrahedron, and $\mathbf{F}$ the average impressed force per unit mass acting on it, the total impressed force on that body of fluid is $\frac{1}{3}hA\rho\mathbf{F}$.

Consider now the equation of motion for this element of fluid. This is obtained by equating the vector sum of all the forces on the element to the product of the total mass and the acceleration of the c.m. If then $\mathbf{a}$ is the acceleration of the c.m., the equation is

$$\tfrac{1}{3}hA\rho\mathbf{F} - \bar{p}A\mathbf{n} + \bar{p}_1A_1\mathbf{i} + \bar{p}_2A_2\mathbf{j} + \bar{p}_3A_3\mathbf{k} = \tfrac{1}{3}hA\rho\mathbf{a},$$

which, on division by A and rearranging, becomes

$$l\bar{p}_1\mathbf{i} + m\bar{p}_2\mathbf{j} + n\bar{p}_3\mathbf{k} - \bar{p}(l\mathbf{i} + m\mathbf{j} + n\mathbf{k}) = \tfrac{1}{3}h\rho(\mathbf{a} - \mathbf{F}).$$

Now let the volume of the element tend to zero, the face LMN moving normally to itself towards the point P. Then h tends to zero; and the average stress-intensities $\bar{p}, \bar{p}_1, \bar{p}_2, \bar{p}_3$ have as their limiting values the stress-intensities p, p_1, p_2, p_3 at the point P across planes perpendicular to $\mathbf{n}$, $\mathbf{i}$, $\mathbf{j}$, $\mathbf{k}$ respectively. Since, then, the second member of the last equation tends to zero, the equation becomes

$$l(p_1 - p)\mathbf{i} + m(p_2 - p)\mathbf{j} + n(p_3 - p)\mathbf{k} = 0.$$

The coefficients of $\mathbf{i}$, $\mathbf{j}$, $\mathbf{k}$ must therefore vanish identically; and since this is true for all values of l, m, n, it follows that

$$p = p_1 = p_2 = p_3,$$

showing that the stress-intensity at P is the same for all surfaces through that point.

Since then p is independent of the direction of the surface, and has a definite value for each point of the fluid, it is a scalar point-function, and will be referred to as the *pressure* at the point P.

34. Local and individual rates of change of a point-function. Let ψ be a (scalar or vector) point-function varying continuously with elapse of time. It is then a function of the position variable $\mathbf{r}$ of the point considered, and also of the time variable t. The rate of change of the value of ψ at a fixed point P is its rate of change relative to t, the variable $\mathbf{r}$ then having a fixed value. This is called the *local* rate of change at P, and is denoted by $\dfrac{\partial\psi}{\partial t}$, being the partial derivative of ψ with respect to t.

Suppose now that a particle of fluid always has associated with it the value of ψ corresponding to the point occupied by it. Then the value of this function associated with the particle at P is altering, partly because the value of ψ at P is altering, and partly because the particle is moving from that point to another. The rate of change of ψ associated with the particle is called the *individual* rate of change, and will be denoted by $\frac{d\psi}{dt}$. Thus $\frac{d\psi}{dt}$ is the sum of the local rate of change $\frac{\partial\psi}{\partial t}$, and the rate of change due to the velocity $\mathbf{v}$ of the particle. Now in a short interval dt the particle moves from P to Q, a distance ds such that

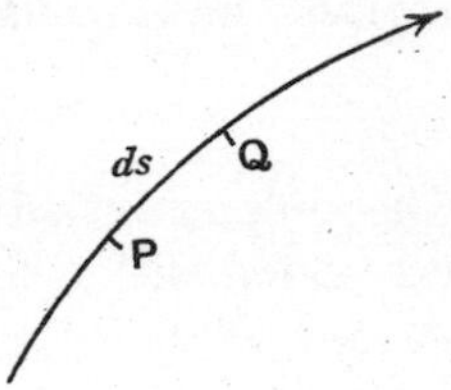

FIG. 17.

$$\overrightarrow{PQ} = \mathbf{v}dt = \mathbf{t}ds,$$

$\mathbf{t}$ being the unit tangent to the path of the particle. Hence the change in ψ due to the motion from P to Q is

$$\frac{\partial\psi}{\partial s}ds = \mathbf{t}\cdot\nabla\psi ds = \mathbf{v}\cdot\nabla\psi dt,$$

so that the rate of change of ψ due to the velocity of the particle is $\mathbf{v}\cdot\nabla\psi$. Thus the local and individual rates of change of ψ are connected by the relation

$$\frac{d\psi}{dt} = \frac{\partial\psi}{\partial t} + \mathbf{v}\cdot\nabla\psi \quad . \quad . \quad . \quad . \quad (1)$$

Suppose for instance we put $\psi = \mathbf{v}$, the velocity of the particle of fluid at the point considered. Then the value of $\mathbf{v}$ associated with a fixed point of the region is the value belonging to the different particles as they successively occupy that point. The rate of change of $\mathbf{v}$ for this fixed point is $\frac{\partial\mathbf{v}}{\partial t}$. But if we fix our attention on a definite particle as it moves from point to point, the rate of change of its velocity is the individual rate of change $\frac{d\mathbf{v}}{dt}$, and this is the acceleration $\mathbf{a}$ of the particle. Thus

$$\mathbf{a} = \frac{d\mathbf{v}}{dt} = \frac{\partial\mathbf{v}}{\partial t} + \mathbf{v}\cdot\nabla\mathbf{v} \quad . \quad . \quad . \quad (2)$$

is the instantaneous acceleration of a particle of the fluid.

35. Equation of continuity. The density ρ of the fluid is a point-function in the region occupied by the fluid. There is an important kinematical relation connecting ρ and $\mathbf{v}$, which is a mathematical expression of the conservation of mass, and is known as the *equation of continuity*.

Consider that portion of the fluid which is contained within a closed surface S *fixed in space*. The rate of increase of the mass enclosed by the surface is

$$\frac{\partial}{\partial t}\int \rho dv = \int \frac{\partial \rho}{\partial t} dv.$$

The differentiation here is local, each element of volume being associated with a fixed point, and ρ being the value of the density at that point. The volume dv does not vary with t. Now the above rate of increase of the enclosed mass must be equal to the rate at which matter is flowing into the region. If $\mathbf{n}$ is the unit outward normal to the surface S, the inward normal velocity is $-\mathbf{n}\cdot\mathbf{v}$ and the mass of fluid entering per second across the element dS is $-\rho\mathbf{n}\cdot\mathbf{v}dS$. Thus the rate of increase of the mass inside S must be equal to

$$-\int \rho\mathbf{n}\cdot\mathbf{v}dS = -\int \text{div }(\rho\mathbf{v})dv$$

by the divergence theorem. Equating this to the original expression we have

$$\int \frac{\partial \rho}{\partial t} dv = -\int \text{div }(\rho\mathbf{v})dv.$$

And as this is true for the region bounded by any closed surface, the integrands must be equal at all points, showing that

$$\frac{\partial \rho}{\partial t} + \text{div }(\rho\mathbf{v}) = 0 \quad . \quad . \quad . \quad . \quad (3)$$

This is the required relation. It may also be written

$$\frac{\partial \rho}{\partial t} + \mathbf{v}\cdot\nabla\rho + \rho \text{ div } \mathbf{v} = 0$$

or

$$\frac{d\rho}{dt} + \rho\cdot\text{div } \mathbf{v} = 0 \quad . \quad . \quad . \quad . \quad (3')$$

Consider a definite element of the fluid, consisting always of the same particles. As it moves, its mass remains constant; or

$$\rho dv = \text{const.}$$

Differentiating logarithmically we have

$$\frac{1}{\rho}\frac{d\rho}{dt} = -\frac{1}{dv}\frac{d(dv)}{dt}.$$

The equation (3′) then gives

$$\text{div } \mathbf{v} = -\frac{1}{\rho}\frac{d\rho}{dt} = \frac{1}{dv}\frac{d(dv)}{dt} \quad . \quad . \quad . \quad (3'')$$

Hence the *physical interpretation*, that the divergence of the velocity is equal to the time rate of increase of volume per unit volume.

If the fluid is *incompressible* the density of any particle is invariable in time, so that $\frac{d\rho}{dt}$ is zero. The equation of continuity for an incompressible fluid is therefore simply

$$\operatorname{div} \mathbf{v} = 0 \quad . \quad . \quad . \quad . \quad (4)$$

For all fluids there is a relation between the pressure and the density. A liquid is practically incompressible, so that ρ is constant. For isothermal changes of a gas p/ρ is constant; while for adiabatic changes p/ρ^γ is constant, γ being the ratio of the two specific heats of the gas, approximately 1·408 in the case of air. For the general changes of a gas p is a function of both ρ and the temperature θ. We shall here confine ourselves to the cases in which p is a function of ρ only,

$$\left.\begin{array}{l} p = f(\rho) \\ \text{or} \quad \rho = F(p) \end{array}\right\} \quad . \quad . \quad . \quad . \quad (5)$$

36. Boundary condition. At the surface of the fluid the equation of continuity is replaced by another kinematical relation. Thus, if the boundary is *fixed*, the normal velocity of the fluid there must be zero, or

$$\mathbf{n} \cdot \mathbf{v} = 0 \quad . \quad . \quad . \quad . \quad . \quad \text{i}$$

At a surface of discontinuity for the velocity, the normal velocity must be the same for particles on either side of the surface, otherwise a fissure would develop there. Thus if $\mathbf{v}_1$, $\mathbf{v}_2$ are the velocities on either side of the surface,

$$\mathbf{n} \cdot \mathbf{v}_1 = \mathbf{n} \cdot \mathbf{v}_2 \quad . \quad . \quad . \quad . \quad \text{ii}$$

This relation also holds at the surface, separating the fluid from a moving solid in contact with it.

More generally, if $F(\mathbf{r}, t) = 0$ is the equation of a boundary surface, the relation

$$\frac{dF}{dt} = 0 \quad . \quad . \quad . \quad . \quad . \quad \text{iii}$$

must hold at every point of it. For the velocity, relative to the boundary, of a particle of fluid at that boundary is tangential to it, otherwise the fluid would be flowing across it, and it would not be a boundary. Since then a particle at this surface is moving instantaneously along it, the individual rate of variation of F for surface particles is zero. Hence the formula iii.

37. Eulerian equation of motion. Consider the fluid within a closed surface S, which moves with the fluid, containing always the same particles and therefore always the same mass. Let dv be the volume of an element of the enclosed region, also moving with the fluid and therefore containing always the same particles. Then the mass ρdv of this element remains constant. If $\mathbf{v}$ is the velocity and $\frac{d\mathbf{v}}{dt}$ the acceleration of a particle of fluid, the rate of increase of the momentum of the above element is $\frac{d\mathbf{v}}{dt}\rho dv$. And if $\mathbf{F}$ is the external force per unit mass acting on the fluid, the force on this element is $\mathbf{F}\rho dv$.

Consider now the whole body of fluid within S. The force on the surface element dS due to pressure of the surrounding fluid is $-p\mathbf{n}dS$. Hence, equating the rate of increase of momentum of the whole fluid to the total force acting on the fluid, we have

$$\begin{aligned}\int\frac{d\mathbf{v}}{dt}\rho dv &= \int\mathbf{F}\rho dv - \int p\mathbf{n}dS\\ &= \int(\rho\mathbf{F} - \nabla p)dv\end{aligned}$$

by (5) of Art. 15. And since this relation holds for the region bounded by any closed surface drawn in the fluid, the integrands must be identical, or

$$\left.\begin{aligned}\mathbf{F} - \frac{1}{\rho}\nabla p &= \frac{d\mathbf{v}}{dt}\\ &= \frac{\partial\mathbf{v}}{\partial t} + \mathbf{v}\cdot\nabla\mathbf{v}\end{aligned}\right\} \quad . \quad . \quad . \quad (6)$$

This is the vector equivalent of Euler's three scalar equations of motion for the fluid.

We may write this equation in a different form. For, by (19) of Art. 8,

$$\tfrac{1}{2}\nabla(\mathbf{v}\cdot\mathbf{v}) = \mathbf{v}\cdot\nabla\mathbf{v} + \mathbf{v}\times\text{curl }\mathbf{v}.$$

Subtracting this from the second form of (6) we have

$$\mathbf{F} - \frac{1}{\rho}\nabla p - \tfrac{1}{2}\nabla\mathbf{v}^2 = \frac{\partial\mathbf{v}}{\partial t} - \mathbf{v}\times\text{curl }\mathbf{v} \quad . \quad . \quad (6')$$

a form of the equation which is frequently found useful.

Suppose now that the external forces form a *conservative system*; that is to say, that $\mathbf{F}$ is the gradient of a scalar point-function. Then we may write

$$\mathbf{F} = -\nabla V.$$

Further, since p is a function of the density ρ, we may define a function P by the equation

$$\frac{1}{\rho}\nabla p = \nabla P.$$

Then for an infinitesimal displacement $d\mathbf{r}$ of the current point we have

$$\frac{1}{\rho}d\mathbf{r}\cdot\nabla p = d\mathbf{r}\cdot\nabla P;$$

or, by (5) of Art. 3, if dp and dP are the corresponding increments in p and P, we may write this

$$\frac{dp}{\rho} = dP.$$

On integration we find then

$$P = \int^p \frac{dp}{\rho}$$

for the explicit expression of the function P. The equation (6′) then becomes

$$\frac{\partial \mathbf{v}}{\partial t} - \mathbf{v}\times\text{curl }\mathbf{v} = -\nabla(V + P + \tfrac{1}{2}\mathbf{v}^2)$$

$$= \nabla U \quad . \quad . \quad . \quad . \quad . \quad (7)$$

where

$$U = -(V + P + \tfrac{1}{2}\mathbf{v}^2)$$

is a scalar point-function. Or, writing curl $\mathbf{v} = 2\mathbf{w}$, we have for the equation of motion of a fluid acted on by a conservative system of forces

$$\frac{\partial \mathbf{v}}{\partial t} - 2\mathbf{v}\times\mathbf{w} = \nabla U \quad . \quad . \quad . \quad . \quad (7')$$

38. Definitions. A *line of flow* is a line drawn in the fluid such that, at any point of it, the direction of the tangent is that of the velocity of the fluid.

The quantity $\mathbf{w} = \frac{1}{2}$ curl $\mathbf{v}$ is called the *vorticity* or *molecular rotation*, for a reason that will be explained later. A *vortex line* is one whose direction at any point is the direction of $\mathbf{w}$ for that point.

The *circulation* along any curved path AB in the fluid is the tangential line integral of the velocity along that path; that is,

$$\int_A^B \mathbf{v}\cdot\mathbf{t}ds \quad \text{or} \quad \int_A^B \mathbf{v}\cdot d\mathbf{r}.$$

If the path is *closed*, and S is an open surface bounded by it, Stokes's theorem gives for the circulation round the path

$$\int_0 \mathbf{v}\cdot d\mathbf{r} = \int \mathbf{n}\cdot \text{curl }\mathbf{v}dS = 2\int \mathbf{n}\cdot\mathbf{w}dS.$$

Thus the circulation round a closed path drawn in the fluid is equal to twice the normal surface integral of the vorticity over any open surface bounded by that path, and lying entirely in the fluid.

39. Fluid in equilibrium. For a fluid at rest and in equilibrium, $\mathbf{v}$ and $\frac{d\mathbf{v}}{dt}$ are identically zero, and the equation (6) becomes simply

$$\mathbf{F} = \frac{1}{\rho}\nabla p.$$

When, as we have assumed, the pressure is a function of the density only, this may be written

$$\mathbf{F} = \nabla P,$$

so that equilibrium is then possible only when the impressed force $\mathbf{F}$ has a scalar potential $-V$. Then the last equation becomes

$$\nabla(V + P) = 0,$$
$$V + P = \text{const.}$$

Thus, since P depends only on p, the surfaces of constant force potential coincide with those of constant pressure, and therefore also with those of constant density. In the absence of impressed forces the pressure is constant throughout the fluid.

If, however, p is not a function of ρ only, the equation

$$\rho\mathbf{F} = \nabla p$$

gives, on taking the curl of both members,

$$\rho \text{ curl } \mathbf{F} - \mathbf{F}\times\nabla\rho = 0.$$

When we then form the scalar product of each term with $\mathbf{F}$, the triple product arising from the second term vanishes, showing that

$$\mathbf{F}\cdot \text{curl } \mathbf{F} = 0.$$

In this case the force $\mathbf{F}$ need not have a potential; but equilibrium is possible only when the curl of the impressed force is perpendicular to the force itself.

40. Equation of energy. Consider, as in Art. 37, a closed surface S, moving with the fluid and therefore containing always the same body of fluid. Let dv be the volume of an element consisting always of the same particles, so that $\frac{d}{dt}(\rho dv) = 0$. Then the kinetic energy of the fluid within S is

$$T = \tfrac{1}{2}\int \mathbf{v}^2 \rho dv,$$

and its rate of increase is

$$\frac{dT}{dt} = \int \rho\mathbf{v}\cdot\frac{d\mathbf{v}}{dt}dv$$
$$= \int \rho\mathbf{v}\cdot\mathbf{F}dv - \int \mathbf{v}\cdot\nabla p dv$$

in virtue of (6). Now we may transform the last term thus. By formula (15) of Art. 8,

$$\int \mathbf{v}\cdot\nabla p dv = \int [\text{div } (p\mathbf{v}) - p \text{ div } \mathbf{v}]dv$$
$$= \int p\mathbf{v}\cdot\mathbf{n}dS - \int p\frac{d}{dt}(dv),$$

the last step following by the divergence theorem and formula (3″) above. The expression for the rate of increase of the kinetic energy is therefore equivalent to

$$\frac{dT}{dt} = \int \rho\mathbf{v}\cdot\mathbf{F}dv - \int p\mathbf{v}\cdot\mathbf{n}dS + \int p\frac{d}{dt}(dv).$$

The first term represents the rate at which the impressed forces are doing work on the fluid within S; the second term is the rate at which the pressure is doing work on this fluid; while the last term is the rate at which this body of fluid is doing work in overcoming the pressure; that is to say, the rate at which it is losing intrinsic energy by expansion.

41. Steady motion. The motion of the fluid is said to be *steady* when the values of the functions at any point are invariable with respect to the time, that is, when all their partial derivatives with respect to t are zero. On the assumption of conservative impressed forces, and a functional relation between p and ρ only, the equation of motion then becomes

$$2\mathbf{w}\times\mathbf{v} = -\nabla(V + P + \tfrac{1}{2}\mathbf{v}^2) \quad . \quad . \quad . \quad (8)$$

And since $\frac{\partial\rho}{\partial t} = 0$, the equation of continuity is

$$\text{div } (\rho\mathbf{v}) = 0 \quad . \quad . \quad . \quad . \quad . \quad (9)$$

The scalar product of the first member of (8) with either $\mathbf{v}$ or $\mathbf{w}$ is zero. Hence

$$\mathbf{v}\cdot\nabla U = 0$$

and

$$\mathbf{w}\cdot\nabla U = 0.$$

Since then the gradient of U is perpendicular to both $\mathbf{v}$ and $\mathbf{w}$, the expression $(V + P + \frac{1}{2}\mathbf{v}^2)$ is constant along a line of flow, and also along a vortex line. The level-surfaces of the function U, therefore, contain a double system of lines, viz. lines of flow and vortex lines.

42. Impulsive generation of motion. Suppose that there is a sudden change in the motion of the fluid, due to a very large impressed force $\mathbf{F}$ and a very large pressure p acting for a very short interval of time, so that the displacement of any particle during this short interval is negligible. Then, on the assumption that no waves of compression are set up, we find on integrating the equation of motion (6) through the indefinitely short period of the impulses

$$\int\frac{d\mathbf{v}}{dt}dt = \int\mathbf{F}dt - \frac{1}{\rho}\int\nabla p dt.$$

If then $\mathbf{v}_0$ and $\mathbf{v}$ are the velocities before and after the change, $\mathbf{F}^* = \int\mathbf{F}dt$ the impulsive impressed force,† and $p^* = \int p dt$ the impulsive pressure, we may write the equation of motion in the form

$$\mathbf{v} - \mathbf{v}_0 = \mathbf{F}^* - \frac{1}{\rho}\nabla p^*.$$

In the case of a *liquid* ρ is constant; and if the impulses are superficial to the liquid, $\mathbf{F}^* = 0$. Then, taking the divergence of both members of the last equation, we have in virtue of the equation (4) of continuity

$$\nabla^2 p^* = 0.$$

If the motion of the liquid were generated from rest by an impulsive pressure p^*, we should have

$$\mathbf{v} = -\frac{1}{\rho}\nabla p^*.$$

Irrotational Motion.

43. Velocity potential. If the vorticity is everywhere zero the motion is said to be *irrotational*. In this case, since curl $\mathbf{v}$ vanishes identically, the velocity is the gradient of a scalar point-function, or

$$\mathbf{v} = -\nabla\phi,$$

ϕ being called the *velocity potential*. The lines of flow are then everywhere normal to the level-surfaces of the velocity potential.

The equation of motion can always be integrated when the impressed forces are conservative and the motion is irrotational. For then (7′) becomes

$$\frac{\partial\mathbf{v}}{\partial t} = \nabla U;$$

that is,

$$-\nabla\frac{\partial\phi}{\partial t} = \nabla U.$$

Hence

$$V + P + \tfrac{1}{2}\mathbf{v}^2 - \frac{\partial\phi}{\partial t} = F(t) \quad . \quad . \quad . \quad (10$$

where $F(t)$ is independent of the point considered, and is a function

† *Cf.* Vol. I., Art. 73.

of t only. But an arbitrary additive function of t may be absorbed in the velocity potential, leaving $\nabla\phi$ unaltered. Hence (10) may be written without loss of generality

$$V + P + \tfrac{1}{2}\mathbf{v}^2 - \frac{\partial\phi}{\partial t} = \text{const} \quad . \quad . \quad . \quad (10')$$

The *equation of continuity*, in terms of the velocity potential, is

$$\frac{d\rho}{dt} - \rho\nabla^2\phi = 0 \quad . \quad . \quad . \quad . \quad (11)$$

or

$$\nabla^2\phi - \frac{d}{dt}\log\rho = 0 \quad . \quad . \quad . \quad . \quad (11')$$

which, for an incompressible fluid, is simply

$$\nabla^2\phi = 0 \quad . \quad . \quad . \quad . \quad (11'')$$

In this case, then, the theorems on harmonic functions, proved in Art. 28, apply to the velocity potential.

If the irrotational motion is also *steady*, equation (10′) becomes

$$V + P + \tfrac{1}{2}\mathbf{v}^2 = \text{const} \quad . \quad . \quad . \quad . \quad (12)$$

which was previously shown to hold along a line of flow or a vortex line whether the motion is irrotational or not. If we are dealing with the steady motion of a uniform liquid under the action of gravity, $P = p/\rho$ and $V = gz$ where z is the height of the point above a fixed level. The equation (12) then becomes

$$z + \frac{p}{\rho g} + \frac{\mathbf{v}^2}{2g} = \text{const} \quad . \quad . \quad . \quad . \quad (13)$$

which is known as *Bernoulli's Theorem*.

44. Definition. A *simply connected* (or *acyclic*) *region* is one in which all paths connecting any two points within the region can be deformed into one another without passing outside the region.

For such a region, given a closed curve lying entirely within it, there always exists an open surface bounded by this curve and lying entirely within the region.

Theorem 1. *For the irrotational motion of a fluid in a simply connected region, the velocity potential must be single-valued.*

For, along any path joining two points A, R, the change in the velocity potential from A to R is

$$\phi_R - \phi_A = \int_A^R \nabla\phi\cdot d\mathbf{r} = -\int_A^R \mathbf{v}\cdot d\mathbf{r},$$

and this is the same for all paths. For if we consider the closed curve made up of two separate paths APR, AQR (Fig. 5), and an open surface bounded by this curve and lying within the region,

Stokes's theorem gives

$$\int_0 \mathbf{v}\cdot d\mathbf{r} = \int \mathbf{n}\cdot \operatorname{curl} \mathbf{v} dS,$$

which is zero because curl $\mathbf{v}$ vanishes identically. Hence $\phi_B - \phi_A$ is the same for all paths.

Cor. *In irrotational motion, the circulation round any closed path drawn in the fluid is zero.*

Theorem 2. *An incompressible fluid filling a simply connected region within a rigid shell cannot have an irrotational motion relative to the shell.*

Assuming such a motion possible, let $\mathbf{v}$ be the velocity of the fluid relative to the shell and ϕ the velocity potential. The equation of continuity is $\nabla^2\phi = 0$. If S is the surface of the shell bounding the fluid, Green's theorem gives

$$\int \mathbf{v}^2 dv = \int (-\nabla\phi)^2 dv = -\int \phi\mathbf{v}\cdot\mathbf{n} dS - \int \phi\nabla^2\phi dv.$$

Now both these integrals vanish ; the last on account of the equation of continuity, and the other because at the boundary S the normal velocity $\mathbf{v}\cdot\mathbf{n}$ relative to the shell is zero. Therefore the first member vanishes, or

$$\int \mathbf{v}^2 dv = 0.$$

And since this definite integral is the sum of a number of essentially positive terms, the integrand must vanish identically, giving $\mathbf{v} = 0$ throughout the fluid. Thus the theorem is established.

45. Theorem 3. *If a mass of liquid is set in motion by giving prescribed velocities to its boundaries, the kinetic energy in the actual motion is less than that in any other motion consistent with the same velocities of the boundaries.*

Let T be the kinetic energy of the actual motion and ϕ the velocity potential ; T_1 the kinetic energy and $\mathbf{v}_1$ the velocity in any other possible state of motion. Then div $\mathbf{v}_1 = 0$ is the equation of continuity. And since the boundary has the same velocity in both cases, the condition to be satisfied there is by Art. 36 :

$$\mathbf{n}\cdot\mathbf{v} = \mathbf{n}\cdot\mathbf{v}_1 \quad . \quad . \quad . \quad . \quad \text{i}$$

Now

$$T_1 - T = \tfrac{1}{2}\rho\int(\mathbf{v}_1{}^2 - \mathbf{v}^2)dv$$

$$= \tfrac{1}{2}\rho\int[2\mathbf{v}\cdot(\mathbf{v}_1 - \mathbf{v}) + (\mathbf{v}_1 - \mathbf{v})^2]dv.$$

Now the first part of this expression may be written

$$\rho\int \mathbf{v}\cdot(\mathbf{v}_1 - \mathbf{v})dv = -\rho\int \nabla\phi\cdot(\mathbf{v}_1 - \mathbf{v})dv$$
$$= -\rho\int [\text{div}\ \phi(\mathbf{v}_1 - \mathbf{v}) - \phi\ \text{div}\ (\mathbf{v}_1 - \mathbf{v})]dv.$$

The last term vanishes in virtue of the equation of continuity. Then by the divergence theorem the integral is equal to

$$-\rho\int \phi(\mathbf{v}_1 - \mathbf{v})\cdot\mathbf{n}dS,$$

which vanishes on account of i. Hence finally

$$T_1 - T = \tfrac{1}{2}\rho\int (\mathbf{v}_1 - \mathbf{v})^2 dv,$$

and is therefore positive because the integrand is positive and not zero. This proves the theorem.

46. Source, sink, or doublet in a liquid. In the theory of moving liquids the conception of a source is sometimes useful. A *source* is a point from which the liquid is imagined to flow out uniformly in all directions. The velocity is then a function of the distance r from the source. If the flux outward across a closed surface surrounding the source is $4\pi m$, the source is said to be of " strength " m. A negative source is called a *sink*.

The motion of a liquid due to a source in it is irrotational. For, by symmetry, the velocity at any point is of the form $f(r)\mathbf{r}$, where $\mathbf{r}$ is the position vector of the point relative to the source, and $f(r)$ is a scalar function of r. Then

$$2\mathbf{w} = \text{curl}\ \mathbf{v} = \nabla f \times \mathbf{r} + f\ \text{curl}\ \mathbf{r}.$$

The first term vanishes in virtue of (9) Art. 5, and the second because curl $\mathbf{r}$ is zero. Thus the vorticity is everywhere zero. There is therefore a velocity potential ϕ whose value is

$$\phi = \frac{m}{r}.$$

For this makes the velocity

$$\mathbf{v} = -\nabla\phi = \frac{m\mathbf{r}}{r^3},$$

giving the correct value $4\pi m$ for the total outward flux across, say, a spherical surface with centre at the source. And the equation of continuity $\nabla^2\phi = 0$ is also satisfied, because $\frac{1}{r}$ is a solution of Laplace's equation.

Imagine a combination of equal and opposite sources of strengths

$\pm m'$, the sink being at the origin and the source at the neighbouring point $\delta\mathbf{s}$. Let $\delta\mathbf{s}$ tend to zero in such a way that the product of its module δs and the strength m' remains finite and equal to μ. Then the limiting arrangement is called a "double source" or *doublet* of strength μ. The axis of the doublet is the line through it in the limiting direction of $\delta\mathbf{s}$. The velocity potential due to the doublet is the sum of those due to the source and the sink. The sink at the origin gives rise to a velocity potential,

$$\phi_1 = -\frac{m'}{r},$$

and the source at the point $\delta\mathbf{s}$ to the potential

$$-(\phi_1 + \delta\mathbf{s}\cdot\nabla\phi_1) = \frac{m'}{r} + \delta\mathbf{s}\cdot\nabla\left(\frac{m'}{r}\right).$$

Hence the combined velocity potential is

$$\phi = m'\delta\mathbf{s}\cdot\nabla\left(\frac{1}{r}\right) = \mu\hat{\mathbf{s}}\cdot\nabla\left(\frac{1}{r}\right),$$

$\hat{\mathbf{s}}$ being the unit vector parallel to the axis of the doublet.

47. Differential equation of sound propagation. Consider next the motion of a compressible fluid which takes place in the propagation of sound waves. In the case of all ordinary sounds the velocity of each particle is so small that its square may be neglected. We assume the fluid frictionless and the impressed force negligible. The motion will then be irrotational with velocity potential ϕ, and the equation (10′) becomes

$$P - \frac{\partial\phi}{\partial t} = \text{const} \quad . \quad . \quad . \quad . \quad \text{i}$$

The variations of density are small, and we may write

$$\rho = \rho_0(1 + s)$$

where ρ_0 is the equilibrium density of the fluid, and s a small quantity called the *condensation*. The quantity P has the value

$$P = \int\frac{dp}{\rho} = \int\frac{dp}{d\rho}\frac{d\rho}{\rho},$$

and, neglecting a quantity of the second order, we may write this

$$P = \left(\frac{dp}{d\rho}\right)_0\int_{\rho_0}^{\rho}\frac{d\rho}{\rho} = \left(\frac{dp}{d\rho}\right)_0\log\frac{\rho}{\rho_0}.$$

Differentiating this result with respect to t, and writing $c^2 = \left(\frac{dp}{d\rho}\right)_0$, we have

$$\frac{\partial P}{\partial t} = c^2\frac{\partial}{\partial t}\log\rho = c^2\frac{d}{dt}\log\rho$$

where we have neglected the second order term $\mathbf{v}\cdot\nabla \log \rho$ in replacing the local rate of change by the individual rate. Then in virtue of the equation (11′) of continuity, this relation is equivalent to

$$\frac{\partial P}{\partial t} = c^2\nabla^2\phi.$$

But from i by differentiation we have

$$\frac{\partial P}{\partial t} = \frac{\partial^2 \phi}{\partial t^2}.$$

From these two results it follows that

$$\frac{\partial^2 \phi}{\partial t^2} = c^2\nabla^2\phi \quad . \quad . \quad . \quad . \quad \text{ii}$$

which is the differential equation for sound propagation, the velocity of the sound waves being therefore

$$c = \sqrt{\left(\frac{dp}{d\rho}\right)_0}.$$

Vortex Motion.

48. Vorticity. Consider an element of the fluid whose centre of mass is the point G, and whose principal moments of inertia at G are equal. Then the moments of inertia about all axes through G are equal, and their common value will be denoted by I. Let $\mathbf{v}$ be the velocity of the particle at G. Then that of a neighbouring particle, whose position vector relative to G is $\mathbf{r}$, is

$$\mathbf{v} + \mathbf{r}\cdot\nabla\mathbf{v}.$$

Hence if m is the mass of this particle, the angular momentum of the element about G is

$$\Sigma m\mathbf{r}\times(\mathbf{v} + \mathbf{r}\cdot\nabla\mathbf{v}).$$

Now the first term is zero; for it is equal to $(\Sigma m\mathbf{r})\times\mathbf{v}$, and $\Sigma m\mathbf{r}$ vanishes because the c.m. is the origin of position vectors. If then $\mathbf{i}, \mathbf{j}, \mathbf{k}$ are unit vectors parallel to the principal axes of the element at G, and $\mathbf{r} = x\mathbf{i} + y\mathbf{j} + z\mathbf{k}$, the above expression for the angular momentum about G may be written

$$\Sigma m(x\mathbf{i} + y\mathbf{j} + z\mathbf{k})\times\left(x\frac{\partial\mathbf{v}}{\partial x} + y\frac{\partial\mathbf{v}}{\partial y} + z\frac{\partial\mathbf{v}}{\partial z}\right)$$
$$= \Sigma m\left(x^2\mathbf{i}\times\frac{\partial\mathbf{v}}{\partial x} + y^2\mathbf{j}\times\frac{\partial\mathbf{v}}{\partial y} + z^2\mathbf{k}\times\frac{\partial\mathbf{v}}{\partial z}\right),$$

because the products of inertia vanish. And, since the principal moments of inertia are equal, we have

$$\Sigma mx^2 = \Sigma my^2 = \Sigma mz^2 = \tfrac{1}{2}I,$$

and the angular momentum is equal to

$$\tfrac{1}{2}I\left(\mathbf{i}\times\frac{\partial \mathbf{v}}{\partial x}+\mathbf{j}\times\frac{\partial \mathbf{v}}{\partial y}+\mathbf{k}\times\frac{\partial \mathbf{v}}{\partial z}\right)=\tfrac{1}{2}I \text{ curl } \mathbf{v}.$$

Suppose now that the element is suddenly solidified and detached from the rest of the fluid. Since the impulses for this solidification are entirely internal, the A.M. of the element about G remains unaltered; and the motion of the element relative to G after solidification is therefore an angular velocity $\mathbf{A}$ such that

$$I\mathbf{A}=\tfrac{1}{2}I \text{ curl } \mathbf{v}.$$

Hence

$$\mathbf{A}=\tfrac{1}{2} \text{ curl } \mathbf{v}=\mathbf{w}.$$

This gives the physical meaning of the *vorticity* $\mathbf{w}$, and explains the name " molecular rotation " sometimes given to it. The motion of a fluid in which $\mathbf{w}$ is not zero is called *vortex motion* or " rotational motion."

49. Vortex tubes and filaments. As already defined, a *vortex line* is a line drawn in the fluid such that, at each point, the vector $\mathbf{w}$ is parallel to the tangent to the line. All the vortex lines intersecting a closed curve bound a portion of the fluid called a *vortex tube*. A vortex tube of infinitesimal cross-section is called a *vortex filament*.

FIG. 18.

Suppose that a vortex tube is intersected by any surface, and that S is the portion of the surface lying within the tube. Then the value of the normal surface integral $\int \mathbf{w}\cdot\mathbf{n}dS$ taken over S is the same for all such surfaces. For consider the portion of the tube cut off by two such surfaces S and S', and apply the divergence theorem to this region and the function curl $\mathbf{v}$. The boundary of the region consists of the end surfaces S, S', and the curved surface of the tube lying between these; and Gauss's theorem states that

$$\int \mathbf{n}\cdot \text{curl } \mathbf{v}dS=\int \text{div curl } \mathbf{v}dv.$$

Now the integrand in the second member vanishes identically. Also over the surface of the vortex tube $\mathbf{n}\cdot$ curl $\mathbf{v}$ is zero, because the vorticity is everywhere tangential to the tube. The surface integral need therefore be considered only over the ends S, S' of this portion of the tube; and $\mathbf{n}$ has at each of these the direction *outward* from the region. If, however, we give $\mathbf{n}$ at both ends the same sense along the tube, the above equation may be written

$$\int_S \mathbf{w}\cdot\mathbf{n}dS = \int_{S'} \mathbf{w}\cdot\mathbf{n}dS',$$

which proves the theorem. The constant value of this integral is called the *strength* of the vortex tube. In the case of a vortex filament, if A is the area of the normal section and $\mathbf{w}$ the vorticity at that point, the strength of the filament is Aw, where $w = \text{mod. } \mathbf{w}$.

If C is a closed curve drawn on the surface of a vortex tube, and enveloping the tube *once* only, the value of the circulation round the path, in the sense which is positive relative to $\mathbf{w}$, is by Stokes's theorem

$$\int_0 \mathbf{v}\cdot d\mathbf{r} = \int \mathbf{n}\cdot \text{curl } \mathbf{v} dS$$

where the surface integral is extended over an open surface bounded by C. The value of this integral has just been proved equal to twice the strength of the tube. Hence the circulation is the same for all such curves drawn on the surface of the tube, and enclosing it only once.

50. Kelvin's circulation theorem. *The circulation round any closed curve moving with the fluid does not alter with elapse of time.*

Consider a closed curve C moving with the fluid; that is to say, consisting always of the same particles. Let $d\mathbf{r}$ be the elementary vector joining always the same two particles P, Q, and let

$$d\mathbf{r} = \mathbf{t}ds,$$

$\mathbf{t}$ being the unit tangent at P to the curve, and ds the length of the element of arc PQ (Fig. 17). The rate of increase of $d\mathbf{r}$ is the difference of the velocities of Q and P; that is,

$$\frac{d}{dt}(d\mathbf{r}) = (d\mathbf{r}\cdot\nabla)\mathbf{v} = \mathbf{t}\cdot\nabla\mathbf{v}ds = \frac{\partial\mathbf{v}}{\partial s}ds.$$

On the assumption of a force potential and a relation between p and ρ only, the equation of motion for the fluid may be expressed

$$\frac{d\mathbf{v}}{dt} = -\nabla(V+P).$$

Now the rate of change of the circulation round the closed curve C is

$$\begin{aligned}\frac{d}{dt}\int_0 \mathbf{v}\cdot d\mathbf{r} &= \int_0\left(\frac{d\mathbf{v}}{dt}\cdot d\mathbf{r} + \mathbf{v}\cdot\frac{d}{dt}d\mathbf{r}\right)\\ &= \int_0\left[-\mathbf{t}\cdot\nabla(V+P) + \mathbf{v}\cdot\frac{\partial\mathbf{v}}{\partial s}\right]ds\\ &= -\int_0 \frac{\partial}{\partial s}(V+P-\tfrac{1}{2}\mathbf{v}^2)ds.\end{aligned}$$

But since the path is closed, and $\mathbf{v}^2$, P, V are single-valued point-functions, the above integral is equal to zero. Thus the time rate of change of the circulation vanishes; or the circulation remains constant for a closed circuit moving with the fluid.

Cor. 1. If the *motion* is *initially irrotational*, the circulation is zero for every closed circuit. Hence if these move with the fluid the circulation remains zero for each of them, and the motion therefore *remains irrotational*.

Cor. 2. Take any closed circuit C drawn on the surface of a vortex tube and not embracing the tube. Since $\mathbf{w} \cdot \mathbf{n}$ is zero at every point of the surface S of the tube, it follows by Stokes's theorem that the circulation is zero round the curve C. Let the surface S move with the fluid, and likewise all such circuits C. Then the circulation remains zero round each circuit, and therefore the surface S remains a surface composed of vortex lines; that is to say, vortex tubes move with the fluid. This is true for tubes of infinitesimal section. Thus *vortex tubes and vortex lines move with the fluid.*

Cor. 3. Take a circuit drawn on the surface of a vortex tube and embracing it once. The circulation round such a curve has been proved equal to twice the strength of the tube. But while the circuit moves with the fluid the circulation remains constant. Hence *the strength of a vortex tube is invariable with respect to the time.*

51. Helmholtz's Theorem. Vector potential. Let the fluid be supposed to extend to infinity, and to be at rest there. Then, by Art. 26, the velocity $\mathbf{v}$ at any point of the fluid may be expressed as the sum of a lamellar and a solenoidal component in the form

$$\mathbf{v} = \nabla\phi + \operatorname{curl} \mathbf{H},$$

the values of the point-functions ϕ, $\mathbf{H}$ at any point P being given by

$$\phi = -\frac{1}{4\pi}\int \frac{\operatorname{div} \mathbf{v}}{r} dv,$$

$$\mathbf{H} = \frac{1}{4\pi}\int \frac{\operatorname{curl} \mathbf{v}}{r} dv,$$

r being the distance from the point P to the variable point Q, at which is situated the element of the fluid of volume dv, and for which the values of div $\mathbf{v}$ and curl $\mathbf{v}$ are to be taken in the integrands. Thus ϕ is a scalar potential and $\mathbf{H}$ a vector potential. In the case of an incompressible fluid div $\mathbf{v}$ is identically zero, and therefore the function ϕ vanishes at all points.

Consider the component of the velocity due to the vortices, that is, the part arising from the *vector potential* $\mathbf{H}$. In the case of an incompressible fluid this is the only component. This part of the velocity is

$$\mathbf{v}_1 = \frac{1}{2\pi}\,\text{curl}\int\frac{\mathbf{w}}{r}dv = \frac{1}{2\pi}\int\text{curl}_P\left(\frac{\mathbf{w}}{r}\right)dv,$$

the curl being taken with respect to P as variable point, and the value $\mathbf{w}$ of the vorticity at Q being therefore constant for this differentiation. Now if $\hat{\mathbf{r}}$ is the unit vector in the direction $\overrightarrow{QP}$,

$$\text{curl}_P\left(\frac{\mathbf{w}}{r}\right) = \nabla_P\left(\frac{1}{r}\right)\times\mathbf{w} = -\frac{\hat{\mathbf{r}}}{r^2}\times\mathbf{w},$$

and therefore

$$\mathbf{v}_1 = \frac{1}{2\pi}\int\frac{\mathbf{w}\times\hat{\mathbf{r}}}{r^2}dv.$$

Take for dv the volume of an element of a vortex filament at Q. If ds is the length of this element, dS the area of the normal cross-section, and μ the strength of the filament,

$$\mathbf{w}dv = \mathbf{w}dSds = wdSd\mathbf{s} = \mu d\mathbf{s},$$

where $d\mathbf{s}$ is the elementary vector of length ds and having the direction of $\mathbf{w}$. Then since μ is constant along the filament we may write

$$\mathbf{v}_1 = -\frac{1}{2\pi}\Sigma\mu\int\frac{\hat{\mathbf{r}}\times d\mathbf{s}}{r^2},$$

the integration extending over the whole length of the filament, and Σ denoting summation with respect to all the filaments.

We may say, then, that the element $d\mathbf{s}$ at Q, of a filament of strength μ, produces at P a velocity

$$-\frac{\mu}{2\pi}\frac{\mathbf{r}\times d\mathbf{s}}{r^3}$$

where $\mathbf{r}$ is the vector $\overrightarrow{QP}$ and r its module. This velocity is connected with the vorticity of the filament in the same way as the magnetic intensity with the strength of the current producing it, the above expression giving the magnetic intensity at P due to the element of circuit ds carrying a current of strength $\mu/2\pi$ (cf. Chap. IX., Arts. 116 and 120).

52. Kinetic energy. Consider the kinetic energy of a body of homogeneous incompressible fluid, supposed to extend to infinity and to be at rest there, all the vortices being within a finite region. The function ϕ is zero and $\mathbf{v} = \text{curl}\,\mathbf{H}$. Hence the kinetic energy of the fluid is

$$T = \tfrac{1}{2}\int\rho\mathbf{v}^2dv = \tfrac{1}{2}\rho\int\mathbf{v}\cdot\text{curl}\,\mathbf{H}\,dv,$$

$$= \tfrac{1}{2}\rho\int(\text{div}\,\mathbf{H}\times\mathbf{v} + \mathbf{H}\cdot\text{curl}\,\mathbf{v})dv$$

by (17) of Art. 8. Transforming the first part by the divergence theorem we obtain

$$T = \tfrac{1}{2}\rho\int \mathbf{H}\times\mathbf{v}\cdot\mathbf{n}dS + \rho\int \mathbf{H}\cdot\mathbf{w}dv,$$

the surface integral being taken over an infinite boundary. But this integral vanishes, because at infinity $\mathbf{H}$ vanishes like $\frac{1}{R}$ and $\mathbf{v}$ like $\frac{1}{R^2}$, while the area of the surface of integration is infinite only like R^2. The value of the surface integral is therefore zero. Substituting in the volume integral the above expression for $\mathbf{H}$, we have

$$T = \frac{\rho}{2\pi}\iint \frac{\mathbf{w}\cdot\mathbf{w}'}{r}dvdv'$$

where r is the mutual distance between the elements dv, dv' at which the vorticities are $\mathbf{w}$ and $\mathbf{w}'$ respectively. Or if, as above, we put

$$\mathbf{w}dv = \mu d\mathbf{s}\,; \quad \mathbf{w}'dv' = \mu' d\mathbf{s}'$$

and integrate by filaments, we have

$$T = \Sigma\frac{\mu\mu'\rho}{2\pi}\iint\frac{d\mathbf{s}\cdot d\mathbf{s}'}{r}$$

where the integration for each variable extends over the whole length of a vortex filament, and Σ denotes summation with respect to all pairs of such filaments.

EXERCISES ON CHAPTER IV.

1. Give the Cartesian equivalents of the equation of continuity (3) or (3′), and of the two forms (6) and (6′) of the equation of motion.

2. Express the same equations in orthogonal curvilinear coordinates; in particular, in spherical polar and cylindrical coordinates.

3. A body of liquid rotates with constant and uniform angular velocity $\mathbf{A}$ about a vertical axis, under the action of gravity only. By integrating the equation of motion show that the free surface is a paraboloid of revolution, with axis vertical, and that the vorticity at any point of the fluid is equal to $\mathbf{A}$.

4. If in the previous exercise the angular velocity $\mathbf{A}$ is a function of the perpendicular distance r from the axis of rotation, show that, in order that the motion should be irrotational,

$$\mathbf{A} = \frac{\mu\mathbf{k}}{r^2}$$

where μ is a constant, and $\mathbf{k}$ the unit vector whose direction is vertical. Prove that the pressure is then given by

$$\frac{p}{\rho} = \text{const} - \tfrac{1}{2}\frac{\mu^2}{r^2} - gz$$

where z is measured vertically upward.

5. For a fluid moving in a fine tube of variable section β, prove that the equation of continuity is

$$\frac{\partial}{\partial t}(\beta\rho) + \frac{\partial}{\partial s}(\beta\rho v) = 0$$

where v is the speed at a point P, and s the length of the tube up to that point.

6. If F $(\mathbf{r}, t) = 0$ is the equation of a moving surface, show that the resolute of the velocity of any point in the direction of the normal to the surface is

$$\frac{dF}{dt}\Big/|\nabla F|.$$

7. A liquid is in equilibrium under the action of an external force $\mathbf{F} = \mu(y+z)\mathbf{i} + \mu(z+x)\mathbf{j} + \mu(x+y)\mathbf{k}$. Show that the surfaces of equal pressure are hyperboloids of revolution.

8. If, in the steady motion of an elastic fluid under no force, the velocity at the point x, y, z is $\mu(y+z)\mathbf{i} + \mu(z+x)\mathbf{j} + \mu(x+y)\mathbf{k}$, show that the surfaces of equal pressure are oblate spheroids, the eccentricity of the generating ellipse being $\sqrt{3}/2$.

9. If the motion of a homogeneous liquid be given by a single-valued velocity potential, prove that the angular momentum of any spherical portion of the liquid about its centre is always zero.

10. For a homogeneous liquid moving irrotationally, prove, with the notation of this chapter, that $\nabla^2\mathbf{v}^2$ is positive, and that $\nabla^2 p$ is negative provided V is harmonic. Hence prove that the speed v cannot have a maximum value, or p a minimum value, at a point in the interior of the liquid.

11. If the vorticity $\mathbf{w}$ at every point of an incompressible fluid is constant, show that $\nabla^2\mathbf{v} = 0$.

12. On the assumption of a conservative system of external forces, prove Helmholtz's formulæ

$$\frac{d}{dt}\left(\frac{\mathbf{w}}{\rho}\right) = \frac{\mathbf{w}}{\rho}\cdot\nabla\mathbf{v} \quad . \quad . \quad . \quad . \quad \text{i}$$

$$\frac{d^2}{dt^2}\left(\frac{\mathbf{w}}{\rho}\right) = \left(\frac{d}{dt}\frac{\mathbf{w}}{\rho}\right)\cdot\nabla\mathbf{v} + \frac{\mathbf{w}}{\rho}\cdot\frac{d}{dt}\nabla\mathbf{v} \quad . \quad . \quad . \quad \text{ii}$$

Taking the curl of both members of (7) Art. 37 we have

$$\frac{\partial\mathbf{w}}{\partial t} + \text{curl}\ (\mathbf{w}\times\mathbf{v}) = 0.$$

Expanding the second term by (18) of Art. 8, and using the formula

(1) of this chapter, we may write the result

$$0 = \frac{d\mathbf{w}}{dt} + \mathbf{w}\ \mathrm{div}\ \mathbf{v} - \mathbf{w}\cdot\nabla\mathbf{v}$$
$$= \frac{d\mathbf{w}}{dt} - \frac{\mathbf{w}}{\rho}\frac{d\rho}{dt} - \mathbf{w}\cdot\nabla\mathbf{v}$$

by the equation of continuity. On division by ρ this becomes

$$\frac{d}{dt}\left(\frac{\mathbf{w}}{\rho}\right) = \frac{\mathbf{w}}{\rho}\cdot\nabla\mathbf{v} \quad . \quad . \quad . \quad . \quad \mathrm{i}$$

By differentiating this we arrive at the second formula.

13. Prove that in the steady motion of an incompressible fluid under the action of conservative forces,

$$\mathbf{v}\cdot\nabla\mathbf{w} - \mathbf{w}\cdot\nabla\mathbf{v} = 0.$$

14. For a liquid whose velocity potential changes from ϕ to ϕ' owing to an impulsive pressure p^* and impulsive forces $\mathbf{F}^* = -\nabla V^*$, show that

$$p^* + \rho V^* + \rho(\phi' - \phi) = \text{const.}$$

Apply the equations of impulsive action to show that, if liquid be contained within a closed surface, the circulation and the vorticity cannot be altered by any impulse applied to the boundary.

15. In the steady motion of a liquid parallel to the xy plane under conservative forces, show that

$$v_2\nabla^2 v_1 - v_1\nabla^2 v_2 = 0$$

where

$$\mathbf{v} = v_1\mathbf{i} + v_2\mathbf{j}$$

and

$$\nabla^2 = \frac{\partial^2}{\partial x^2} + \frac{\partial^2}{\partial y^2}.$$

16. For the irrotational motion of a liquid in two dimensions under conservative forces, prove that

$$\nabla^2 \log \nabla^2 p = 0.$$

17. If $\mathbf{v}_m$ is the velocity of the particle at the point $\mathbf{r}$ relative to a moving frame of reference, which is rotating about the origin with angular velocity $\mathbf{A}$, show that the equation of motion of the fluid is expressible as

$$\mathbf{F} - \frac{1}{\rho}\nabla p = \left(\frac{\partial \mathbf{v}_m}{\partial t}\right)_m + \mathbf{v}_m\cdot\nabla\mathbf{v}_m + 2\mathbf{A}\times\mathbf{v}_m + \frac{\partial \mathbf{A}}{\partial t}\times\mathbf{r} + \mathbf{A}\times(\mathbf{A}\times\mathbf{r}),$$

the first term on the right-hand side being the rate of change of $\mathbf{v}_m$ relative to the moving system, *i.e.* the acceleration relative to that system (cf. Vol. I., Art. 95).

Prove also that the equation of continuity is

$$\frac{d\rho}{dt} + \rho\ \mathrm{div}\ \mathbf{v}_m = 0.$$

18. If in the last exercise the fluid is incompressible, the equation of continuity is div $\mathbf{v}_m = 0$. Show also that if $\mathbf{A}$ is constant the equation of motion may be written

$$\left(\frac{\partial \mathbf{v}_m}{\partial t}\right)_m - 2\mathbf{v}_m \times (\mathbf{w}_m - \mathbf{A}) = \mathbf{F} - \nabla\left(\frac{p}{\rho} + \tfrac{1}{2}Q^2\right)$$

where
$$Q^2 = \mathbf{v}_m{}^2 - \mathbf{A}^2\mathbf{r}^2 + (\mathbf{A}\cdot\mathbf{r})^2.$$

19. If in Exercise 17 the motion is irrotational, show that

$$P + V + \tfrac{1}{2}\mathbf{v}_m{}^2 + \mathbf{A}\times\mathbf{r}\cdot\mathbf{v}_m - \frac{\partial \phi}{\partial t}$$

is a function of t, the symbols having the same meanings as in Art. 43.

20. A space is bounded by an ideal fixed surface S drawn in a homogeneous incompressible fluid satisfying the conditions for the continued existence of a velocity potential ϕ under conservative forces. Prove that the rate per unit time at which energy flows across S into the space bounded by it is

$$\rho\int \frac{\partial \phi}{\partial t}\frac{\partial \phi}{\partial n} dS.$$

21. Prove that the kinetic energy of a vortex system of finite dimensions in an infinite liquid at rest at infinity can be expressed in the form

$$2\rho\int \mathbf{v}\cdot\mathbf{r}\times\mathbf{w}\,dv.$$

22. If $r_1, \theta_1;\ r_2, \theta_2 \ldots$ be the polar coordinates at time t of a system of rectilinear vortices of strengths $\mu_1, \mu_2, \ldots$ respectively, prove that

$$\Sigma \mu r^2 = \text{const},$$

and
$$\Sigma \mu r^2 \frac{\partial \theta}{\partial t} = \frac{1}{2\pi}\Sigma \mu_1 \mu_2.$$

23. Show that the kinetic energy of a body of liquid moving irrotationally is

$$T = \tfrac{1}{2}\rho\int \phi\frac{\partial \phi}{\partial n} dS.$$

Also if ϕ, ϕ' are the velocity potentials of two distinct motions of the liquid,

$$\int \phi\frac{\partial \phi'}{\partial n} dS = \int \phi'\frac{\partial \phi}{\partial n} dS.$$

24. Prove that the value of ϕ at any point of a liquid is given in terms of the values of ϕ and $\dfrac{\partial \phi}{\partial n}$ at the boundary by the formula

$$\phi = \frac{1}{4\pi}\int \frac{1}{r}\frac{\partial \phi}{\partial n} dS - \frac{1}{4\pi}\int \phi \frac{\partial}{\partial n}\left(\frac{1}{r}\right) dS.$$

Interpret this in terms of a surface distribution of sources and doublets.

CHAPTER V.

LINEAR VECTOR FUNCTIONS.*

CENTRAL QUADRIC SURFACES.

I. DYADICS.

53. Linear vector function. Suppose that $\mathbf{r}$, $\mathbf{r}'$ are two point-functions in a certain region. Then $\mathbf{r}'$ is said to be a linear vector function of $\mathbf{r}$ when, for each point, the scalar components of $\mathbf{r}'$ parallel to three non-coplanar unit vectors $\mathbf{l}$, $\mathbf{m}$, $\mathbf{n}$ are linear functions of the scalar components of $\mathbf{r}$ in the same directions. Let

$$\mathbf{r} = \xi\mathbf{l} + \eta\mathbf{m} + \zeta\mathbf{n}$$
$$\mathbf{r}' = \xi'\mathbf{l} + \eta'\mathbf{m} + \zeta'\mathbf{n}.$$

Then if

$$\xi' = a_{11}\xi + a_{12}\eta + a_{13}\zeta$$
$$\eta' = a_{21}\xi + a_{22}\eta + a_{23}\zeta$$
$$\zeta' = a_{31}\xi + a_{32}\eta + a_{33}\zeta$$

where the coefficients of ξ, η, ζ are constant, $\mathbf{r}'$ is said to be a linear vector function of $\mathbf{r}$.

We lose no generality by taking the three directions as those of three mutually perpendicular (unit) vectors $\mathbf{i}$, $\mathbf{j}$, $\mathbf{k}$. Let the direction cosines of the two systems of vectors with respect to each other be those indicated in the table, and let

	$\mathbf{i}$	$\mathbf{j}$	$\mathbf{k}$
$\mathbf{l}$	l_1	l_2	l_3
$\mathbf{m}$	m_1	m_2	m_3
$\mathbf{n}$	n_1	n_2	n_3

$$\mathbf{r} = x\mathbf{i} + y\mathbf{j} + z\mathbf{k}$$
$$\mathbf{r}' = x'\mathbf{i} + y'\mathbf{j} + z'\mathbf{k}$$

Then by projecting the vector $\mathbf{r}'$ on a line parallel to $\mathbf{i}$ we find

$$x' = l_1\xi' + m_1\eta' + n_1\zeta'$$
$$= l_1(a_{11}\xi + a_{12}\eta + a_{13}\zeta) + m_1(a_{21}\xi + \ldots) + \ldots$$

* The reader who desires a more complete treatment of the linear vector function than is given in the present chapter is referred to Prof. E. B. Wilson's admirable and exhaustive discussion in his *Vector Analysis* (chap. v.), to which the author is considerably indebted.

while y', z' are equal to similar linear functions of ξ, η, ζ. But x, y, z are also linear functions of these variables, viz.

$$x = l_1\xi + m_1\eta + n_1\zeta$$
$$y = l_2\xi + m_2\eta + n_2\zeta$$
$$z = l_3\xi + m_3\eta + n_3\zeta.$$

Therefore by eliminating ξ, η, ζ we obtain x', y', z' as linear functions of x, y, z. We may then state that $\mathbf{r}'$ is a linear vector function of $\mathbf{r}$, when the scalar resolutes of the former parallel to $\mathbf{i}$, $\mathbf{j}$, $\mathbf{k}$ are linear functions of the scalar resolutes of the latter. Let these relations be put in the form

$$x' = a_1x + a_2y + a_3z$$
$$y' = b_1x + b_2y + b_3z$$
$$z' = c_1x + c_2y + c_3z,$$

which are equivalent to

$$x' = \mathbf{a}\cdot\mathbf{r}, \quad y' = \mathbf{b}\cdot\mathbf{r}, \quad z' = \mathbf{c}\cdot\mathbf{r},$$

$\mathbf{a}$, $\mathbf{b}$, $\mathbf{c}$ being the vectors whose scalar resolutes are (a_1, a_2, a_3), (b_1, b_2, b_3), and (c_1, c_2, c_3) respectively. Then

$$\mathbf{r}' = x'\mathbf{i} + y'\mathbf{j} + z'\mathbf{k}$$
$$= \mathbf{r}\cdot\mathbf{a}\,\mathbf{i} + \mathbf{r}\cdot\mathbf{b}\,\mathbf{j} + \mathbf{r}\cdot\mathbf{c}\,\mathbf{k}.$$

We write this more briefly

$$\mathbf{r}' = \mathbf{r}\cdot(\mathbf{a}\,\mathbf{i} + \mathbf{b}\,\mathbf{j} + \mathbf{c}\,\mathbf{k}) \quad . \quad . \quad . \quad (1)$$

where the expression in brackets is an operator called a *dyadic*, of which $\mathbf{a}$, $\mathbf{b}$, $\mathbf{c}$ are the *antecedents* and $\mathbf{i}$, $\mathbf{j}$, $\mathbf{k}$ the *consequents*. The scalar product of $\mathbf{r}$ and any antecedent is the coefficient of the consequent in the same term of the dyadic. Each term of the dyadic is called a *dyad*.

54. Dyadics. The dyadic in (1) comes after the vector $\mathbf{r}$, and is therefore called a *postfactor*. But the relation between $\mathbf{r}'$ and $\mathbf{r}$ might be equally well written

$$\mathbf{r}' = \mathbf{i}\,\mathbf{a}\cdot\mathbf{r} + \mathbf{j}\,\mathbf{b}\cdot\mathbf{r} + \mathbf{k}\,\mathbf{c}\cdot\mathbf{r},$$

a number placed after a vector having the same significance as when placed before it. And this is equivalent to

$$\mathbf{r}' = (\mathbf{i}\,\mathbf{a} + \mathbf{j}\,\mathbf{b} + \mathbf{k}\,\mathbf{c})\cdot\mathbf{r} \quad . \quad . \quad . \quad (2)$$

in which the dyadic now precedes the vector and is called a *prefactor*. It will be noticed that the dyadics in (1) and (2) are not identical, the antecedents of either being the consequents of the other. Such dyadics are said to be *conjugate*; and any dyadic used as a prefactor is equivalent to its conjugate used as a postfactor.

Capital Greek letters $\Phi, \Psi, \Omega, \ldots$ will be used to indicate dyadics.

Their conjugates will be denoted by Φ_c, Ψ_c, Ω_c, . . . respectively. If Φ is the dyadic in (1), the relation between $\mathbf{r}'$ and $\mathbf{r}$ is written

$$\mathbf{r}' = \mathbf{r}\cdot\Phi = \Phi_c\cdot\mathbf{r},$$

the middle expression being pronounced "$\mathbf{r}$ *dot* Φ," and called the *scalar* or *direct product* of $\mathbf{r}$ and the dyadic Φ used as a postfactor.

Thus any linear vector function of $\mathbf{r}$ is expressible in the form $\mathbf{r}\cdot\Phi$ or $\Phi_c\cdot\mathbf{r}$, where Φ is a dyadic determined by the particular function. And conversely, this expression is a linear vector function of $\mathbf{r}$, for its resolutes are linear functions of those of $\mathbf{r}$.

We may have dyadics in which neither the antecedents nor the consequents are the vectors $\mathbf{i}$, $\mathbf{j}$, $\mathbf{k}$, while the number of dyads is quite arbitrary. Thus

$$\Psi = \mathbf{a}_1\mathbf{b}_1 + \mathbf{a}_2\mathbf{b}_2 + \mathbf{a}_3\mathbf{b}_3 + \ldots$$

is a dyadic, whose operation upon $\mathbf{r}$ gives

$$\mathbf{r}\cdot\Psi = \Sigma\mathbf{r}\cdot\mathbf{a}\,\mathbf{b}$$

or

$$\Psi\cdot\mathbf{r} = \Sigma\mathbf{a}\,\mathbf{b}\cdot\mathbf{r} = \mathbf{r}\cdot\Psi_c,$$

and each of these is a linear vector function of $\mathbf{r}$. For if the terms are expanded it is easily seen that the resolutes of either $\mathbf{r}\cdot\Psi$ or $\Psi\cdot\mathbf{r}$ are linear functions of those of $\mathbf{r}$.

Moreover, the *distributive law* holds for the operation of a dyadic upon a sum of vectors; that is to say,

$$\Psi\cdot(\mathbf{r}_1 + \mathbf{r}_2) = \Psi\cdot\mathbf{r}_1 + \Psi\cdot\mathbf{r}_2 \quad . \quad . \quad . \quad (3)$$

For, with the above notation,

$$\begin{aligned}\Psi\cdot(\mathbf{r}_1 + \mathbf{r}_2) &= \Sigma\mathbf{a}\,\mathbf{b}\cdot(\mathbf{r}_1 + \mathbf{r}_2)\\ &= \Sigma\mathbf{a}\,\mathbf{b}\cdot\mathbf{r}_1 + \Sigma\mathbf{a}\,\mathbf{b}\cdot\mathbf{r}_2\\ &= \Psi\cdot\mathbf{r}_1 + \Psi\cdot\mathbf{r}_2,\end{aligned}$$

and similarly for the sum of any number of vectors.

Also if V is either a scalar point-function or a constant scalar,

$$\begin{aligned}\Psi\cdot(V\mathbf{r}) &= \Sigma\mathbf{a}\,\mathbf{b}\cdot(V\mathbf{r}) = V\Sigma\mathbf{a}\,\mathbf{b}\cdot\mathbf{r}\\ &= V\Psi\cdot\mathbf{r} \quad . \quad . \quad . \quad . \quad . \quad (4)\end{aligned}$$

Thus a scalar factor is passed over by the operation of Ψ.

The sum of two dyadics $\Psi_1 = \Sigma\mathbf{a}\,\mathbf{b}$ and $\Psi_2 = \Sigma\mathbf{c}\,\mathbf{d}$ is denoted by $\Psi_1 + \Psi_2$, and is defined by

$$\Psi_1 + \Psi_2 = \Sigma\mathbf{a}\,\mathbf{b} + \Sigma\mathbf{c}\,\mathbf{d}.$$

From this it is clear that

$$\mathbf{r}\cdot(\Psi_1 + \Psi_2) = \mathbf{r}\cdot\Psi_1 + \mathbf{r}\cdot\Psi_2,$$

so that the distributive law holds for the direct or *dot* product of a vector and a sum of dyadics.

55. Distributive law for dyads.

Definition. If

$$\mathbf{r}\cdot\Phi = \mathbf{r}\cdot\Psi$$

and

$$\Phi\cdot\mathbf{r} = \Psi\cdot\mathbf{r}$$

for all values of $\mathbf{r}$, the dyadics Φ and Ψ are said to be *equal*.

If either vector in a dyad is expressed as the sum of two others, the result may be expanded according to the *distributive law*; that is,

$$\mathbf{a}(\mathbf{b} + \mathbf{c}) = \mathbf{a}\,\mathbf{b} + \mathbf{a}\,\mathbf{c}\,. \qquad . \qquad . \qquad . \qquad (5)$$

For whatever the vector $\mathbf{r}$,

$$\begin{aligned}[\mathbf{a}(\mathbf{b} + \mathbf{c})]\cdot\mathbf{r} = \mathbf{a}(\mathbf{b} + \mathbf{c})\cdot\mathbf{r} &= \mathbf{a}\,\mathbf{b}\cdot\mathbf{r} + \mathbf{a}\,\mathbf{c}\cdot\mathbf{r} \\ &= (\mathbf{a}\,\mathbf{b} + \mathbf{a}\,\mathbf{c})\cdot\mathbf{r}.\end{aligned}$$

In the same way

$$\begin{aligned}\mathbf{r}\cdot[\mathbf{a}(\mathbf{b} + \mathbf{c})] = \mathbf{r}\cdot\mathbf{a}(\mathbf{b} + \mathbf{c}) &= \mathbf{r}\cdot\mathbf{a}\,\mathbf{b} + \mathbf{r}\cdot\mathbf{a}\,\mathbf{c} \\ &= \mathbf{r}\cdot(\mathbf{a}\,\mathbf{b} + \mathbf{a}\,\mathbf{c}),\end{aligned}$$

and therefore the relation (5) is true. Similarly we may show that

$$(\mathbf{a} + \mathbf{b})\mathbf{c} = \mathbf{a}\,\mathbf{c} + \mathbf{b}\,\mathbf{c}\,. \qquad . \qquad . \qquad . \qquad (5')$$

Continued application of these results shows that, if each vector of a dyad is expressed as the sum of any number of others, the dyad may be expanded by the ordinary rules of algebra, provided the order of the vectors in each term is maintained. Thus

$$(\mathbf{a} + \mathbf{b} + \ldots)(\mathbf{l} + \mathbf{m} + \ldots) = \mathbf{a}\,\mathbf{l} + \mathbf{a}\,\mathbf{m} + \ldots + \mathbf{b}\,\mathbf{l} + \mathbf{b}\,\mathbf{m} + \ldots + \ldots$$

For this reason a dyad is spoken of as the *indeterminate* or *open* product of the two vectors which form its antecedent and consequent.

The *negative sign* with a dyad is interpreted according to the convention

$$-(\mathbf{a}\,\mathbf{b}) = (-\mathbf{a})\mathbf{b} = \mathbf{a}(-\mathbf{b}),$$

the same rule of signs applying as for algebraic products. In agreement with the above it is obvious that

$$(-\mathbf{a})(-\mathbf{b}) = \mathbf{a}\,\mathbf{b}.$$

If all the antecedents and consequents of a dyadic Φ are expressed in terms of the unit vectors $\mathbf{i}$, $\mathbf{j}$, $\mathbf{k}$, and the separate dyads then expanded according to the distributive law, only nine different dyads will result; and if the like dyads are collected we may put the dyadic in the form

$$\left.\begin{aligned}\Phi = a_{11}\mathbf{i}\,\mathbf{i} + a_{12}\mathbf{i}\,\mathbf{j} + a_{13}\mathbf{i}\,\mathbf{k} \\ + a_{21}\mathbf{j}\,\mathbf{i} + a_{22}\mathbf{j}\,\mathbf{j} + a_{23}\mathbf{j}\,\mathbf{k} \\ + a_{31}\mathbf{k}\,\mathbf{i} + a_{32}\mathbf{k}\,\mathbf{j} + a_{33}\mathbf{k}\,\mathbf{k}\end{aligned}\right\}. \qquad . \qquad . \qquad . \qquad (6)$$

This expansion, involving nine independent dyads, is called the *nonion* form of Φ. Clearly two dyadics will be equal if the coefficients of the like dyads in their nonion forms are equal.

Any dyadic may be expressed as the sum of three dyads, of which *either* the antecedents *or* the consequents are three arbitrarily chosen non-coplanar vectors **a**, **b**, **c**. For if we express all the antecedents and all the consequents in terms of **a**, **b**, **c** and expand the separate dyads, we obtain dyads of nine different kinds in **a**, **b**, **c**. Combining those whose antecedents are **a**, those whose antecedents are **b**, and those whose antecedents are **c**, we may write the expansion

$$\mathbf{a}(a_1\mathbf{a} + a_2\mathbf{b} + a_3\mathbf{c}) + \mathbf{b}(b_1\mathbf{a} + b_2\mathbf{b} + b_3\mathbf{c}) + \mathbf{c}(c_1\mathbf{a} + c_2\mathbf{b} + \ldots),$$

which is of the form

$$\mathbf{a}\,\mathbf{A} + \mathbf{b}\,\mathbf{B} + \mathbf{c}\,\mathbf{C}.$$

Similarly by combining the dyads whose consequents are **a**, those whose consequents are **b**, and those whose consequents are **c**, we could express the dyadic in the form

$$\mathbf{A}'\mathbf{a} + \mathbf{B}'\mathbf{b} + \mathbf{C}'\mathbf{c},$$

which proves the theorem.

56. Scalar and vector of a dyadic. The *scalar* of a dyadic Φ is the sum of the scalar products of the antecedent and consequent in each term of the dyadic. Thus if

$$\Phi = \mathbf{a}_1\mathbf{b}_1 + \mathbf{a}_2\mathbf{b}_2 + \ldots$$

its scalar is

$$\Phi_s = \mathbf{a}_1\cdot\mathbf{b}_1 + \mathbf{a}_2\cdot\mathbf{b}_2 + \ldots \quad . \quad . \quad . \quad (7)$$

being denoted by the symbol of the dyadic with the suffix *s* appended. Similarly the *vector* of Φ is the sum of the vector products of the antecedent and consequent in each term of the dyadic. Thus

$$\Phi_v = \mathbf{a}_1\times\mathbf{b}_1 + \mathbf{a}_2\times\mathbf{b}_2 + \ldots \quad . \quad . \quad . \quad (8)$$

the suffix *v* being used in this case.*

The scalar and the vector of a dyadic are invariant; that is to say, their values are not altered by expressing the antecedents and consequents in terms of other vectors, expanding the separate dyads, and then forming the scalar and vector of the expansion. This is an immediate consequence of the fact that dyads are expanded according to the same distributive law as the scalar and vector products of two vectors.

In terms of the coefficients in the nonion form (6)of Φ we may write

$$\Phi_s = a_{11} + a_{22} + a_{33} \quad . \quad . \quad . \quad . \quad (7')$$

* Gibbs used $\Phi_\times$ for the *vector* of Φ.

and

$$\Phi_v = (a_{23} - a_{32})\mathbf{i} + (a_{31} - a_{13})\mathbf{j} + (a_{12} - a_{21})\mathbf{k} \quad . \quad (8')$$

These may also be written in the convenient forms

$$\Phi_s = \mathbf{i}\cdot\Phi\cdot\mathbf{i} + \mathbf{j}\cdot\Phi\cdot\mathbf{j} + \mathbf{k}\cdot\Phi\cdot\mathbf{k} \quad . \quad . \quad . \quad (7'')$$

$$-\Phi_v = \mathbf{i}\cdot\Phi\times\mathbf{i} + \mathbf{j}\cdot\Phi\times\mathbf{j} + \mathbf{k}\cdot\Phi\times\mathbf{k} \quad . \quad . \quad (8'')$$

57. Products of dyadics. The scalar or direct product of the two dyads **a b** and **c d**, the first as a prefactor and the second as a postfactor, is denoted by placing a dot between them, and is defined by

$$(\mathbf{a\,b})\cdot(\mathbf{c\,d}) = \mathbf{b}\cdot\mathbf{c}(\mathbf{a\,d}).$$

It is therefore itself a dyad, whose antecedent and consequent are the antecedent of the first dyad and the consequent of the second respectively, the scalar product **b·c** of the intermediate vectors forming a numerical coefficient.

The product of two dyadics is defined by the formal expansion, according to the distributive law, of two sums of dyads. Thus, if

$$\Phi = \mathbf{a}_1\mathbf{b}_1 + \mathbf{a}_2\mathbf{b}_2 + \mathbf{a}_3\mathbf{b}_3 + \ldots$$

and

$$\Psi = \mathbf{c}_1\mathbf{d}_1 + \mathbf{c}_2\mathbf{d}_2 + \ldots$$

their scalar or direct product, with Φ as prefactor, is

$$\begin{aligned}\Phi\cdot\Psi &= (\mathbf{a}_1\mathbf{b}_1)\cdot(\mathbf{c}_1\mathbf{d}_1) + (\mathbf{a}_1\mathbf{b}_1)\cdot(\mathbf{c}_2\mathbf{d}_2) + \ldots + (\mathbf{a}_2\mathbf{b}_2)\cdot(\mathbf{c}_1\mathbf{d}_1) \\ &\qquad + (\mathbf{a}_2\mathbf{b}_2)\cdot(\mathbf{c}_2\mathbf{d}_2) + \ldots + \ldots \\ &= \sum_{m,\,n} \mathbf{b}_m\cdot\mathbf{c}_n(\mathbf{a}_m\mathbf{d}_n),\end{aligned}$$

and is therefore itself a dyadic. And from the above definition it is also obvious that, if Ψ_1 and Ψ_2 are two dyadics,

$$\left.\begin{aligned}\Phi\cdot(\Psi_1 + \Psi_2) &= \Phi\cdot\Psi_1 + \Phi\cdot\Psi_2 \\ \text{and} \quad (\Psi_1 + \Psi_2)\cdot\Phi &= \Psi_1\cdot\Phi + \Psi_2\cdot\Phi\end{aligned}\right\} \quad . \quad . \quad . \quad (9)$$

so that the *distributive law* holds for the product of dyadics.

The *associative law* for the product of several dyadics is also true; that is,

$$(\Phi\cdot\Psi)\cdot\Omega = \Phi\cdot(\Psi\cdot\Omega) \quad . \quad . \quad . \quad (10)$$

For, taking the product of three dyads, we have

$$\begin{aligned}[(\mathbf{a\,b})\cdot(\mathbf{c\,d})]\cdot(\mathbf{e\,f}) &= \mathbf{b}\cdot\mathbf{c}(\mathbf{a\,d})\cdot(\mathbf{e\,f}) \\ &= \mathbf{b}\cdot\mathbf{c}\,\mathbf{d}\cdot\mathbf{e}(\mathbf{a\,f}),\end{aligned}$$

and similarly

$$\begin{aligned}(\mathbf{a\,b})\cdot[(\mathbf{c\,d})\cdot(\mathbf{e\,f})] &= \mathbf{d}\cdot\mathbf{e}(\mathbf{a\,b})\cdot(\mathbf{c\,f}) \\ &= \mathbf{b}\cdot\mathbf{c}\,\mathbf{d}\cdot\mathbf{e}(\mathbf{a\,f}),\end{aligned}$$

showing that the two products are equal. And since the product of the dyadics is obtained by the formal expansion, according to the distributive law, of the product of sums of dyads, the result also holds for the three dyadics. Since, then, the associative law (10) holds, the brackets are unnecessary, and we may write the product of the three dyadics simply $\Phi \cdot \Psi \cdot \Omega$. Successive applications of this result show that the same law holds for the product of any number of dyadics, *provided the order of the dyadics is not altered.*

The associative law also holds for the product of a vector $\mathbf{r}$ with a product of dyadics. To show, for instance, that

$$\mathbf{r} \cdot (\Phi \cdot \Psi) = (\mathbf{r} \cdot \Phi) \cdot \Psi \quad . \quad . \quad . \quad . \quad (11)$$

take two dyads, $\mathbf{a\,b}$, $\mathbf{c\,d}$, one from each dyadic. Then

$$\mathbf{r} \cdot [(\mathbf{a\,b}) \cdot (\mathbf{c\,d})] = \mathbf{r} \cdot (\mathbf{a\,d}) \mathbf{b} \cdot \mathbf{c} = \mathbf{r} \cdot \mathbf{a\,b} \cdot \mathbf{c\,d}.$$

Similarly

$$[\mathbf{r} \cdot (\mathbf{a\,b})] \cdot (\mathbf{c\,d}) = \mathbf{r} \cdot \mathbf{a\,b} \cdot (\mathbf{c\,d}) = \mathbf{r} \cdot \mathbf{a\,b} \cdot \mathbf{c\,d},$$

so that the two results are identical. Then, on account of the distributive law, the formula (11) holds for dyadics also.

Operating on both sides of (11) with another dyadic, Ω, as postfactor, we have

$$\begin{aligned} [\mathbf{r} \cdot (\Phi \cdot \Psi)] \cdot \Omega &= [(\mathbf{r} \cdot \Phi) \cdot \Psi] \cdot \Omega \\ &= (\mathbf{r} \cdot \Phi) \cdot (\Psi \cdot \Omega) \quad . \quad . \quad \text{by (11)} \\ &= \mathbf{r} \cdot (\Phi \cdot \Psi \cdot \Omega). \end{aligned}$$

The result may be extended to any number of dyadics, and is true whether $\mathbf{r}$ comes first or last in the product. Thus the associative law holds for the product of any number of dyadics and a vector $\mathbf{r}$, provided $\mathbf{r}$ occurs as an extreme factor and the order of the dyadics is not altered.

58. The cross product $\Phi \times \mathbf{r}$. The *cross product* of a dyad $\mathbf{a\,b}$ and a vector $\mathbf{r}$ is defined by

$$(\mathbf{a\,b}) \times \mathbf{r} = \mathbf{a\,b} \times \mathbf{r}$$

when the dyad is a prefactor; or

$$\mathbf{r} \times (\mathbf{a\,b}) = \mathbf{r} \times \mathbf{a\,b}$$

when it is a postfactor. Each of these is itself a dyad. Similarly for the dyadic $\Phi = \Sigma(\mathbf{a\,b})$ we have

$$\begin{aligned} \Phi \times \mathbf{r} &= (\mathbf{a}_1\mathbf{b}_1 + \mathbf{a}_2\mathbf{b}_2 + \dots) \times \mathbf{r} \\ &= \mathbf{a}_1\mathbf{b}_1 \times \mathbf{r} + \mathbf{a}_2\mathbf{b}_2 \times \mathbf{r} + \dots \\ &= \Sigma(\mathbf{a\,b} \times \mathbf{r}), \end{aligned}$$

which is also a dyadic, and

$$\mathbf{r} \times \Phi = \mathbf{r} \times \Sigma(\mathbf{a\,b}) = \Sigma(\mathbf{r} \times \mathbf{a\,b}).$$

It may be shown, as in the case of the direct or dot product, that the associative law holds for the cross product of $\mathbf{r}$ with a product of dyadics, provided $\mathbf{r}$ is an extreme factor in the product. For example

$$\left.\begin{aligned}(\mathbf{r}\times\Phi)\cdot\Psi &= \mathbf{r}\times(\Phi\cdot\Psi)\\ \text{and}\qquad \Phi\cdot(\Psi\times\mathbf{r}) &= (\Phi\cdot\Psi)\times\mathbf{r}\end{aligned}\right\} \quad . \quad . \quad . \quad (12)$$

but the order of the factors must not be changed.

Also, as in the case of the scalar product of three vectors where the dot and cross are interchangeable, we have the formulæ

$$\left.\begin{aligned}\Phi\cdot(\mathbf{r}\times\mathbf{s}) &= (\Phi\times\mathbf{r})\cdot\mathbf{s}\\ \text{and}\qquad (\mathbf{r}\times\mathbf{s})\cdot\Phi &= \mathbf{r}\cdot(\mathbf{s}\times\Phi)\end{aligned}\right\} \quad . \quad . \quad . \quad . \quad (13)$$

To prove the first let $\Phi = \Sigma(\mathbf{a}\,\mathbf{b})$. Then

$$\begin{aligned}\Phi\cdot(\mathbf{r}\times\mathbf{s}) &= \Sigma(\mathbf{a}\,\mathbf{b})\cdot(\mathbf{r}\times\mathbf{s}) = \Sigma(\mathbf{a}\,\mathbf{b}\cdot\mathbf{r}\times\mathbf{s})\\ &= \Sigma(\mathbf{a}\,\mathbf{b}\times\mathbf{r}\cdot\mathbf{s}) = (\Phi\times\mathbf{r})\cdot\mathbf{s},\end{aligned}$$

and the second may be proved in the same way.

59. The Idemfactor or Identical Dyadic. If the scalar product of a dyadic Φ and a vector $\mathbf{r}$ is always equal to the same vector $\mathbf{r}$, the dyadic is said to be an *Idemfactor*, and is denoted by I. Thus if

$$\Phi\cdot\mathbf{r} = \mathbf{r} \quad \text{and} \quad \mathbf{r}\cdot\Phi = \mathbf{r}$$

for all values of $\mathbf{r}$, Φ is an idemfactor.

It has been shown * that if $\mathbf{a}$, $\mathbf{b}$, $\mathbf{c}$ are non-coplanar vectors and $\mathbf{a}'$, $\mathbf{b}'$, $\mathbf{c}'$ the reciprocal set, then

$$\mathbf{r} = \mathbf{r}\cdot\mathbf{a}'\mathbf{a} + \mathbf{r}\cdot\mathbf{b}'\mathbf{b} + \mathbf{r}\cdot\mathbf{c}'\mathbf{c}$$

and

$$\mathbf{r} = \mathbf{r}\cdot\mathbf{a}\,\mathbf{a}' + \mathbf{r}\cdot\mathbf{b}\,\mathbf{b}' + \mathbf{r}\cdot\mathbf{c}\,\mathbf{c}'.$$

These may be written

$$\left.\begin{aligned}\mathbf{r} &= \mathbf{r}\cdot(\mathbf{a}'\mathbf{a} + \mathbf{b}'\mathbf{b} + \mathbf{c}'\mathbf{c})\\ \text{and}\qquad \mathbf{r} &= \mathbf{r}\cdot(\mathbf{a}\,\mathbf{a}' + \mathbf{b}\,\mathbf{b}' + \mathbf{c}\,\mathbf{c}')\end{aligned}\right\} \quad . \quad . \quad . \quad (14)$$

for all values of $\mathbf{r}$. Hence the dyadic

$$\mathbf{a}'\mathbf{a} + \mathbf{b}'\mathbf{b} + \mathbf{c}'\mathbf{c}$$

is equal to its conjugate, and is an idemfactor. In particular

$$\mathrm{I} = \mathbf{i}\,\mathbf{i} + \mathbf{j}\,\mathbf{j} + \mathbf{k}\,\mathbf{k} \quad . \quad . \quad . \quad . \quad (15)$$

is an idemfactor, since the system $\mathbf{i}$, $\mathbf{j}$, $\mathbf{k}$ is its own reciprocal. When

* Cf. *Elem. Vector Anal.*, Art. 47.

expressed in nonion form an idemfactor must always be as in (15). This is easily proved by taking the nonion form (6) for the dyadic, and using the conditions for an idemfactor

$$\mathbf{I}\cdot\mathbf{i} = \mathbf{i}, \quad \mathbf{I}\cdot\mathbf{j} = \mathbf{j}, \quad \mathbf{I}\cdot\mathbf{k} = \mathbf{k}.$$

The direct product of any dyadic Φ and the idemfactor is equal to Φ. For

$$(\Phi\cdot\mathbf{I})\cdot\mathbf{r} = \Phi\cdot(\mathbf{I}\cdot\mathbf{r}) = \Phi\cdot\mathbf{r}$$

for all values of $\mathbf{r}$. Hence $\Phi\cdot\mathbf{I} = \Phi$,

and in a similar manner $\mathbf{I}\cdot\Phi = \Phi$.

Thus the idemfactor in direct multiplication leaves either a vector or a dyadic unaltered.

60. Reciprocal dyadics. When the direct product of two dyadics is equal to the idemfactor, the dyadics are said to be *reciprocal*; or each is the reciprocal of the other. Thus if

$$\Phi\cdot\Psi = \mathbf{I} \quad . \quad . \quad . \quad . \quad . \qquad \text{i}$$

Φ and Ψ are reciprocal dyadics. If this relation is satisfied, then

$$\Psi\cdot\Phi = \mathbf{I} \quad . \quad . \quad . \quad . \quad . \qquad \text{ii}$$

is also satisfied, the order of the dyadics being reversed. For from i it follows that for all values of $\mathbf{r}$

$$\mathbf{r}\cdot(\Phi\cdot\Psi) = \mathbf{r}\cdot\mathbf{I} = \mathbf{r},$$

and therefore, because of the associative law,

$$(\mathbf{r}\cdot\Phi)\cdot(\Psi\cdot\Phi) = \mathbf{r}\cdot\Phi.$$

Hence $\Psi\cdot\Phi$ is equal to the idemfactor as stated. The reciprocal dyadic of Φ is often written Φ^{-1}. Thus in the above case

$$\Phi = \Psi^{-1} \quad \text{and} \quad \Psi = \Phi^{-1}.$$

As an example, consider the dyadic reciprocal to

$$\Phi = \mathbf{a}\,\mathbf{l} + \mathbf{b}\,\mathbf{m} + \mathbf{c}\,\mathbf{n}$$

where $\mathbf{a}$, $\mathbf{b}$, $\mathbf{c}$; $\mathbf{l}$, $\mathbf{m}$, $\mathbf{n}$ are two sets of three non-coplanar vectors. Then, if the reciprocal sets of vectors are $\mathbf{a}'$, $\mathbf{b}'$, $\mathbf{c}'$; $\mathbf{l}'$, $\mathbf{m}'$, $\mathbf{n}'$ respectively,

$$\Phi^{-1} = \mathbf{l}'\mathbf{a}' + \mathbf{m}'\mathbf{b}' + \mathbf{n}'\mathbf{c}'.$$

This is easily verified by forming the product of these dyadics and using the properties of reciprocal vectors. In particular the dyadics

$$a^2\mathbf{i}\,\mathbf{i} + b^2\mathbf{j}\,\mathbf{j} + c^2\mathbf{k}\,\mathbf{k}$$

and

$$\frac{1}{a^2}\mathbf{i}\,\mathbf{i} + \frac{1}{b^2}\mathbf{j}\,\mathbf{j} + \frac{1}{c^2}\mathbf{k}\,\mathbf{k}$$

are reciprocal, as is easily verified by forming their product.

The reciprocal of the product of any number of dyadics is equal to the product of their reciprocals taken in the opposite order. To show, for instance, that the reciprocal of $\Phi \cdot \Psi$ is $\Psi^{-1} \cdot \Phi^{-1}$, we have only to show that their product is equal to I. Thus

$$(\Phi \cdot \Psi) \cdot (\Psi^{-1} \cdot \Phi^{-1}) = \Phi \cdot (\Psi \cdot \Psi^{-1}) \cdot \Phi^{-1} = \Phi \cdot \mathrm{I} \cdot \Phi^{-1}$$
$$= \Phi \cdot \Phi^{-1} = \mathrm{I},$$

proving the theorem in the case of two dyadics. And in a similar manner it may be proved for any number of dyadics.

The product of n dyadics, each equal to Φ, is called the nth *power* of Φ and is denoted by Φ^n. From the theorem just proved it follows that

$$(\Phi^n)^{-1} = \Phi^{-1} \cdot \Phi^{-1} \cdot \ldots \text{ to } n \text{ factors}$$
$$= (\Phi^{-1})^n \qquad . \quad . \quad . \quad . \quad . \quad (16)$$

Thus the reciprocal of any positive integral power of Φ is equal to the same power of the reciprocal of Φ.

61. Conjugate dyadics. We have already defined the conjugate of Φ as the dyadic Φ_c whose antecedents and consequents are the consequents and antecedents respectively of Φ. Each of these dyadics is therefore the conjugate of the other. It is also obvious that the conjugate of the sum of two dyadics is equal to the sum of their conjugates ; that is,

$$(\Phi + \Psi)_c = \Phi_c + \Psi_c.$$

The conjugate of the product of several dyadics is equal to the product of their conjugates taken in the opposite order. Taking the case of two dyadics Φ, Ψ we have for all values of $\mathbf{r}$

$$\mathbf{r} \cdot (\Phi \cdot \Psi)_c = (\Phi \cdot \Psi) \cdot \mathbf{r} = \Phi \cdot (\Psi \cdot \mathbf{r}) = (\Psi \cdot \mathbf{r}) \cdot \Phi_c = \mathbf{r} \cdot (\Psi_c \cdot \Phi_c),$$

and therefore

$$(\Phi \cdot \Psi)_c = \Psi_c \cdot \Phi_c \qquad . \quad . \quad . \quad . \quad . \quad (17)$$

The relation thus proved for two dyadics may be extended to the case of any number.

If in the theorem we take n dyadics each equal to Φ we obtain the relation

$$(\Phi^n)_c = (\Phi_c)^n \qquad . \quad . \quad . \quad . \quad . \quad (18)$$

That is to say, the conjugate of the nth power of a dyadic is equal to the nth power of its conjugate.

The conjugate of the reciprocal of a dyadic is equal to the reciprocal of its conjugate ; or

$$(\Phi^{-1})_c = (\Phi_c)^{-1} \qquad . \quad . \quad . \quad . \quad . \quad (19)$$

To prove this we have only to show that the product of $(\Phi^{-1})_c$ and Φ_c

is equal to the idemfactor. Now by formula (17)

$$(\Phi^{-1})_c \cdot \Phi_c = (\Phi \cdot \Phi^{-1})_c = I_c = I,$$

for the idemfactor is equal to its conjugate, as is obvious from (15). The theorem is therefore true, and we may write either the conjugate of the reciprocal, or the reciprocal of the conjugate, simply Φ_c^{-1}.

Definition. A dyadic which is equal to its conjugate is said to be *self-conjugate*. A dyadic which is equal to its conjugate with the sign changed is said to be *anti-self-conjugate*.

Thus if Φ is self-conjugate, $\mathbf{r} \cdot \Phi = \Phi \cdot \mathbf{r}$. If Ψ is anti-self-conjugate, $\mathbf{r} \cdot \Psi = -\Psi \cdot \mathbf{r}$.

62. Theorem. *Any dyadic Φ may be expressed as the sum of a self-conjugate and an anti-self-conjugate dyadic.* For

$$\begin{aligned} \Phi &= \tfrac{1}{2}(\Phi + \Phi_c) + \tfrac{1}{2}(\Phi - \Phi_c) \quad . \quad . \quad . \quad (20) \\ &= \Psi + \Omega \text{ (say).} \end{aligned}$$

The first part Ψ is clearly self-conjugate, and the second part Ω anti-self-conjugate. For

$$\Omega_c = \tfrac{1}{2}(\Phi_c - \Phi) = -\Omega.$$

Then for any vector $\mathbf{r}$ we have

$$\Phi \cdot \mathbf{r} = \Psi \cdot \mathbf{r} + \Omega \cdot \mathbf{r} \quad . \quad . \quad . \quad . \quad \text{i}$$

The last term of this equation may be transformed thus. Let Φ be expressed as

$$\Phi = \mathbf{a\,l} + \mathbf{b\,m} + \mathbf{c\,n}.$$

Then

$$\begin{aligned} \Omega &= \tfrac{1}{2}(\Phi - \Phi_c) \\ &= \tfrac{1}{2}(\mathbf{a\,l} - \mathbf{l\,a} + \mathbf{b\,m} - \mathbf{m\,b} + \mathbf{c\,n} - \mathbf{n\,c}), \end{aligned}$$

and therefore

$$\begin{aligned} \Omega \cdot \mathbf{r} &= \tfrac{1}{2}[(\mathbf{a\,l} \cdot \mathbf{r} - \mathbf{l\,a} \cdot \mathbf{r}) + (\mathbf{b\,m} \cdot \mathbf{r} - \mathbf{m\,b} \cdot \mathbf{r}) + \ldots] \\ &= -\tfrac{1}{2}[(\mathbf{a} \times \mathbf{l}) \times \mathbf{r} + (\mathbf{b} \times \mathbf{m}) \times \mathbf{r} + (\mathbf{c} \times \mathbf{n}) \times \mathbf{r}] \\ &= -\tfrac{1}{2}(\mathbf{a} \times \mathbf{l} + \mathbf{b} \times \mathbf{m} + \mathbf{c} \times \mathbf{n}) \times \mathbf{r} \\ &= -\tfrac{1}{2}\Phi_v \times \mathbf{r} \quad . \quad . \quad . \quad . \quad . \quad . \quad \text{ii} \end{aligned}$$

where Φ_v is the vector of Φ. Thus i may be written

$$\Phi \cdot \mathbf{r} = \Psi \cdot \mathbf{r} - \tfrac{1}{2}\Phi_v \times \mathbf{r} \quad . \quad . \quad . \quad . \quad (21)$$

Ψ being the self-conjugate part of Φ, whose value is $\frac{1}{2}(\Phi + \Phi_c)$. And similarly we may prove the relation

$$\mathbf{r} \cdot \Phi = \mathbf{r} \cdot \Psi - \tfrac{1}{2}\mathbf{r} \times \Phi_v \quad . \quad . \quad . \quad . \quad (21')$$

in which Φ occurs as a postfactor.

We note in passing that *the vector of a self-conjugate dyadic is zero.* For in this case $\Phi = \Psi$, and the last term in (21) must vanish for all values of **r**. This necessitates $\Phi_v = 0$. The same is also obvious *a priori*. For by interchanging antecedents and consequents we change the sign of every term in the vector of the dyadic. Hence

$$\Phi_v = -(\Phi_c)_v.$$

But if Φ is self-conjugate, and therefore equal to Φ_c, we must have

$$\Phi_v = (\Phi_c)_v.$$

Hence the vector must be identically zero.

Conversely, if Φ_v is zero, Φ is self-conjugate. For then (21) and (21′) show that $\Phi = \Psi = \frac{1}{2}(\Phi + \Phi_c)$; that is, $\Phi = \Phi_c$.

63. Theorem. *Any vector* **a**, *used in cross multiplication with* **r**, *may be replaced by a dyadic* $\mathrm{I}\times\mathbf{a}$ *used in direct multiplication.* For

$$\mathbf{a}\times\mathbf{r} = (\mathrm{I}\cdot\mathbf{a})\times\mathbf{r} = (\mathrm{I}\times\mathbf{a})\cdot\mathbf{r} \quad . \quad . \quad . \quad (22)$$

in virtue of (13). The expression may also be written

$$[(\mathrm{I}\times\mathbf{a})\cdot\mathrm{I}]\cdot\mathbf{r} = [\mathrm{I}\cdot(\mathbf{a}\times\mathrm{I})]\cdot\mathbf{r},$$

since the dot and cross in the triple product of each term of the expansion can be interchanged; and the last expression is equal to $(\mathbf{a}\times\mathrm{I})\cdot\mathbf{r}$. Thus the dyadics $\mathbf{a}\times\mathrm{I}$ and $\mathrm{I}\times\mathbf{a}$ are identical. This is also obvious if we use the values

$$\mathbf{a} = a_1\mathbf{i} + a_2\mathbf{j} + a_3\mathbf{k},$$
$$\mathrm{I} = \mathbf{i}\,\mathbf{i} + \mathbf{j}\,\mathbf{j} + \mathbf{k}\,\mathbf{k},$$

when each of the dyadics $\mathbf{a}\times\mathrm{I}$ and $\mathrm{I}\times\mathbf{a}$ is seen to be equal to

$$a_1(\mathbf{k}\,\mathbf{j} - \mathbf{j}\,\mathbf{k}) + a_2(\mathbf{i}\,\mathbf{k} - \mathbf{k}\,\mathbf{i}) + a_3(\mathbf{j}\,\mathbf{i} - \mathbf{i}\,\mathbf{j}),$$

a dyadic which is clearly anti-self-conjugate.

Hence a vector **a** preceding another **r** in cross multiplication is equivalent to the anti-self-conjugate dyadic $\mathrm{I}\times\mathbf{a}$ or $\mathbf{a}\times\mathrm{I}$ used as a prefactor to **r** in direct multiplication. In the same way we may prove that

$$\mathbf{r}\times\mathbf{a} = \mathbf{r}\cdot(\mathrm{I}\times\mathbf{a}) = \mathbf{r}\cdot(\mathbf{a}\times\mathrm{I}) \quad . \quad . \quad . \quad (22')$$

64. Theorem. *Any self-conjugate dyadic may be reduced to the form*

$$a_1\mathbf{i}\,\mathbf{i} + a_2\mathbf{j}\,\mathbf{j} + a_3\mathbf{k}\,\mathbf{k} \quad . \quad . \quad . \quad . \quad (23)$$

where a_1, a_2, a_3 are scalars which may be positive or negative.

Let the dyadic be expressed in its nonion form (6). Then, since it is self-conjugate,

$$a_{12} = a_{21}, \quad a_{13} = a_{31}, \quad a_{23} = a_{32}.$$

Endeavour to find, if possible, a vector **r** such that $\Phi\cdot\mathbf{r}$ is parallel to **r**. If

$$\mathbf{r} = x\mathbf{i} + y\mathbf{j} + z\mathbf{k},$$

the conditions of parallelism of these vectors may be written

$$\frac{a_{11}x + a_{12}y + a_{13}z}{x} = \frac{a_{21}x + a_{22}y + a_{23}z}{y} = \ldots = \lambda \text{ (say).}$$

These again are equivalent to the equations

$$\left.\begin{array}{r}(a_{11} - \lambda)x + a_{12}y + a_{13}z = 0\\ a_{21}x + (a_{22} - \lambda)y + a_{23}z = 0\\ a_{31}x + a_{32}y + (a_{33} - \lambda)z = 0\end{array}\right\} \quad . \quad . \quad . \quad \text{i}$$

We may eliminate x, y, z from these and obtain

$$\begin{vmatrix} a_{11} - \lambda & a_{12} & a_{13} \\ a_{21} & a_{22} - \lambda & a_{23} \\ a_{31} & a_{32} & a_{33} - \lambda \end{vmatrix} = 0 \quad . \quad . \quad \text{ii}$$

which is a cubic equation in λ, and therefore possesses at least one real root λ_1. With this value of λ any two of the equations i determine the ratios $x : y : z$, giving the direction of a vector **r** which remains parallel to itself after being operated on by Φ. The directions of the orthogonal vectors **i**, **j**, **k** are at our disposal. Choose **i** parallel to the direction just determined. Then since $\Phi \cdot \mathbf{i}$ is parallel to **i**, it follows that

$$a_{12} = a_{13} = 0.$$

Next try for a direction perpendicular to **i** and possessing the same property. Any vector perpendicular to **i** is of the form $y\mathbf{j} + z\mathbf{k}$; and if $\Phi \cdot (y\mathbf{j} + z\mathbf{k})$ is parallel to this vector, we must have

$$\frac{a_{22}y + a_{23}z}{y} = \frac{a_{32}y + a_{33}z}{z} = \mu \text{ (say),}$$

which may be written

$$\left.\begin{array}{r}(a_{22} - \mu)y + a_{23}z = 0\\ a_{32}y + (a_{33} - \mu)z = 0\end{array}\right\} \quad . \quad . \quad . \quad \text{iii}$$

Elimination of the ratio $y : z$ leads to the quadratic

$$(a_{22} - \mu)(a_{33} - \mu) - a_{23}^2 = 0 \quad . \quad . \quad . \quad \text{iv}$$

for determining μ. The roots of this equation are easily shown to be real. With a value of μ equal to one of these roots, either of the equations iii gives the ratio $y : z$, which determines the direction of a vector possessing the required property. Take the vector **j** parallel to this direction. Then $\Phi \cdot \mathbf{j}$ is parallel to **j**, which requires $a_{23} = 0$. Hence with the orthogonal vectors **i**, **j**, **k** in these directions, the nonion form of the self-conjugate dyadic reduces to

$$a_{11}\mathbf{i}\,\mathbf{i} + a_{22}\mathbf{j}\,\mathbf{j} + a_{33}\mathbf{k}\,\mathbf{k},$$

as was to be proved. The coefficients a_{11}, a_{22}, a_{33} may be positive or negative. It is also obvious that now $\Phi\cdot(z\mathbf{k}) = a_{33}z\mathbf{k}$; so that any vector parallel to either **i**, **j**, or **k** has its direction unchanged by direct multiplication with Φ. These directions may be called the *principal directions* for the self-conjugate dyadic. There are in general only three such, since the cubic in λ has only three roots, and we have shown that they are mutually perpendicular.

If the equation iv has *equal roots*, then $a_{22} = a_{33}$ and $a_{23} = 0$, and the roots are equal to $a_{22} = a_{33}$. The equations iii are then satisfied for all values of the ratio $y : z$; that is to say, any vector perpendicular to **i** possesses the required property. The nonion form of the dyadic is then

$$a_{11}\mathbf{i}\,\mathbf{i} + a_{22}(\mathbf{j}\,\mathbf{j} + \mathbf{k}\,\mathbf{k}).$$

65. Invariants. The quantity λ introduced in the preceding Art. is the ratio of the two parallel vectors $\Phi\cdot\mathbf{r}$ and $\mathbf{r}$, the three values of λ corresponding to the three directions for which they are parallel. Now this ratio depends only on the dyadic Φ and the vector **r**, and is independent of the set of rectangular axes chosen for the expression of the dyadic in nonion form. Hence the cubic equation ii for determining λ must be the same for all rectangular systems of axes; that is to say, the coefficients of the equation are *invariants*. These are easily calculated to be

$$a_{11} + a_{22} + a_{33},$$
$$a_{11}a_{22} + a_{22}a_{33} + a_{33}a_{11} - a_{12}^2 - a_{23}^2 - a_{31}^2,$$
$$a_{11}a_{22}a_{33} + 2a_{12}a_{23}a_{31} - a_{11}a_{23}^2 - a_{22}a_{31}^2 - a_{33}a_{12}^2.$$

The first is the sum of the terms in the leading diagonal of the determinant

$$\begin{vmatrix} a_{11} & a_{12} & a_{13} \\ a_{21} & a_{22} & a_{23} \\ a_{31} & a_{32} & a_{33} \end{vmatrix}$$

formed from the coefficients of the nonion form of the dyadic. This is the *scalar* of the dyadic defined above, and denoted by Φ_s. The third invariant is the value of this determinant, and is denoted by Φ_3 or $|\,\Phi\,|$. It is called the *determinant* of the dyadic.

II. Central Quadric Surfaces.

66. Equation of surface. The most general scalar homogeneous expression, quadratic in the position vector **r** of a variable point P, is of the form

$$\Sigma(p\mathbf{r}\cdot\mathbf{r} + q\mathbf{r}\cdot\mathbf{a}\,\mathbf{r}\cdot\mathbf{b})$$

where $p, q, \mathbf{a}, \mathbf{b}$ are independent of $\mathbf{r}$; and this may be written

$$\begin{aligned}&\Sigma[\mathbf{r}\cdot(p\mathrm{I})\cdot\mathbf{r} + \mathbf{r}\cdot(q\mathbf{a}\,\mathbf{b})\cdot\mathbf{r}]\\ &= \mathbf{r}\cdot[\Sigma(p\mathrm{I} + q\mathbf{a}\,\mathbf{b})]\cdot\mathbf{r}\\ &= \mathbf{r}\cdot\Phi\cdot\mathbf{r}\end{aligned}$$

where Φ is the constant dyadic in square brackets. This dyadic may be expressed as the sum of a self-conjugate dyadic Ψ and an anti-self-conjugate dyadic Ω. But for the latter

$$\mathbf{r}\cdot\Omega = -\Omega\cdot\mathbf{r},$$

and therefore

$$\mathbf{r}\cdot\Omega\cdot\mathbf{r} = -\mathbf{r}\cdot\Omega\cdot\mathbf{r},$$

so that the expression vanishes identically. Hence the most general homogeneous scalar quadratic expression in $\mathbf{r}$ is of the form

$$\mathbf{r}\cdot\Phi\cdot\mathbf{r}$$

where Φ is a self-conjugate dyadic. Putting this in the simple form proved always possible in Art. 64, we may write the quadratic expression

$$\begin{aligned}&\mathbf{r}\cdot(a_1\mathbf{i}\,\mathbf{i} + a_2\mathbf{j}\,\mathbf{j} + a_3\mathbf{k}\,\mathbf{k})\cdot\mathbf{r}\\ &= a_1x^2 + a_2y^2 + a_3z^2.\end{aligned}$$

Points for which this quadratic expression has a constant value lie on the surface

$$\mathbf{r}\cdot\Phi\cdot\mathbf{r} = \text{const} \quad . \quad . \quad . \quad . \quad (24)$$

or

$$a_1x^2 + a_2y^2 + a_3z^2 = \text{const},$$

which represents a central quadric surface with centre at the origin. If the coefficients a_1, a_2, a_3 are all positive, and the constant value of the expression also positive, the surface is an ellipsoid. If one of the coefficients is negative, the surface is an hyperboloid of one sheet; if two are negative, an hyperboloid of two sheets. The most important case physically is that of the ellipsoid, for which Φ may be put in the standard form

$$\frac{1}{a^2}\mathbf{i}\,\mathbf{i} + \frac{1}{b^2}\mathbf{j}\,\mathbf{j} + \frac{1}{c^2}\mathbf{k}\,\mathbf{k}.$$

67. Tangent plane. The equation (24) for the central quadric may be written with equal generality

$$\mathbf{r}\cdot\Phi\cdot\mathbf{r} = 1. \quad . \quad . \quad . \quad . \quad . \quad (25)$$

for the dyadic may be divided by the value of the constant. We take this as the standard form of the equation for a central quadric surface.

Consider the points of intersection of the surface with the straight line through the point D parallel to the *unit* vector $\mathbf{b}$. The equation of this line is

$$\mathbf{r} = \mathbf{d} + t\mathbf{b} \qquad . \quad . \quad . \quad . \quad (26)$$

where $\mathbf{d}$ is the position vector of D. The values of $\mathbf{r}$ for the points of intersection satisfy both (25) and (26). Eliminating $\mathbf{r}$ between the equations, we find for the values of t corresponding to the points of intersection the quadratic equation

$$(\mathbf{d} + t\mathbf{b})\cdot\Phi\cdot(\mathbf{d} + t\mathbf{b}) = 1\,;$$

that is,

$$t^2(\mathbf{b}\cdot\Phi\cdot\mathbf{b}) + 2t(\mathbf{b}\cdot\Phi\cdot\mathbf{d}) + \mathbf{d}\cdot\Phi\cdot\mathbf{d} = 1 \qquad . \quad . \quad (27)$$

since Φ is self-conjugate. The straight line therefore cuts the surface in two points,

$$\mathbf{d} + t_1\mathbf{b}, \quad \mathbf{d} + t_2\mathbf{b},$$

real or imaginary according as the roots t_1, t_2 of (27) are real or imaginary.

If D is a point on the quadric surface, $\mathbf{d}\cdot\Phi\cdot\mathbf{d} = 1$, and one root of (27) is zero. In order that the straight line should touch the surface the other root also must be zero, for a tangent line intersects the surface in two consecutive points. For this to be the case we must have

$$\mathbf{b}\cdot\Phi\cdot\mathbf{d} = 0.$$

If $\mathbf{r}$ is any point on the straight line (26), this condition is equivalent to

$$(\mathbf{r} - \mathbf{d})\cdot\Phi\cdot\mathbf{d} = 0 \qquad . \quad . \quad . \quad . \quad (28)$$

This is the equation of a plane through the point $\mathbf{d}$ perpendicular to $\Phi\cdot\mathbf{d}$; showing that all tangent lines through $\mathbf{d}$ lie on this plane, which is therefore the *tangent plane* at that point. Since $\mathbf{d}$ lies on the surface, and therefore satisfies (25), the last equation may be written

$$\mathbf{r}\cdot\Phi\cdot\mathbf{d} = 1. \qquad . \quad . \quad . \quad . \quad (29)$$

which we take as the standard form of the equation of the tangent plane at the point $\mathbf{d}$. The vector

$$\Phi\cdot\mathbf{d} = \mathbf{N} \text{ (say)}$$

is perpendicular to the tangent plane, and therefore normal to the surface at the point $\mathbf{d}$. The length p of the perpendicular from the centre to the tangent plane (29) is (Vol. I., Art. 30)

$$p = \frac{1}{N} = \frac{1}{\sqrt{(\Phi\cdot\mathbf{d})^2}}$$

where N is mod. $\mathbf{N}$; and the vector perpendicular is

$$\mathbf{p} = p\frac{\mathbf{N}}{N} = \frac{\Phi\cdot\mathbf{d}}{(\Phi\cdot\mathbf{d})^2}.$$

It was shown in Art. 64 that there are three directions for which $\Phi \cdot \mathbf{d}$ is parallel to $\mathbf{d}$; that is, three directions to points on the surface whose position vectors are parallel to the normals at the points. These directions are those of the principal axes of the surface.

68. Condition of tangency. Let us find the condition that the plane

$$\mathbf{r} \cdot \mathbf{n} = q \quad . \quad . \quad . \quad . \quad (30)$$

should touch the quadric surface. If it is a tangent plane at the point $\mathbf{d}$, it is identical with the plane (29). This requires

$$q \Phi \cdot \mathbf{d} = \mathbf{n} ;$$

that is

$$q \mathbf{d} = \Phi^{-1} \cdot \mathbf{n}.$$

And therefore, since the point $\mathbf{d}$ lies on the plane (30),

$$\mathbf{n} \cdot \Phi^{-1} \cdot \mathbf{n} = q \mathbf{d} \cdot \mathbf{n} = q^2 \quad . \quad . \quad . \quad (31)$$

which is the required condition of tangency. If Φ is expressed in the standard form (23),

$$\Phi^{-1} = \frac{1}{a_1} \mathbf{i}\,\mathbf{i} + \frac{1}{a_2} \mathbf{j}\,\mathbf{j} + \frac{1}{a_3} \mathbf{k}\,\mathbf{k}.$$

To find the locus of the point of intersection of three mutually perpendicular tangent planes, let the equations of the planes be

$$\begin{aligned} \mathbf{r} \cdot \mathbf{n}_1 &= \sqrt{\mathbf{n}_1 \cdot \Phi^{-1} \cdot \mathbf{n}_1} \\ \mathbf{r} \cdot \mathbf{n}_2 &= \sqrt{\mathbf{n}_2 \cdot \Phi^{-1} \cdot \mathbf{n}_2} \\ \mathbf{r} \cdot \mathbf{n}_3 &= \sqrt{\mathbf{n}_3 \cdot \Phi^{-1} \cdot \mathbf{n}_3}, \end{aligned}$$

in which $\mathbf{n}_1$, $\mathbf{n}_2$, $\mathbf{n}_3$ are *unit* vectors, mutually perpendicular. On squaring and adding these three equations we have

$$\begin{aligned} \mathbf{r}^2 &= \mathbf{n}_1 \cdot \Phi^{-1} \cdot \mathbf{n}_1 + \mathbf{n}_2 \cdot \Phi^{-1} \cdot \mathbf{n}_2 + \mathbf{n}_3 \cdot \Phi^{-1} \cdot \mathbf{n}_3 \\ &= \Phi_s^{-1} \qquad \text{by } (7'') \\ &= \frac{1}{a_1} + \frac{1}{a_2} + \frac{1}{a_3}. \end{aligned}$$

Hence the required locus is a sphere with centre at the origin.

69. Polar plane. The tangent plane at the point $\mathbf{d}$ is given by (29). If this passes through the point $\mathbf{h}$, then

$$\mathbf{h} \cdot \Phi \cdot \mathbf{d} = 1.$$

Further, every point such as $\mathbf{d}$, the tangent plane at which passes through $\mathbf{h}$, satisfies this relation and therefore lies on the plane whose equation is

$$\mathbf{h} \cdot \Phi \cdot \mathbf{r} = 1 \quad . \quad . \quad . \quad . \quad (32)$$

This is called the *polar plane* of the point $\mathbf{h}$, and is perpendicular to $\mathbf{h} \cdot \Phi$. It cuts the quadric surface in a curve C, which is the locus of those points whose tangent planes pass through **h**. The lines joining **h** to points on C form the *tangent cone* from the point **h** to the surface, touching the surface along the curve C.

If the polar plane of the point H passes through G, then the polar plane of G passes through H. Let **h**, **g** be the position vectors of these points. Then if G lies on the polar plane of H,

$$\mathbf{h}\cdot\Phi\cdot\mathbf{g} = 1.$$

But since Φ is self-conjugate, this relation is symmetrical in **h**, **g**, showing that H lies on the polar plane of G.

Any straight line drawn from the point H to intersect the surface is cut harmonically by the surface and the polar plane of H. The equation of such a line is

$$\mathbf{r} = \mathbf{h} + t\mathbf{b}$$

where we take **b** as a *unit* vector; and then the value t_1 of t for the point S at which this line cuts the polar plane is given by

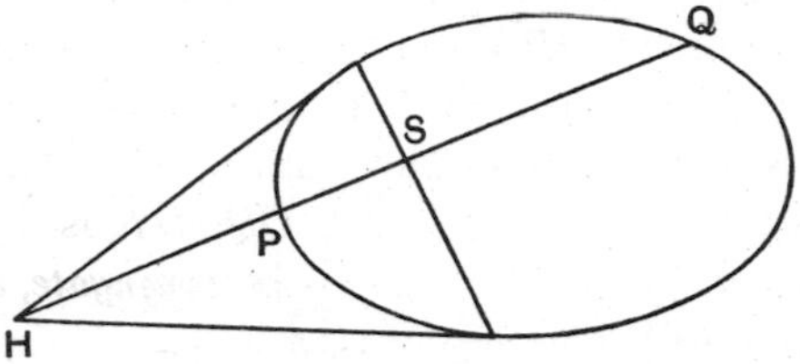

FIG. 19.

$$\mathbf{h}\cdot\Phi\cdot(\mathbf{h} + t_1\mathbf{b}) = 1\,;$$

that is,

$$t_1 = \frac{1 - \mathbf{h}\cdot\Phi\cdot\mathbf{h}}{\mathbf{h}\cdot\Phi\cdot\mathbf{b}}.$$

Similarly the values t_2 and t_3 of t for the points P, Q at which the same line cuts the surface are the roots of the equation (27) with **h** in place of **d**. Hence

$$\frac{1}{t_2} + \frac{1}{t_3} = \frac{t_2 + t_3}{t_2 t_3} = -\frac{2\mathbf{b}\cdot\Phi\cdot\mathbf{h}}{(\mathbf{h}\cdot\Phi\cdot\mathbf{h} - 1)} = \frac{2}{t_1}.$$

But t_1, t_2, t_3 measure the lengths of HS, HP, HQ respectively, and therefore

$$\frac{1}{HP} + \frac{1}{HQ} = \frac{2}{HS},$$

which proves the theorem.

70. Diametral plane. Conjugate diameters. Consider again the points of intersection of the quadric surface (25) with the straight line through the point **d** parallel to **b**. The roots of the equation (27) will be equal and opposite if

$$\mathbf{b}\cdot\Phi\cdot\mathbf{d} = 0,$$

and **d** will then be the mid-point of the chord of intersection. This relation shows that all points such as $\mathbf{d}$, bisecting the chords parallel to $\mathbf{b}$, lie on the plane whose equation is

$$\mathbf{b}\cdot\Phi\cdot\mathbf{r} = 0 \qquad (33)$$

This plane, which passes through the centre of the quadric surface and is perpendicular to $\mathbf{b}\cdot\Phi$, bisects all chords parallel to $\mathbf{b}$, and is called the *diametral plane* for such chords. It is parallel to the tangent planes at the ends of the diameter which is parallel to $\mathbf{b}$.

Since the origin O is the centre of the quadric surface, the symmetry of the equation (33) shows that if the point Q is on the diametral plane of OP, then will P be on the diametral plane of OQ. Further, let OR be the line of intersection of the diametral planes of OP and OQ. Then since the diametral planes of OP and OQ pass through OR, that of OR will pass through P and Q, and will therefore be the plane POQ. Thus the plane through any two of the three lines OP, OQ, OR is diametral to the third. Three such planes are said to be *conjugate*, and their lines of intersection are called *conjugate diameters*.

Let $\mathbf{a}$, $\mathbf{b}$, $\mathbf{c}$ be three points on an **ellipsoid** at the extremities of conjugate diameters. Then since each lies on the diametral planes of the other two,

$$\mathbf{a}\cdot\Phi\cdot\mathbf{b} = \mathbf{b}\cdot\Phi\cdot\mathbf{c} = \mathbf{c}\cdot\Phi\cdot\mathbf{a} = 0 \qquad (34)$$

And because each point is on the ellipsoid,

$$\mathbf{a}\cdot\Phi\cdot\mathbf{a} = \mathbf{b}\cdot\Phi\cdot\mathbf{b} = \mathbf{c}\cdot\Phi\cdot\mathbf{c} = 1 \qquad (35)$$

From these relations it follows that the three vectors

$$\mathbf{a}' = \Phi\cdot\mathbf{a}, \quad \mathbf{b}' = \Phi\cdot\mathbf{b}, \quad \mathbf{c}' = \Phi\cdot\mathbf{c}$$

are the reciprocal system to $\mathbf{a}$, $\mathbf{b}$, $\mathbf{c}$ (Vol. I., Art. 47). In terms of these the dyadic Φ may be written

$$\Phi = \mathbf{a}'\mathbf{a}' + \mathbf{b}'\mathbf{b}' + \mathbf{c}'\mathbf{c}',$$

for this satisfies (34) and (35) identically; while it follows by Art. 60 that

$$\Phi^{-1} = \mathbf{a}\,\mathbf{a} + \mathbf{b}\,\mathbf{b} + \mathbf{c}\,\mathbf{c}.$$

Again, writing the dyadic Φ for the ellipsoid in the standard form,

$$\Phi = \frac{\mathbf{i}\,\mathbf{i}}{a^2} + \frac{\mathbf{j}\,\mathbf{j}}{b^2} + \frac{\mathbf{k}\,\mathbf{k}}{c^2},$$

we may introduce another,

$$\Psi = \frac{\mathbf{i}\,\mathbf{i}}{a} + \frac{\mathbf{j}\,\mathbf{j}}{b} + \frac{\mathbf{k}\,\mathbf{k}}{c},$$

such that $\Psi^2 = \Phi$. The relations (34) and (35) are then equivalent to

$$(\mathbf{a}\cdot\Psi)\cdot(\Psi\cdot\mathbf{b}) = (\mathbf{b}\cdot\Psi)\cdot(\Psi\cdot\mathbf{c}) = (\mathbf{c}\cdot\Psi)\cdot(\Psi\cdot\mathbf{a}) = 0$$

and
$$(\mathbf{a}\cdot\Psi)^2 = (\mathbf{b}\cdot\Psi)^2 = (\mathbf{c}\cdot\Psi)^2 = 1 \quad . \quad . \quad . \quad (35')$$
from which it follows that
$$\mathbf{a}\cdot\Psi, \quad \mathbf{b}\cdot\Psi, \quad \mathbf{c}\cdot\Psi$$
are three mutually perpendicular unit vectors. The equation of the ellipsoid itself is
$$1 = \mathbf{r}\cdot\Phi\cdot\mathbf{r} = (\mathbf{r}\cdot\Psi)\cdot(\Psi\cdot\mathbf{r}) = (\mathbf{r}\cdot\Psi)^2.$$
Thus if $\mathbf{r}$ is a point on the ellipsoid, the vector $\mathbf{r}' = \mathbf{r}\cdot\Psi$ is one of unit length, so that the point $\mathbf{r}'$ lies on a unit sphere. We may then say briefly that the dyadic Ψ transforms the ellipsoid into a sphere ; three conjugate diameters of the ellipsoid transforming into three mutually perpendicular diameters of the sphere.

The sum of the squares on three conjugate diameters of an ellipsoid is constant. For with the above notation, and writing $\mathbf{a}\cdot\Psi = \mathbf{a}''$, $\mathbf{b}\cdot\Psi = \mathbf{b}''$, and $\mathbf{c}\cdot\Psi = \mathbf{c}''$, we have
$$\begin{aligned}\mathbf{a}^2 + \mathbf{b}^2 + \mathbf{c}^2 &= (\mathbf{a}''\cdot\Psi^{-1})\cdot(\Psi^{-1}\cdot\mathbf{a}'') + (\mathbf{b}''\cdot\Psi^{-1})\cdot(\Psi^{-1}\cdot\mathbf{b}'') + \ldots \\ &= \mathbf{a}''\cdot\Phi^{-1}\cdot\mathbf{a}'' + \mathbf{b}''\cdot\Phi^{-1}\cdot\mathbf{b}'' + \mathbf{c}''\cdot\Phi^{-1}\cdot\mathbf{c}''.\end{aligned}$$
And since $\mathbf{a}''$, $\mathbf{b}''$, $\mathbf{c}''$ are mutually perpendicular unit vectors, this expression represents the scalar of Φ^{-1}, whose value is $a^2 + b^2 + c^2$. Hence the theorem.

Other theorems may be established in a similar manner ; but we have done sufficient to illustrate the vector method.

71. Reciprocal quadric surfaces. Consider the quadric surfaces
$$\mathbf{r}\cdot\Phi\cdot\mathbf{r} = c \quad . \quad . \quad (36)$$
$$\mathbf{s}\cdot\Phi^{-1}\cdot\mathbf{s} = c' \quad . \quad . \quad (37)$$
whose self-conjugate dyadics are reciprocal, and whose constants c, c' are connected by the reciprocal relation
$$cc' = \epsilon^4$$
where ϵ is a constant. The tangent plane to the first at the point P, whose position vector relative to the centre O is $\mathbf{r}$, is
$$\mathbf{R}\cdot\Phi\cdot\mathbf{r} = c$$
where $\mathbf{R}$ is the current point on the plane ; and the length of the perpendicular OQ from the centre to this plane is *
$$p = \frac{c}{\operatorname{mod} \Phi\cdot\mathbf{r}}.$$

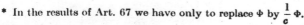

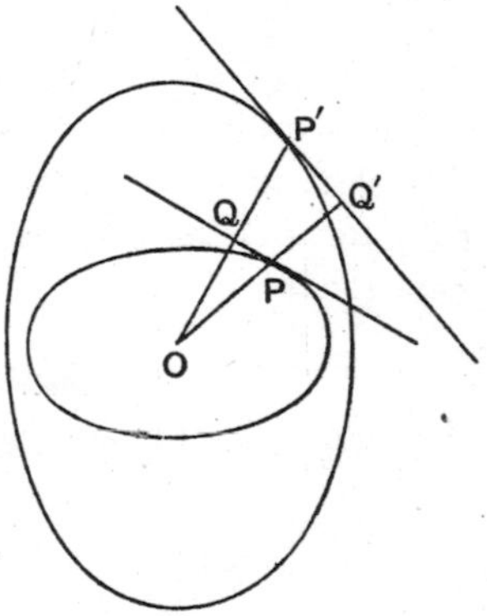

FIG. 20.

* In the results of Art. 67 we have only to replace Φ by $\frac{1}{c}\Phi$.

If P' is the point $\mathbf{s}$ on the quadric (37) in the direction $\overrightarrow{OQ}$, then $\mathbf{s} = k\Phi\cdot\mathbf{r}$ where k is some scalar. Hence

$$\Phi^{-1}\cdot\mathbf{s} = k\Phi^{-1}\cdot\Phi\cdot\mathbf{r} = k\mathbf{r},$$

showing that the tangent plane at P' to the quadric (37) is perpendicular to $\mathbf{r}$; that is to say, OP cuts this tangent plane at right angles. Thus if OP' is perpendicular to the tangent plane at P, then OP is perpendicular to that at P'. The relation is therefore a reciprocal one.

Moreover, the unit vector $\hat{\mathbf{s}}$ in the direction $\overrightarrow{OQ}$ is $\Phi\cdot\mathbf{r}/\text{mod } \Phi\cdot\mathbf{r}$. Hence the length l of OP' is given by

$$l^2\hat{\mathbf{s}}\cdot\Phi^{-1}\cdot\hat{\mathbf{s}} = c';$$

that is,

$$c' = \frac{l^2(\mathbf{r}\cdot\Phi)\cdot\Phi^{-1}\cdot(\Phi\cdot\mathbf{r})}{(\Phi\cdot\mathbf{r})^2} = \frac{l^2\mathbf{r}\cdot\Phi\cdot\mathbf{r}}{(\Phi\cdot\mathbf{r})^2}.$$

The numerator of this expression has the value l^2c, while the denominator is equal to c^2/p^2. The whole expression therefore has the value l^2p^2/c, showing that

$$l^2p^2 = cc' = \epsilon^4;$$

that is,

$$OQ.OP' = lp = \epsilon^2.$$

Similarly we may show that

$$OP.OQ' = \epsilon^2.$$

Thus P', Q' are inverse points to Q, P respectively in a sphere of radius ϵ and centre O. The points P, P' are the poles of $P'Q'$ and PQ respectively with respect to this sphere; and the quadric surfaces (36) and (37) are said to be *reciprocal* to each other with respect to this sphere.

EXERCISES ON CHAPTER V.

1. Show that $\Phi\cdot\Phi_c$ is self-conjugate; and that

$$(\Phi\times\mathbf{a})_c = -\mathbf{a}\times\Phi_c.$$

2. Show that

$$(\mathrm{I}\times\mathbf{a})\cdot\Phi = \mathbf{a}\times\Phi$$

and

$$(\mathbf{a}\times\mathrm{I})\cdot\Phi = \mathbf{a}\times\Phi.$$

3. If $\Phi\cdot\mathbf{r} = 0$ for three non-coplanar values of $\mathbf{r}$, show that $\Phi = 0$.

4. Prove that

$$\begin{aligned}\mathbf{a}\,\mathbf{b}\times\mathbf{c} + \mathbf{b}\,\mathbf{c}\times\mathbf{a} + \mathbf{c}\,\mathbf{a}\times\mathbf{b} &= [\mathbf{abc}]\mathrm{I}\\ &= \mathbf{b}\times\mathbf{c}\,\mathbf{a} + \mathbf{c}\times\mathbf{a}\,\mathbf{b} + \mathbf{a}\times\mathbf{b}\,\mathbf{c}.\end{aligned}$$

5. Show that

$$(\Phi\cdot\Psi\cdot\Omega)_s = (\Psi\cdot\Omega\cdot\Phi)_s = (\Omega\cdot\Phi\cdot\Psi)_s.$$

6. If the dyadics Φ_1, Φ_2, Φ_3, . . . are *small* (that is to say, one vector in each dyad is small), prove that, neglecting squares and products as well as indeterminate products of small vectors,

$$(I + \Phi_1)\cdot(I + \Phi_2)\cdot \; . \; . \; . \; \cdot(I + \Phi_n) = I + \sum_1^n \Phi,$$

and that

$$(I + \Phi_1)^n = I + n\Phi_1.$$

If Φ is small, prove that, to the same order of approximation as above, $(I + \Phi)$ and $(I - \Phi)$ are reciprocal.

7. Show that the dyadic $(I + a\mathbf{i}\,\mathbf{i} + b\mathbf{j}\,\mathbf{j} + c\mathbf{k}\,\mathbf{k})$, in direct multiplication with vectors parallel to **i**, **j**, and **k**, leaves their directions unaltered but increases their lengths in the ratios $1 + a : 1$, $1 + b : 1$, $1 + c : 1$ respectively.

8. If

$$\Phi = I + \frac{\beta - 1}{v^2}\mathbf{v}\,\mathbf{v}$$

and

$$\frac{1}{\beta} = \sqrt{1 - \frac{\mathbf{v}^2}{c^2}},$$

prove that

$$\Phi^2 = I + \frac{\beta^2}{c^2}\mathbf{v}\,\mathbf{v}$$

and

$$\Phi^{-1} = I - \frac{\beta - 1}{\beta v^2}\mathbf{v}\,\mathbf{v} = \Phi - \frac{\beta}{c^2}\mathbf{v}\,\mathbf{v}.$$

Also show that Φ "stretches" vectors parallel to **v** in the ratio $\beta : 1$, but leaves vectors perpendicular to **v** unaltered.

9. With the same notation as in the last Ex. if

$$\mathbf{r}' = \Phi\cdot\mathbf{r} - \beta t\mathbf{v}$$

and

$$t' = \beta\left(t - \frac{\mathbf{v}\cdot\mathbf{r}}{c^2}\right),$$

prove that

$$\mathbf{r} = \Phi\cdot\mathbf{r}' + \beta t'\mathbf{v}$$

and

$$t = \beta\left(t' + \frac{\mathbf{v}\cdot\mathbf{r}'}{c^2}\right).$$

10. In the case of a rigid body moving about a fixed point (the origin) with angular velocity **A**, show that the A.M. about that point is

$$\mathbf{H} = \Sigma\mathbf{r}\times(m\mathbf{A}\times\mathbf{r}) = \Phi\cdot\mathbf{A}$$

where

$$\Phi = \Sigma m(\mathbf{r}^2 \mathrm{I} - \mathbf{r}\,\mathbf{r}),$$

and that the kinetic energy is

$$T = \tfrac{1}{2}\Sigma m(\mathbf{A}\times\mathbf{r})^2 = \tfrac{1}{2}\mathbf{A}\cdot\Phi\cdot\mathbf{A} = \tfrac{1}{2}\mathbf{A}\cdot\mathbf{H}.$$

11. Show that the volume of a parallelepiped, whose edges are three conjugate radii of an ellipsoid, is constant.

12. Give the Cartesian equivalents of the relations (34) and (35).

13. The sum of the squares of the reciprocals of the three perpendiculars dropped from the origin upon a system of three conjugate tangent planes of an ellipsoid is constant.

14. The equation of the plane through the points **a**, **b**, **c** at the extremities of three conjugate diameters of an ellipsoid is

$$\mathbf{r}\cdot\Phi\cdot(\mathbf{a} + \mathbf{b} + \mathbf{c}) = 1.$$

15. The locus of the centroid of the ends of three conjugate semi-diameters of an ellipsoid is a similar ellipsoid.

16. Prove that the tangent planes at the extremities of three conjugate diameters of an ellipsoid meet on a similar ellipsoid.

17. If the sum of the squares on the lines joining a point P to the six ends of three conjugate diameters of an ellipsoid is constant, the locus of P is a sphere.

18. Chords of a central quadric which are bisected by the point **d** lie in the plane

$$(\mathbf{r} - \mathbf{d})\cdot\Phi\cdot\mathbf{d} = 0.$$

19. The necessary and sufficient condition that the quadrics

$$\mathbf{r}\cdot\Phi\cdot\mathbf{r} = 1, \quad \mathbf{r}\cdot\Psi\cdot\mathbf{r} = 1$$

be confocal, is that Φ^{-1} and Ψ^{-1} differ by a multiple of the idemfactor.

20. If two confocals intersect they do so orthogonally.

21. If $\mathbf{r}' = \Phi\cdot\mathbf{r}$, find the locus of the point $\mathbf{r}'$ when the point $\mathbf{r}$ lies

(i) on the plane $\mathbf{r}\cdot\mathbf{n} = q$ (a plane);
(ii) on the straight line $\mathbf{r} = \mathbf{a} + t\mathbf{b}$ (a straight line);
(iii) on the sphere $\mathbf{r}^2 = \mathbf{a}^2$ (an ellipsoid);
(iv) on the ellipsoid $\mathbf{r}\cdot\Phi\cdot\mathbf{r} = 1$ (a reciprocal ellipsoid).

CHAPTER VI.

THE RIGID BODY.

INERTIA DYADIC. MOTION ABOUT A FIXED POINT.

I. The Inertia Dyadic.

72. Moments and products of inertia. Second moments. The moment of inertia of a rigid body about a given axis, and its products of inertia relative to a set of rectangular axes through a given point, were discussed in our elementary volume, Arts. 90–91. We shall here consider them from a different point of view.

Let m be the mass of a particle of the body at P, and $\mathbf{r}$ its position vector relative to a fixed point O. The *second moment* or *moment of inertia* of the body about an axis through O parallel to the unit vector $\mathbf{a}$ is equal to Σmp^2, where p is the length of the perpendicular PN from P to the given axis, and the summation includes all the particles of the body. But (Fig. 21)

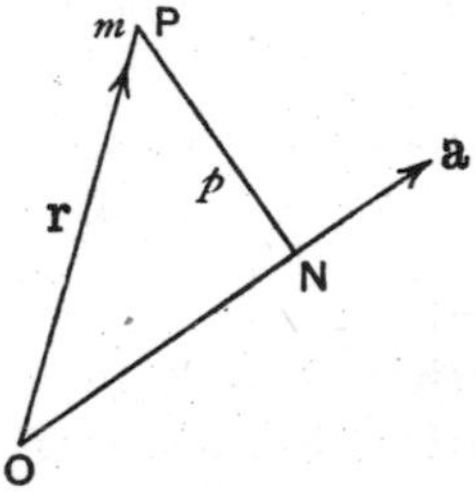

FIG. 21.

$$p^2 = (\mathbf{r}\times\mathbf{a})^2,$$

and therefore

$$\begin{aligned}\Sigma mp^2 &= \Sigma m(\mathbf{r}\times\mathbf{a})^2\\ &= \Sigma m[\mathbf{r}^2 - (\mathbf{r}\cdot\mathbf{a})^2]\\ &= \mathbf{a}\cdot[\Sigma m(\mathbf{r}^2\mathrm{I} - \mathbf{r}\,\mathbf{r})]\cdot\mathbf{a}\\ &= \mathbf{a}\cdot\Phi\cdot\mathbf{a}\end{aligned}$$

where the self-conjugate dyadic Φ is defined by

$$\Phi = \Sigma m(\mathbf{r}^2\mathrm{I} - \mathbf{r}\,\mathbf{r}) \quad . \quad . \quad . \quad . \quad (1)$$

and is called the *inertia dyadic* relative to the point O. Thus for an axis through O parallel to the unit vector $\mathbf{a}$, the moment of inertia or second moment is given by $\mathbf{a}\cdot\Phi\cdot\mathbf{a}$. If this expression has the value Mk^2 where $M \equiv \Sigma m$ is the mass of the whole body, k is called the *radius of gyration* of the body about the axis considered.

It will be found convenient to define the second moment or *product of inertia* of the body about a pair of axes through O parallel to the unit vectors **a**, **b** as equal to $\mathbf{a}\cdot\Phi\cdot\mathbf{b}$. This makes the moment of inertia a particular case of the product, for which the axes are coincident. And in the case of rectangular axes through O parallel to **i**, **j**, **k**, we then have for the product of inertia relative to the last two

$$\begin{aligned}\mathbf{j}\cdot\Phi\cdot\mathbf{k} &= \mathbf{j}\cdot[\Sigma m(\mathbf{r}^2\mathrm{I} - \mathbf{r}\,\mathbf{r})]\cdot\mathbf{k} \\ &= -\Sigma m(\mathbf{r}\cdot\mathbf{j})(\mathbf{r}\cdot\mathbf{k}) \\ &= -\Sigma myz,\end{aligned}$$

which is of opposite sign to the product as usually defined. However, considering the generality of definition, the uniformity gained in treating moments and products of inertia, and the "eruption" of negative signs that will be apparent from the following, it seems worth while to make this change in the current practice.*

73. Theorem of parallel axes. Let G be the centre of mass of the body, $\bar{\mathbf{r}}$ its position vector relative to O, and $\mathbf{r}'$ that of P relative to G. Then $\mathbf{r} = \bar{\mathbf{r}} + \mathbf{r}'$. The dyadic Φ for the point O may then be written

$$\begin{aligned}\Phi &= \Sigma m(\mathbf{r}^2\mathrm{I} - \mathbf{r}\,\mathbf{r}) \\ &= \Sigma m[(\bar{\mathbf{r}}^2 + 2\bar{\mathbf{r}}\cdot\mathbf{r}' + \mathbf{r}'^2)\mathrm{I} - (\bar{\mathbf{r}}\,\bar{\mathbf{r}} + \bar{\mathbf{r}}\,\mathbf{r}' + \mathbf{r}'\bar{\mathbf{r}} + \mathbf{r}'\mathbf{r}')].\end{aligned}$$

Now since G is the centre of mass

$$\Sigma m\bar{\mathbf{r}}\cdot\mathbf{r}' = \bar{\mathbf{r}}\cdot\Sigma m\mathbf{r}' = 0.$$

Similarly

$$\Sigma m\bar{\mathbf{r}}\,\mathbf{r}' = \bar{\mathbf{r}}\Sigma m\mathbf{r}' = 0$$

and

$$\Sigma m\mathbf{r}'\bar{\mathbf{r}} = (\Sigma m\mathbf{r}')\bar{\mathbf{r}} = 0.$$

Omitting these zero terms from the dyadic we have

$$\begin{aligned}\Phi &= \Sigma m(\bar{\mathbf{r}}^2\mathrm{I} - \bar{\mathbf{r}}\,\bar{\mathbf{r}}) + \Sigma m(\mathbf{r}'^2\mathrm{I} - \mathbf{r}'\mathbf{r}') \\ &= \overline{\Phi} + \Phi'. \qquad (2)\end{aligned}$$

where Φ' is the inertia dyadic relative to G, and $\overline{\Phi}$ that relative to O when the whole mass $M = \Sigma m$ is supposed collected at G. Therefore

$$\mathbf{a}\cdot\Phi\cdot\mathbf{a} = \mathbf{a}\cdot\overline{\Phi}\cdot\mathbf{a} + \mathbf{a}\cdot\Phi'\cdot\mathbf{a} \qquad (2')$$

The first member is the moment of inertia I about an axis through O parallel to **a**; the last term is the moment of inertia I' about a parallel axis through the c.m. The middle term, being the moment of inertia about the former axis of a particle of mass M at G, is equal to Md^2, where d is the perpendicular distance between the parallel axes. Hence

$$I = I' + Md^2,$$

which is the *theorem of parallel axes*.

* This suggestion is due to Prof. J. H. Michell, F.R.S.

Similarly for the products of inertia about pairs of axes through O and G parallel to **a** and **b** we have

$$\mathbf{a}\cdot\Phi\cdot\mathbf{b} = \mathbf{a}\cdot\overline{\Phi}\cdot\mathbf{b} + \mathbf{a}\cdot\Phi'\cdot\mathbf{b} \quad . \quad . \quad . \quad (2'')$$

74. Nonion form of Φ. When expressed in terms of the unit vectors **i**, **j**, **k**, let Φ take the form

$$\Phi = A\mathbf{i}\,\mathbf{i} + B\mathbf{j}\,\mathbf{j} + C\mathbf{k}\,\mathbf{k} + D(\mathbf{j}\,\mathbf{k} + \mathbf{k}\,\mathbf{j}) + E(\mathbf{k}\,\mathbf{i} + \mathbf{i}\,\mathbf{k}) + F(\mathbf{i}\,\mathbf{j} + \mathbf{j}\,\mathbf{i}) \quad (3)$$

the coefficients in conjugate dyads being equal because the dyadic is self-conjugate. From this it follows that

$$A = \mathbf{i}\cdot\Phi\cdot\mathbf{i}, \quad B = \mathbf{j}\cdot\Phi\cdot\mathbf{j}, \quad C = \mathbf{k}\cdot\Phi\cdot\mathbf{k},$$
$$D = \mathbf{j}\cdot\Phi\cdot\mathbf{k}, \quad E = \mathbf{k}\cdot\Phi\cdot\mathbf{i}, \quad F = \mathbf{i}\cdot\Phi\cdot\mathbf{j}.$$

That is to say, A, B, C are equal to the moments of inertia about axes through O parallel to **i**, **j**, **k** respectively; while D, E, F are the products of inertia about axes through O parallel to **j** and **k**, **k** and **i**, **i** and **j** respectively. If in the expression (1) for Φ we put as usual

$$\mathbf{r} = x\mathbf{i} + y\mathbf{j} + z\mathbf{k},$$

we easily calculate the values of these coefficients to be

$$A = \Sigma m(y^2 + z^2), \quad B = \Sigma m(z^2 + x^2), \quad C = \Sigma m(x^2 + y^2),$$
$$D = -\Sigma myz, \quad E = -\Sigma mzx, \quad F = -\Sigma mxy.$$

Using the value of Φ given by (3), we find for the moment of inertia about an axis through O parallel to the unit vector $\mathbf{a} = l\mathbf{i} + m\mathbf{j} + n\mathbf{k}$ the expression

$$\begin{aligned} I(\mathbf{a}) &= \mathbf{a}\cdot\Phi\cdot\mathbf{a} \\ &= Al^2 + Bm^2 + Cn^2 + 2Dmn + 2Enl + 2Flm. \end{aligned}$$

Similarly if $\mathbf{b} = l'\mathbf{i} + m'\mathbf{j} + n'\mathbf{k}$ is another unit vector, the product of inertia about axes through O parallel to **a** and **b** is

$$\begin{aligned} P(\mathbf{a}, \mathbf{b}) &= \mathbf{a}\cdot\Phi\cdot\mathbf{b} \\ &= All' + Bmm' + Cnn' + D(mn' + m'n) \\ &\qquad + E(nl' + n'l) + F(lm' + l'm). \end{aligned}$$

It was shown in Art. 64 that a set of rectangular unit vectors **i**, **j**, **k** could always be found in terms of which the self-conjugate dyadic Φ took the simple form

$$\Phi = A\mathbf{i}\,\mathbf{i} + B\mathbf{j}\,\mathbf{j} + C\mathbf{k}\,\mathbf{k} \quad . \quad . \quad . \quad (4)$$

The coefficients A, B, C are the moments of inertia about axes through O parallel to **i**, **j**, **k** respectively, and are always positive and finite. We call these axes the *principal axes* of inertia at O, and A, B, C the principal moments of inertia at O. The products of inertia relative to these axes are all zero, for $\mathbf{j}\cdot\Phi\cdot\mathbf{k}$, etc., now vanish identically. It was also shown in Art. 64 that, if the quadratic in μ had *equal roots*, any direction perpendicular to **i** was a principal direction for the dyadic, and two of the coefficients in the form (23) of that Art. were equal. In this case any axis through O perpendicular to **i** is a principal axis, and two of the principal moments of inertia B, C are equal. The reduced form for Φ is then

$$\Phi = A\mathbf{i}\,\mathbf{i} + B(\mathbf{j}\,\mathbf{j} + \mathbf{k}\,\mathbf{k}) \quad . \quad . \quad . \quad (4')$$

Consider the principal axis of inertia at O parallel to **i**, and any perpendicular axis through O, *e.g.* parallel to the unit vector $f\mathbf{j} + g\mathbf{k}$. Then the product of inertia relative to these is

$$\begin{aligned}\mathbf{i}\cdot\Phi\cdot(f\mathbf{j} + g\mathbf{k}) &= f\mathbf{i}\cdot\Phi\cdot\mathbf{j} + g\mathbf{i}\cdot\Phi\cdot\mathbf{k} \\ &= 0.\end{aligned}$$

Thus the product of inertia with respect to a principal axis and any perpendicular axis through O is zero.

75. Momental ellipsoid, and ellipsoid of gyration. Consider the quadric surface

$$\mathbf{r}\cdot\Phi\cdot\mathbf{r} = M\epsilon^4 \quad . \quad . \quad . \quad . \quad (5)$$

where Φ is the inertia dyadic for the origin O, M the mass of the body, and ϵ a constant. Let P be the point of the surface whose position vector is $\mathbf{r} = r\hat{\mathbf{r}}$ with the usual notation. Then (5) is equivalent to

$$\hat{\mathbf{r}}\cdot\Phi\cdot\hat{\mathbf{r}} = \frac{M\epsilon^4}{r^2}.$$

But the first member is equal to the moment of inertia of the body about the axis OP, and is finite for all axes, and never zero. Hence r is finite for all points on the surface, which is therefore an ellipsoid with centre at O. And the moment of inertia (M.I.) of the body about an axis through O is inversely proportional to the square of the semi-diameter of the ellipsoid along that axis. This ellipsoid is called the *momental ellipsoid* of the body at the point O. Its size depends on the choice of the constant ϵ; but its shape is determined only by the distribution of mass about the point O.

Consider now the quadric surface reciprocal to the momental ellipsoid (5) with respect to a sphere of radius ϵ and centre O. In virtue of Art. 71 this reciprocal surface has for equation

$$\mathbf{s}\cdot\Phi^{-1}\cdot\mathbf{s} = \frac{1}{M} \quad . \quad . \quad . \quad . \quad (6)$$

The two surfaces are such that if P' (Fig. 20) is a point of (6) lying on the perpendicular from O to the tangent plane at P, then P lies on the perpendicular from O to the tangent plane at P'. Also

P', Q' are inverse points to Q, P respectively with respect to the sphere of radius ϵ; so that

$$OQ'.OP = \epsilon^2$$

or

$$p' = \frac{\epsilon^2}{r}.$$

The above value for the M.I. of the body about OP is therefore equivalent to

$$I(\hat{\mathbf{r}}) = \frac{M\epsilon^4}{r^2} = Mp'^2 \quad . \quad . \quad . \quad . \quad (7)$$

Thus the M.I. of the body about the axis OP is proportional to the square of the perpendicular OQ' to the tangent plane at the corresponding point P' on (6). From (7) it follows that the length of this perpendicular is equal to the radius of gyration of the body about OP. In particular when OP is an axis of the momental ellipsoid, that is, a principal axis of inertia at O, it is also an axis of the ellipsoid (6), and p' is the length of the semi-axis of (6) in this direction. Thus the semi-axes of this ellipsoid are equal to the radii of gyration of the body about the principal axes of inertia at O. Hence the name *ellipsoid of gyration* which is given to the reciprocal surface (6).

76. Principal axes at any point. Binet's theorem. Take the centre of mass of the body as origin, and let $\mathbf{r}$ be the position vector of the point P. If Φ is the inertia dyadic for the c.m., that for the point P is

$$\Psi = \Phi + M(r^2\mathrm{I} - \mathbf{r}\,\mathbf{r}). \quad . \quad \text{i}$$

by Art. 73. Let us endeavour to *find the principal axes of inertia at P.*

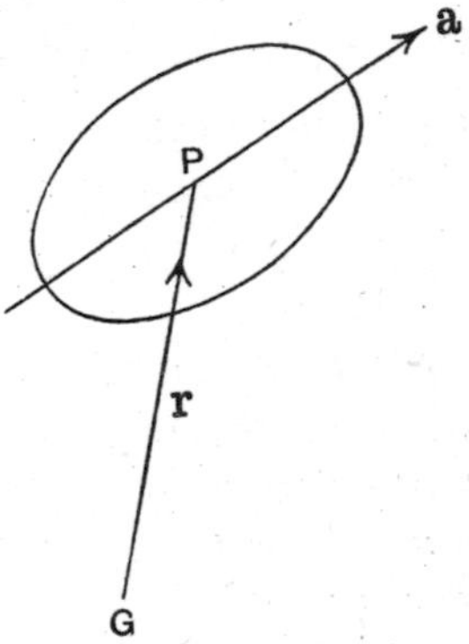

FIG. 22.

If the unit vector $\mathbf{a}$ is parallel to a principal axis at P, the normal to the momental ellipsoid for P, at the point in the direction of $\mathbf{a}$ from P, must be parallel to $\mathbf{a}$; that is

$$\Psi\cdot\mathbf{a} = \lambda\mathbf{a} \quad . \quad . \quad . \quad \text{ii}$$

where λ is a scalar factor. This requires

$$\mathbf{a}\cdot\Psi\cdot\mathbf{a} = \lambda,$$

so that λ is the corresponding principal M.I. at P. Denote it by Mk^2, where k is the corresponding principal radius of gyration at P. Substituting in ii the values of Ψ and λ, and transposing terms, we may write it

$$[\Phi + (Mr^2 - Mk^2)\mathrm{I}]\cdot\mathbf{a} = M\mathbf{r}\cdot\mathbf{a}\,\mathbf{r} \quad . \quad . \quad \text{iii}$$

Then multiplying both sides by the dyadic reciprocal to that in square brackets, we obtain

$$\mathbf{a} = M\mathbf{r}\cdot\mathbf{a}[\Phi + M(r^2 - k^2)\mathrm{I}]^{-1}\cdot\mathbf{r} \quad . \quad . \quad . \quad \text{iv}$$

Lastly, forming the scalar product of each member with $\mathbf{r}$, we may write the result

$$\mathbf{r}\cdot[\Phi + M(r^2 - k^2)\mathrm{I}]^{-1}\cdot\mathbf{r} = \frac{1}{M} \quad . \quad . \quad . \quad \text{v}$$

This is an equation in k^2, from which the values of the principal radii of gyration at P may be found. That it is a cubic equation becomes obvious if we write Φ in its normal form,

$$\Phi = A\mathbf{i}\,\mathbf{i} + B\mathbf{j}\,\mathbf{j} + C\mathbf{k}\,\mathbf{k}$$

where A, B, C are the principal moments of inertia at the c.m. Then

$$\Phi + M(r^2 - k^2)\mathrm{I} = (A + Mr^2 - Mk^2)\mathbf{i}\,\mathbf{i} + \ldots + \ldots .$$

and therefore

$$[\Phi + M(r^2 - k^2)\mathrm{I}]^{-1} = \frac{\mathbf{i}\,\mathbf{i}}{A + M(r^2 - k^2)} + \frac{\mathbf{j}\,\mathbf{j}}{B + M(r^2 - k^2)} + \ldots$$

Thus if P is the point (x, y, z), the equation v for k^2 may be written

$$\frac{x^2}{A + M(r^2 - k^2)} + \frac{y^2}{B + M(r^2 - k^2)} + \ldots = \frac{1}{M} \quad . \quad . \quad \text{vi}$$

which is clearly a cubic in k^2 for determining the principal radii of gyration at P.

The equation v shows that P lies on the quadric surfaces

$$\mathbf{R}\cdot[\Phi + M(r^2 - k^2)\mathrm{I}]^{-1}\cdot\mathbf{R} = \frac{1}{M} \quad . \quad . \quad . \quad \text{vii}$$

for the three values of k^2 given by vi ; and these surfaces are confocal to the ellipsoid of gyration at the c.m., viz.

$$\mathbf{r}\cdot\Phi^{-1}\cdot\mathbf{r} = \frac{1}{M}$$

(*cf*. Ex. 19, Chap. V.). It also follows from iv that $\mathbf{a}$, or the direction of a principal axis at P, is normal at that point to the particular confocal given by that value of k^2. Thus the principal axes of inertia at P are the normals at P to the three confocal quadric surfaces vii, for the values of k^2 determined from v. This is *Binet's theorem*.

II. Motion about a Fixed Point.

77. Kinematical. Consider the case of a rigid body turning about a point O, which is fixed in the body and also in space.* Let $\mathbf{A}$

* That is to say, fixed in the frame of reference relative to which the motion of the body is expressed.

be the angular velocity of the body at any instant. Then the velocity of a particle at the point P, whose position vector relative to O is $\mathbf{r}$, is given by (Vol. I., Art. 87)

$$\mathbf{v} = \mathbf{A} \times \mathbf{r}.$$

If m is the mass of this particle, its linear momentum is $m\mathbf{A}\times\mathbf{r}$; and its moment of momentum or angular momentum (A.M.) about O is $\mathbf{r}\times(m\mathbf{A}\times\mathbf{r})$. The A.M. of the whole body about O is then

$$\begin{aligned} \mathbf{H} &= \Sigma\mathbf{r}\times(m\mathbf{A}\times\mathbf{r}) \\ &= \Sigma m(\mathbf{r}\cdot\mathbf{r}\,\mathbf{A} - \mathbf{r}\cdot\mathbf{A}\,\mathbf{r}) \\ &= [\Sigma m(\mathbf{r}^2\mathrm{I} - \mathbf{r}\,\mathbf{r})]\cdot\mathbf{A} \\ &= \Phi\cdot\mathbf{A}\,. \qquad (8) \end{aligned}$$

where Φ is the inertia dyadic for the origin O. Similarly the kinetic energy T of the body is $\frac{1}{2}\Sigma m\mathbf{v}^2$; so that

$$\begin{aligned} 2T &= \Sigma m(\mathbf{A}\times\mathbf{r})\cdot(\mathbf{A}\times\mathbf{r}) \\ &= \Sigma m[\mathbf{A}^2\mathbf{r}^2 - (\mathbf{A}\cdot\mathbf{r})^2] \\ &= \mathbf{A}\cdot[\Sigma m(\mathbf{r}^2\mathrm{I} - \mathbf{r}\,\mathbf{r})]\cdot\mathbf{A} \\ &= \mathbf{A}\cdot\Phi\cdot\mathbf{A} \qquad (9) \\ &= \mathbf{A}\cdot\mathbf{H}\,. \qquad (9') \end{aligned}$$

The momental ellipsoid at the point O is given by the equation

$$\mathbf{r}\cdot\Phi\cdot\mathbf{r} = M\epsilon^4.$$

The normal at the point $\mathbf{r}$ is parallel to $\Phi\cdot\mathbf{r}$. It follows then from (8) that $\mathbf{H}$ is perpendicular to the tangent plane at the point of the surface in the direction of $\mathbf{A}$; so that $\mathbf{H}$ and $\mathbf{A}$ have the same direction only for a rotation about a principal axis. If $\mathbf{r}$ is the position vector of the point of the surface in the direction of $\mathbf{A}$, the length p of the perpendicular from O to the tangent plane at that point is

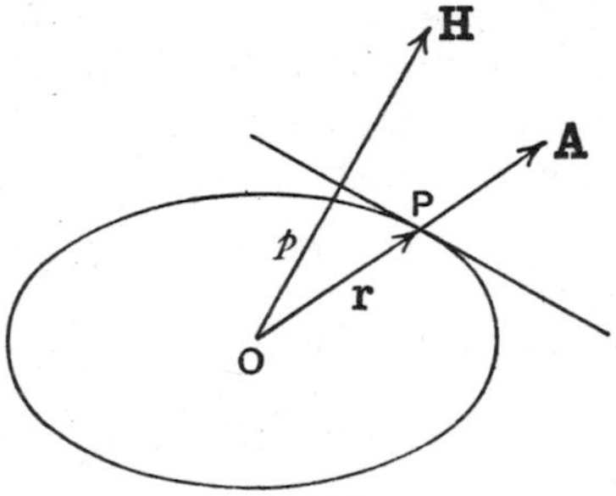

FIG. 23.

$$p = \frac{M\epsilon^4}{\text{mod}\ \Phi\cdot\mathbf{r}} = \frac{M\epsilon^4}{H}\cdot\frac{\omega}{r} \qquad (10)$$

where $\omega = \text{mod}\ \mathbf{A}$ and $H = \text{mod}\ \mathbf{H}$.

78. Equation of motion. Let $\mathbf{L}$ denote the torque about O of all the external forces acting on the body. Then (Vol. I., Art. 84)

$$\mathbf{L} = \frac{d\mathbf{H}}{dt} \qquad (11)$$

This rate of change is relative to a frame of reference S_1 outside the body and considered as fixed. If we introduce also a frame of reference S_2 fixed in the body, and denote rates of change relative to this by a suffix 2, then by Vol. I., Art. 94, the above formula becomes

$$\mathbf{L} = \left(\frac{d\mathbf{H}}{dt}\right)_2 + \mathbf{A}\times\mathbf{H}.$$

The dyadic Φ depends upon the distribution of matter about the point O, and is constant relative to the frame S_2 fixed in the body. Thus $\left(\frac{d\Phi}{dt}\right)_2 = 0$. If then we substitute in the last equation the value of $\mathbf{H}$ given by (8), it becomes

$$\mathbf{L} = \Phi\cdot\left(\frac{d\mathbf{A}}{dt}\right)_2 + \mathbf{A}\times(\Phi\cdot\mathbf{A}).$$

And, since the rate of increase of $\mathbf{A}$ is the same for both frames of reference, we may write this simply

$$\mathbf{L} = \Phi\cdot\frac{d\mathbf{A}}{dt} + \mathbf{A}\times(\Phi\cdot\mathbf{A}). \quad . \quad . \quad . \quad (12)$$

This is a convenient form of the *equation of motion* of the body about the fixed point O. If we express all the vectors in terms of their rectangular components parallel to the principal axes of the body at O, the equation (12) gives Euler's dynamical equations for the body, already found in Vol. I., Art. 96.

If we form the scalar product of each side of (12) with $\mathbf{A}$, the last term disappears, being then a scalar triple product with a repeated factor. Thus

$$\mathbf{L}\cdot\mathbf{A} = \mathbf{A}\cdot\Phi\cdot\frac{d\mathbf{A}}{dt} = \mathbf{H}\cdot\frac{d\mathbf{A}}{dt} \quad . \quad . \quad . \quad (13)$$

Further, the rate of increase of the kinetic energy T is given by

$$\begin{aligned} 2\frac{dT}{dt} &= \frac{d}{dt}(\mathbf{A}\cdot\mathbf{H}) = \frac{d\mathbf{A}}{dt}\cdot\mathbf{H} + \mathbf{A}\cdot\frac{d\mathbf{H}}{dt} \\ &= \mathbf{L}\cdot\mathbf{A} + \mathbf{A}\cdot\mathbf{L} \quad . \quad . \quad . \quad . \quad \text{by (13)} \\ &= 2\mathbf{L}\cdot\mathbf{A} \quad . \quad . \quad . \quad . \quad . \quad . \quad (14) \end{aligned}$$

Thus the rate of increase of the kinetic energy is equal to $\mathbf{L}\cdot\mathbf{A}$. This expression therefore measures the rate at which the external forces are doing work on the body, and is called the *activity* of the forces. The system of external forces is equivalent to the torque $\mathbf{L}$ about O together with a force at O equal to their vector sum. The latter does no work because O is fixed.

Suppose the body to be rotating about an *axis fixed in space*, that is, in the frame S_1. Let the directions of $\mathbf{i}, \mathbf{j}, \mathbf{k}$ be also fixed in space,

i being parallel to the axis of rotation, so that $\mathbf{A} = \omega\mathbf{i}$. The equation of motion (12) then becomes

$$\frac{d\omega}{dt}\Phi\cdot\mathbf{i} + \omega^2\mathbf{i}\times(\Phi\cdot\mathbf{i}) = \mathbf{L}.$$

But if Φ is expressed in its nonion form (3),

$$\Phi\cdot\mathbf{i} = A\mathbf{i} + F\mathbf{j} + E\mathbf{k}$$

where A, F, E are the moment and products of inertia relative to the axis of rotation and perpendicular axes through O. The above equation is therefore equivalent to

$$\mathbf{L} = A\frac{d\omega}{dt}\mathbf{i} + \left(F\frac{d\omega}{dt} - E\omega^2\right)\mathbf{j} + \left(E\frac{d\omega}{dt} + F\omega^2\right)\mathbf{k}.$$

The torque **L** is the resultant of the torques due to the impressed forces and the constraint of the fixed axis.

If there are no impressed forces, the constraint of the axis will vanish only if the second member of the last equation is zero. This requires the coefficients of **i**, **j**, **k** to vanish separately. Thus $\left(\frac{d\omega}{dt}\right)$ must be zero, and therefore ω constant. Then the other components will vanish only if $E = F = O$; that is to say, if the fixed axis is a principal axis of inertia. Thus *an axis of free rotation of the body through a fixed point O must be a principal axis at that point.*

79. Motion under no forces. Suppose that a rigid body, turning about a fixed point O, is acted on by no forces except the constraint at O. Then the torque **L** is zero; and the equations

$$\mathbf{L} = \frac{d\mathbf{H}}{dt}, \quad \mathbf{L}\cdot\mathbf{A} = \frac{dT}{dt},$$

show that both the angular momentum **H** and the kinetic energy T are constant.

Let $\mathbf{r} = \overrightarrow{OP}$ be the radius vector of the momental ellipsoid for O in the direction of **A** (Fig. 23). Then

$$\mathbf{r}\cdot\Phi\cdot\mathbf{r} = M\epsilon^4.$$

But the kinetic energy is given by

$$\mathbf{A}\cdot\Phi\cdot\mathbf{A} = 2T.$$

From these two equations it follows, since **r** and **A** are parallel, that

$$\frac{\mathbf{A}^2}{\mathbf{r}^2} = \frac{2T}{M\epsilon^4} = \text{const} \quad . \quad . \quad . \quad . \quad (15)$$

Thus the angular velocity is proportional to the radius of the momental ellipsoid in the direction of the instantaneous axis. And using the value of the ratio $\omega : r$ given by this equation, we find from (10) for the length p of the perpendicular from O to the tangent plane at the point P

$$p = \frac{1}{H}\sqrt{2TM\epsilon^4} = \text{const} \quad . \quad . \quad . \quad (16)$$

The length of this perpendicular is constant, and its direction is also constant, being the direction of **H**. Therefore the tangent plane at the point P is a plane fixed in space. It is called the *invariable plane*, and the line through O perpendicular to it the *invariable line*. Further, the instantaneous motion of the body is a rotation about the line OP. Therefore the motion may be described by saying that the momental ellipsoid rolls (without slipping) on the invariable plane. The path which the point of contact P traces out on the momental ellipsoid (fixed in the body) is called the *polhode*; that which it traces out on the invariable plane is the *herpolhode*. This description of the motion is due to *Poinsot*.

We may find the *equation of the polhode* as the intersection of two surfaces. For

$$\mathbf{H}^2 = (\mathbf{A}\cdot\Phi)\cdot(\Phi\cdot\mathbf{A}) = \mathbf{A}\cdot\Phi^2\cdot\mathbf{A} \quad . \quad . \quad . \quad (17)$$

where, referred to the principal directions at O,

$$\Phi^2 = \Phi\cdot\Phi = A^2\mathbf{i}\,\mathbf{i} + B^2\mathbf{j}\,\mathbf{j} + C^2\mathbf{k}\,\mathbf{k}.$$

Then using the value of $\omega : r$ given by (15) we may write (17) as

$$\mathbf{r}\cdot\Phi^2\cdot\mathbf{r} = \frac{H^2M\epsilon^4}{2T} \quad . \quad . \quad . \quad . \quad (18)$$

This is the equation of an ellipsoid with centre at O. Also P lies on the momental ellipsoid

$$\mathbf{r}\cdot\Phi\cdot\mathbf{r} = M\epsilon^4 \quad . \quad . \quad . \quad . \quad (19)$$

and the polhode is therefore the intersection of the two surfaces (18) and (19). In Cartesian coordinates, referred to the principal axes at O, these surfaces are

$$A^2x^2 + B^2y^2 + C^2z^2 = H^2M\epsilon^4/2T \quad . \quad . \quad (18')$$

and

$$Ax^2 + By^2 + Cz^2 = M\epsilon^4 \quad . \quad . \quad . \quad (19')$$

Eliminating z from these equations we find

$$A(A - C)x^2 + B(B - C)y^2 = (H^2 - 2CT)M\epsilon^4/2T$$

for the equation of the projection of the polhode on the xy plane. This is an ellipse if C is either the greatest or the least of the principal moments of inertia. In this case, if the body is slightly disturbed from a steady rotation about that principal axis, the polhode will be a small curve round the end of that axis of the momental ellipsoid, and the axis of rotation will remain in the neighbourhood of the principal axis, which is therefore a *stable* axis for steady rotation. But if C is intermediate between A and B, the projection of the polhode on the xy plane is an hyperbola, and the axis of rotation will depart further and further from this principal axis, which is therefore an *unstable* axis for steady rotation.

80. The free motion of a body about a fixed point O may also be expressed in terms of the ellipsoid of gyration, which is the reciprocal of the momental ellipsoid with respect to a sphere of radius ϵ and centre O. Since the tangent plane PQ (Fig. 20) to the momental ellipsoid is invariable, the corresponding point P' of the ellipsoid of gyration is invariable. Thus *the ellipsoid of gyration moves so that its surface always passes through a point P' fixed in space*, at a distance from O along the invariable line equal to

$$OP' = \frac{\epsilon^2}{p} = \frac{H}{\sqrt{2MT}} \quad . \quad . \quad . \quad . \quad \text{by (16)}$$

Further, OP is perpendicular to the tangent plane at P'; and the length of the perpendicular OQ' to this tangent plane is

$$p' = \frac{\epsilon^2}{r} = \frac{1}{\omega}\sqrt{\frac{2T}{M}} \quad . \quad . \quad . \quad . \quad \text{by (15)}$$

Therefore *the perpendicular from O to the tangent plane at the fixed point P' is the instantaneous axis of rotation; and the angular velocity of the body varies inversely as the length of this perpendicular.*

The scalar resolute ω' of the angular velocity about the invariable line is given by

$$\omega' = \omega \cos POQ = \frac{\omega p}{r} = \frac{2T}{H}$$

by (15) and (16). Thus *the angular velocity about the invariable line is constant.* This description of the motion is due to *MacCullagh.*

81. Impulsive forces. It was shown in Vol. I., Chap. VII., that the equations of motion of a rigid body acted on by forces $\mathbf{F}_1$, $\mathbf{F}_2$, . . . whose lines of action pass through the points $\mathbf{r}_1$, $\mathbf{r}_2$, . . . respectively, are

$$\left.\begin{aligned} \frac{d\mathbf{M}}{dt} &= \Sigma\mathbf{F} \\ \frac{d\mathbf{H}}{dt} &= \Sigma\mathbf{r}\times\mathbf{F} \end{aligned}\right\} \quad . \quad . \quad . \quad . \quad (20)$$

$\mathbf{M}$ being the linear momentum of the body and $\mathbf{H}$ its angular momentum about the origin. The impulse of a force acting for a definite period was also shown to be the time integral of the force extended over that period ; or

$$\mathbf{F}^* = \int_{t_1}^{t_2} \mathbf{F} dt.$$

When the magnitude of the force is very great, and the interval of time during which it acts very small, while the impulse $\mathbf{F}^*$ is finite, the force is called an impulsive force or *impulse*. The displacement of the body during the interval is infinitesimal. Suppose that the force acts through the point $\mathbf{r}$ during the whole interval, and that its value is $\mathbf{F}$ at any instant. Its torque about the origin O at that instant is $\mathbf{r}\times\mathbf{F}$, and the time integral of this over the brief interval of action is called the *impulsive torque*. Its value is

$$\int_{t_1}^{t_2} \mathbf{r}\times\mathbf{F} dt = \mathbf{r}\times\int_{t_1}^{t_2} \mathbf{F} dt = \mathbf{r}\times\mathbf{F}^*,$$

since $\mathbf{r}$ is constant during the interval. It is therefore equal to the moment of the impulse acting through the point $\mathbf{r}$.

Now integrate the equations (20) with respect to t for the interval t_1 to t_2 during which the impulsive forces act. We then obtain for the increments in the linear and angular momenta

$$\left.\begin{aligned} \Delta\mathbf{M} &= [\mathbf{M}]_{t_1}^{t_2} = \Sigma\int_{t_1}^{t_2} \mathbf{F} dt = \Sigma\mathbf{F}^* \\ \text{and} \quad \Delta\mathbf{H} &= [\mathbf{H}]_{t_1}^{t_2} = \Sigma\int_{t_1}^{t_2} \mathbf{r}\times\mathbf{F} dt = \Sigma\mathbf{r}\times\mathbf{F}^* = \mathbf{L}^* \text{ (say)} \end{aligned}\right\} \quad . \quad (21)$$

Thus the increment $\Delta\mathbf{M}$ in the linear momentum of the body during the interval is equal to the vector sum of the impulses ; and the increment $\Delta\mathbf{H}$ in the A.M. about O is equal to $\mathbf{L}^*$, the vector sum of the impulsive torques.

For a rigid body $\mathbf{H} = \Phi\cdot\mathbf{A}$, where $\mathbf{A}$ is the angular velocity and Φ the inertia dyadic for the point O. Now Φ is invariable during the action of the impulses, so that

$$\left.\begin{aligned} \mathbf{L}^* &= \Delta\mathbf{H} = \Phi\cdot(\Delta\mathbf{A}) \\ \text{or} \quad \Delta\mathbf{A} &= \Phi^{-1}\cdot\mathbf{L}^* \end{aligned}\right\} \quad . \quad . \quad . \quad (22)$$

Thus $\mathbf{L}^*$ is parallel to the normal at the end of the radius vector of the momental ellipsoid whose direction is that of $\Delta\mathbf{A}$; and $\Delta\mathbf{A}$ is parallel to the normal at the end of the radius vector of the ellipsoid of gyration in the direction of $\mathbf{L}^*$. The directions of $\mathbf{L}^*$ and $\Delta\mathbf{A}$ coincide only when parallel to a principal axis at O.

82. Centre of percussion for a given axis. A rigid body is set rotating about a fixed axis through O parallel to the unit vector $\mathbf{a}$, by a blow $\mathbf{F}^*$ at the point P whose position vector $\overrightarrow{OP} = \mathbf{r}$. It is required to find $\mathbf{F}^*$ and $\mathbf{r}$ so that there is no impulsive action on the axis of constraint; that is, so that the initial motion would be one of rotation about this axis if there were no constraint at all.

Let G be the c.m. whose position vector is $\overrightarrow{OG} = \bar{\mathbf{r}}$, and let $\mathbf{A} = \omega\mathbf{a}$ be the angular velocity produced by the blow. The initial velocity of the c.m. is $\mathbf{A}\times\bar{\mathbf{r}}$, and the equations (21) give

$$\left.\begin{aligned} M\mathbf{A}\times\bar{\mathbf{r}} &= \mathbf{F}^* \\ \Phi\cdot\mathbf{A} &= \mathbf{r}\times\mathbf{F}^* \end{aligned}\right\}$$

since there is to be no impulsive action of constraint. The first equation shows that $\mathbf{F}^*$ is perpendicular to the plane of $\mathbf{a}$ and $\bar{\mathbf{r}}$; that is, perpendicular to the plane containing the axis and the c.m. Let N be the foot of the perpendicular from P to this plane. Also, since the axis is to be one of no constraint, we may take the origin anywhere on it. Choose it at the foot of the perpendicular from P to this axis. Then $\mathbf{a}\cdot\mathbf{r} = 0$.

The second equation of motion then gives

$$\begin{aligned} \omega\Phi\cdot\mathbf{a} &= \mathbf{r}\times\mathbf{F}^* \\ &= M\mathbf{r}\times(\mathbf{A}\times\bar{\mathbf{r}}), \end{aligned}$$

and therefore

$$\begin{aligned} \Phi\cdot\mathbf{a} &= M\mathbf{r}\times(\mathbf{a}\times\bar{\mathbf{r}}) \\ &= M(\mathbf{r}\cdot\bar{\mathbf{r}}\,\mathbf{a} - \mathbf{r}\cdot\mathbf{a}\,\bar{\mathbf{r}}) \\ &= M\mathbf{r}\cdot\bar{\mathbf{r}}\,\mathbf{a}. \end{aligned}$$

Thus $\Phi\cdot\mathbf{a}$ is parallel to $\mathbf{a}$, so that the axis is a principal axis at O. If Mk^2 is the moment of inertia about it,

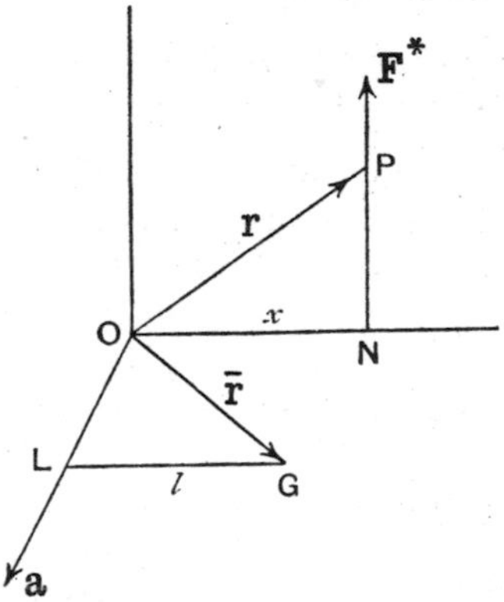

FIG. 24.

$$Mk^2 = \mathbf{a}\cdot\Phi\cdot\mathbf{a} = M\mathbf{r}\cdot\bar{\mathbf{r}} = Mxl$$

where $x = ON$, and l is the perpendicular distance LG of G from the axis. Thus $x = k^2/l$ is the shortest distance between the axis and the line of action of the blow. The required conditions are therefore that

(i) the axis chosen must be a principal axis at one point on it:

(ii) the blow must be applied in a plane through that point perpendicular to the axis, in a direction perpendicular to the plane containing the axis and the c.m., and at a distance k^2/l from the axis.

EXERCISES ON CHAPTER VI.

1. Show that the moment of inertia of a body about the straight line $\mathbf{r} = \mathbf{d} + t\mathbf{a}$ is

$$\mathbf{a}\cdot\Phi\cdot\mathbf{a} + M\mathbf{d}^2 - M(\mathbf{a}\cdot\mathbf{d})^2$$

where $\mathbf{a}$ is a unit vector and Φ is the inertia dyadic for the c.m. which is taken as origin.

Show also that the momental ellipsoid at the point $\mathbf{d}$, referred to its centre as origin, is

$$\mathbf{r}\cdot\Phi\cdot\mathbf{r} + M\mathbf{d}^2\mathbf{r}^2 - M(\mathbf{d}\cdot\mathbf{r})^2 = M\epsilon^4.$$

2. Using the cubic vi of Art. 76 for determining k^2, show that the locus of a point of the body, such that the sum of the principal moments of inertia is constant, is a sphere with centre at the c.m.

Also find the locus when the sum of the products of the principal moments taken two and two together is constant; and when the product of the three principal moments is constant.

3. Any point O in a body being given, and any plane through it, prove that two straight lines at right angles can always be drawn in this plane through O, such that the product of inertia relative to them is zero.

4. *A straight line being given, it is required to find at what point (if any) it is a principal axis of the body, and the condition that such a point should exist.*

With the c.m. of the body as origin, let the straight line be $\mathbf{r} = \mathbf{d} + t\mathbf{a}$ where $\mathbf{a}$ is a unit vector. If Φ is the inertia dyadic for the c.m., that for a point P on this line is (by Art. 76)

$$\Psi = \Phi + M[(\mathbf{d} + t\mathbf{a})^2 \mathrm{I} - M(\mathbf{d} + t\mathbf{a})(\mathbf{d} + t\mathbf{a})].$$

If $\mathbf{b}$, $\mathbf{c}$ are two other unit vectors perpendicular to each other and to $\mathbf{a}$, the conditions that the given line be a principal axis at P are

$$\mathbf{a}\cdot\Psi\cdot\mathbf{b} = 0 = \mathbf{a}\cdot\Psi\cdot\mathbf{c}.$$

These are equivalent to

$$\left.\begin{aligned}\mathbf{a}\cdot\Phi\cdot\mathbf{b} - M(\mathbf{a}\cdot\mathbf{d} + t)\mathbf{d}\cdot\mathbf{b} = 0\\ \mathbf{a}\cdot\Phi\cdot\mathbf{c} - M(\mathbf{a}\cdot\mathbf{d} + t)\mathbf{d}\cdot\mathbf{c} = 0\end{aligned}\right\} \quad . \quad . \quad . \quad \mathrm{i}$$

In order that these equations in t should be consistent we must have

$$\mathbf{d}\cdot\mathbf{c}\; \mathbf{a}\cdot\Phi\cdot\mathbf{b} = \mathbf{d}\cdot\mathbf{b}\; \mathbf{a}\cdot\Phi\cdot\mathbf{c} \quad . \quad . \quad . \quad \mathrm{ii}$$

which is the condition that such a point should exist. The required value of t, that is to say, the distance of this point from the point $\mathbf{d}$, is then given by either of the equations i, say

$$t = \frac{\mathbf{a}\cdot\Phi\cdot\mathbf{b} - M\mathbf{a}\cdot\mathbf{d}\; \mathbf{b}\cdot\mathbf{d}}{M\mathbf{b}\cdot\mathbf{d}} \quad . \quad . \quad . \quad . \quad \mathrm{iii}$$

If the given straight line is parallel to a principal axis at the c.m. G, then

$$\mathbf{a}\cdot\Phi\cdot\mathbf{b} = 0 = \mathbf{a}\cdot\Phi\cdot\mathbf{c} \quad . \quad . \quad . \quad . \quad \mathrm{iv}$$

and the condition ii is satisfied. The value of t given by iii is then

$$t = -\mathbf{a}\cdot\mathbf{d},$$

showing that the required point on the line is the projection of G upon it.

If the given straight line passes through the c.m. ($\mathbf{d} = 0$) and is a principal axis at that point, the equations iv hold, and therefore the relations i are satisfied for all values of t. Thus *if a straight line through the c.m. is a principal axis at that point, it is a principal axis at every point.*

The point on a straight line at which it is a principal axis is called the *principal point* of the line.

5. Having found the principal point of the straight line $\mathbf{r} = \mathbf{d} + t\mathbf{a}$ in the previous exercise, show how to find the other principal axes at that point.

6. The semi-axes of an ellipsoid are a, b, c. If $\mathbf{m} = a\mathbf{i} + b\mathbf{j} + c\mathbf{k}$, and $\mathbf{n} = \frac{1}{a}\mathbf{i} + \frac{1}{b}\mathbf{j} + \frac{1}{c}\mathbf{k}$ where $\mathbf{i}$, $\mathbf{j}$, $\mathbf{k}$ are parallel to the axes of the ellipsoid whose centre is taken as origin, show that the straight line

$$\mathbf{r} = \mathbf{m} + t\mathbf{n}$$

is at some point a principal axis of the ellipsoid.

7. Show that any straight line drawn on a lamina is a principal axis of that lamina at some point if the line does not pass through the centre of mass. Where is this point if the straight line pass through the centre of mass?

8. Show that on any plane there is a point at which it is a principal plane for a given body.

9. For a rigid body of mass M, turning about a fixed point O, and acted on by external forces whose vector sum is $\mathbf{F}$, show that the action $\mathbf{R}$ of the hinge at O is given by

$$\mathbf{F} + \mathbf{R} = M\left[\frac{d\mathbf{A}}{dt}\times\bar{\mathbf{r}} + \mathbf{A}\times(\mathbf{A}\times\bar{\mathbf{r}})\right]$$

where $\bar{\mathbf{r}}$ is the position vector of the c.m. relative to O.

10. A rigid body, hinged at O to a fixed point, is set rotating about a principal axis at O. If it is acted on by no forces but those at the hinge, show that it will continue to rotate with constant angular velocity about the same axis.

If O is the c.m. of the body, show that there is zero action on the hinge; and hence that a principal axis at the c.m. is an axis of free rotation.

11. The sum of the squares of the distances of the extremities of the principal diameters of the momental ellipsoid from the invariable line is constant throughout the motion (Poinsot).

12. A body moves about a fixed point O under the action of no forces. Show that if the surface $\mathbf{r}\cdot\Phi\cdot\mathbf{r} = M\mathbf{r}^4$ be traced in the body, this surface throughout the motion will roll on a fixed sphere.

13. If the body while in motion be acted on by an impulsive torque about O, whose plane is perpendicular to the invariable line, show that the momental ellipsoid will continue to roll on the same plane as before, but that the rate of motion will be altered.

14. In the motion of a body about a fixed point under any forces (Arts. 77, 78), prove the relations

$$\frac{H^2}{2T}=\frac{M\epsilon^4}{p^2}, \quad 2T=M\epsilon^4\left(\frac{\omega}{r}\right)^2, \quad H=\frac{M\epsilon^4\omega}{pr}.$$

If the moment of the impressed forces about the instantaneous axis is always zero, show that the kinetic energy is constant, and that ω is proportional to r throughout the motion.

15. In the same problem show that

$$\mathbf{H}\cdot\frac{d\mathbf{H}}{dt}=\mathbf{H}\cdot\mathbf{L}=\mathbf{L}\cdot\mathbf{\Phi}\cdot\mathbf{A}.$$

Hence show that, when the impressed forces have zero moment about the line through O parallel to $\mathbf{H}$, the scalar H is constant, and that ω varies as pr.

16. When $\mathbf{L}$ is perpendicular to both $\mathbf{A}$ and $\mathbf{H}$, the quantities T, H, p are constant, and ω varies as r.

17. Prove that

$$(\mathbf{A}\times\mathbf{H})\cdot(\mathbf{L}\times\mathbf{H})=\frac{4T^2M\epsilon^4}{p^3}\frac{dp}{dt}.$$

Hence when the projection of $\mathbf{L}$ upon the plane of $\mathbf{A}$ and $\mathbf{H}$ is parallel to $\mathbf{H}$, show that p and therefore $\mathbf{H}^2/T$ is constant.

18. A rigid body moves about a fixed point under the action of a torque $\mathbf{L}$, producing motion such that the kinetic energy is proportional to the square of the angular momentum $\mathbf{H}$. Prove that the plane of $\mathbf{L}$ and $\mathbf{H}$ is perpendicular to that of $\mathbf{A}$ and $\mathbf{H}$.

CHAPTER VII

DYADICS INVOLVING THE OPERATOR ∇.

83. The operator ∇ applied to a vector. We have already seen that the operator ∇ applied to a scalar point-function V yields the vector function

$$\nabla V = \mathbf{i}\frac{\partial V}{\partial x} + \mathbf{j}\frac{\partial V}{\partial y} + \mathbf{k}\frac{\partial V}{\partial z},$$

which is invariant with respect to the choice of orthogonal coordinate axes. So far we have attached no meaning to $\nabla\mathbf{V}$ where $\mathbf{V}$ is a vector point-function. By analogy with the above we define it as the dyadic

$$\nabla\mathbf{V} = \mathbf{i}\frac{\partial \mathbf{V}}{\partial x} + \mathbf{j}\frac{\partial \mathbf{V}}{\partial y} + \mathbf{k}\frac{\partial \mathbf{V}}{\partial z} \quad . \quad . \quad . \quad . \quad (1)$$

each term being a dyad, the indeterminate product of two vectors. Similarly we define $\mathbf{V}\nabla$ as the conjugate dyadic

$$\mathbf{V}\nabla = \frac{\partial \mathbf{V}}{\partial x}\mathbf{i} + \frac{\partial \mathbf{V}}{\partial y}\mathbf{j} + \frac{\partial \mathbf{V}}{\partial z}\mathbf{k} \quad . \quad . \quad . \quad (1')$$

The dyadics thus defined by analogy with the gradient of a scalar function are of very frequent occurrence in more advanced work, where their introduction greatly simplifies the analysis. In the following chapters we shall see their use in the theories of Elasticity and Electro-magnetism.

Both the dyadics are *invariant* with respect to the system of rectangular axes chosen. For if $\hat{\mathbf{a}}$ is any constant unit vector,

$$(\nabla\mathbf{V})\cdot\hat{\mathbf{a}} = \left(\Sigma\mathbf{i}\frac{\partial \mathbf{V}}{\partial x}\right)\cdot\hat{\mathbf{a}} = \Sigma\mathbf{i}\frac{\partial}{\partial x}(\mathbf{V}\cdot\hat{\mathbf{a}})$$
$$= \nabla(\mathbf{V}\cdot\hat{\mathbf{a}}),$$

which is invariant; and similarly

$$\hat{\mathbf{a}}\cdot(\nabla\mathbf{V}) = \hat{\mathbf{a}}\cdot\Sigma\mathbf{i}\frac{\partial \mathbf{V}}{\partial x} = a_1\frac{\partial \mathbf{V}}{\partial x} + a_2\frac{\partial \mathbf{V}}{\partial y} + a_3\frac{\partial \mathbf{V}}{\partial z}$$
$$= (\hat{\mathbf{a}}\cdot\nabla)\mathbf{V} \quad . \quad . \quad . \quad . \quad . \quad . \quad (2)$$

which is the derivative of $\mathbf{V}$ in the direction of $\hat{\mathbf{a}}$, and is invariant. Thus since $\hat{\mathbf{a}}\cdot(\nabla\mathbf{V})$ and $(\nabla\mathbf{V})\cdot\hat{\mathbf{a}}$ are invariant for all values of $\hat{\mathbf{a}}$, the dyadic $\nabla\mathbf{V}$ is invariant. Hence its conjugate $\mathbf{V}\nabla$ is also invariant.

The equation (2) shows that $\hat{\mathbf{a}}\cdot(\nabla\mathbf{V})$ has the same value as the directional derivative $(\hat{\mathbf{a}}\cdot\nabla)\mathbf{V}$. The brackets are therefore unnecessary, as in the case of a scalar function (Art. 4), and either expression may be written simply $\hat{\mathbf{a}}\cdot\nabla\mathbf{V}$. The analogy to the case of a scalar V is very close throughout. If, for instance, $\mathbf{V}$ and $\mathbf{V} + d\mathbf{V}$ are the values of the vector function at the points $\mathbf{r}$ and $\mathbf{r} + d\mathbf{r}$ respectively, putting

$$\mathbf{r} = x\mathbf{i} + y\mathbf{j} + z\mathbf{k},$$

and therefore

$$d\mathbf{r} = dx\mathbf{i} + dy\mathbf{j} + dz\mathbf{k},$$

we have

$$\begin{aligned} d\mathbf{r}\cdot\nabla\mathbf{V} &= (dx\mathbf{i} + dy\mathbf{j} + dz\mathbf{k})\cdot\left(\mathbf{i}\frac{\partial\mathbf{V}}{\partial x} + \mathbf{j}\frac{\partial\mathbf{V}}{\partial y} + \dots\right) \\ &= \frac{\partial\mathbf{V}}{\partial x}dx + \frac{\partial\mathbf{V}}{\partial y}dy + \frac{\partial\mathbf{V}}{\partial z}dz \\ &= d\mathbf{V} \qquad . \quad . \quad . \quad . \quad . \quad . \quad . \qquad (3) \end{aligned}$$

which is of the same form as in Art. 3 for a scalar function, viz.

$$d\mathbf{r}\cdot\nabla V = dV.$$

We may also remark that the scalar of the dyadic $\nabla\mathbf{V}$ is, by (1),

$$(\nabla\mathbf{V})_s = \mathbf{i}\cdot\frac{\partial\mathbf{V}}{\partial x} + \mathbf{j}\cdot\frac{\partial\mathbf{V}}{\partial y} + \mathbf{k}\cdot\frac{\partial\mathbf{V}}{\partial z} = \text{div } \mathbf{V} \qquad . \quad . \qquad (4)$$

and similarly its vector is

$$(\nabla\mathbf{V})_v = \Sigma\mathbf{i}\times\frac{\partial\mathbf{V}}{\partial x} = \text{curl } \mathbf{V} \qquad . \quad . \quad . \qquad (5)$$

The scalar of the conjugate $\mathbf{V}\nabla$ is also equal to div $\mathbf{V}$, but its vector is

$$(\mathbf{V}\nabla)_v = \Sigma\frac{\partial\mathbf{V}}{\partial x}\times\mathbf{i} = -\text{ curl } \mathbf{V} \qquad . \quad . \quad . \qquad (5')$$

In agreement with the notation

$$\nabla\times\mathbf{V} = \Sigma\mathbf{i}\times\frac{\partial\mathbf{V}}{\partial x} = \text{curl } \mathbf{V}$$

we may conveniently write

$$\left.\begin{aligned} \mathbf{V}\times\nabla &= \Sigma\frac{\partial\mathbf{V}}{\partial x}\times\mathbf{i} = -\nabla\times\mathbf{V} \\ \mathbf{V}\cdot\nabla &= \Sigma\frac{\partial\mathbf{V}}{\partial x}\cdot\mathbf{i} = \quad \nabla\cdot\mathbf{V} \end{aligned}\right\} \qquad . \quad . \quad . \qquad (6)$$

Thus the vectors and scalars of the above dyadics are

$$(\nabla \mathbf{V})_v = \nabla \times \mathbf{V}, \quad (\nabla \mathbf{V})_s = \nabla \cdot \mathbf{V}$$
$$(\mathbf{V}\nabla)_v = \mathbf{V} \times \nabla, \quad (\mathbf{V}\nabla)_s = \mathbf{V} \cdot \nabla = \nabla \cdot \mathbf{V}.$$

Since ∇V is a vector, we may form with it the dyadic $\nabla\nabla V$. The scalar of this dyadic is therefore $\nabla \cdot \nabla V = \nabla^2 V$, and its vector

$$(\nabla\nabla V)_v = \nabla \times \nabla V = \text{curl grad } V = 0$$

by Art. 9. Since, then, the vector of the dyadic vanishes identically, the dyadic is *self-conjugate* (Art. 62).

84. Differentiation of dyadics. If **UV** is a dyad of point-functions, we define its derivative with respect to x by the equation

$$\frac{\partial}{\partial x}(\mathbf{UV}) = \frac{\partial \mathbf{U}}{\partial x}\mathbf{V} + \mathbf{U}\frac{\partial \mathbf{V}}{\partial x},$$

the indeterminate product being therefore differentiated by the same rule as other products, the order of the vectors, however, not being reversible. Similarly if Φ is a dyadic, whose antecedents and consequents are vector point-functions, we define $\frac{\partial \Phi}{\partial x}$ as the sum of the derivatives of its dyads.

We now introduce the further functions defined by

$$\nabla \cdot \Phi = \mathbf{i} \cdot \frac{\partial \Phi}{\partial x} + \mathbf{j} \cdot \frac{\partial \Phi}{\partial y} + \mathbf{k} \cdot \frac{\partial \Phi}{\partial z} \quad . \quad . \quad . \quad (7)$$

$$\nabla \times \Phi = \mathbf{i} \times \frac{\partial \Phi}{\partial x} + \mathbf{j} \times \frac{\partial \Phi}{\partial y} + \mathbf{k} \times \frac{\partial \Phi}{\partial z} \quad . \quad . \quad . \quad (8)$$

the former being a vector and the latter a dyadic. It is easily shown that their values are independent of the choice of rectangular axes. For if $\hat{\mathbf{a}}$ is any constant unit vector,

$$(\nabla \cdot \Phi) \cdot \hat{\mathbf{a}} = \left(\Sigma \mathbf{i} \cdot \frac{\partial \Phi}{\partial x}\right) \cdot \hat{\mathbf{a}} = \Sigma \mathbf{i} \cdot \frac{\partial}{\partial x}(\Phi \cdot \hat{\mathbf{a}})$$
$$= \text{div } (\Phi \cdot \hat{\mathbf{a}}),$$

which is invariant. And since this is true for all directions of $\hat{\mathbf{a}}$, the vector $\nabla \cdot \Phi$ is *invariant.* Similarly it may be shown that $\nabla \times \Phi$ is invariant. In agreement with the above definitions we naturally attach to $\Phi \cdot \nabla$ and $\Phi \times \nabla$ the meanings

$$\Phi \cdot \nabla = \frac{\partial \Phi}{\partial x} \cdot \mathbf{i} + \frac{\partial \Phi}{\partial y} \cdot \mathbf{j} + \frac{\partial \Phi}{\partial z} \cdot \mathbf{k} \quad . \quad . \quad . \quad (7')$$

$$\Phi \times \nabla = \frac{\partial \Phi}{\partial x} \times \mathbf{i} + \frac{\partial \Phi}{\partial y} \times \mathbf{j} + \frac{\partial \Phi}{\partial z} \times \mathbf{k} \quad . \quad . \quad . \quad (8')$$

from which it is obvious that

$$\Phi \cdot \nabla = \Sigma \mathbf{i} \cdot \frac{\partial \Phi_c}{\partial x} = \nabla \cdot \Phi_c \quad . \quad . \quad . \quad (7'')$$

and similarly that

$$\Phi \times \nabla = -\left[\Sigma \mathbf{i} \times \frac{\partial \Phi_c}{\partial x} \right]_c = -(\nabla \times \Phi_c)_c \quad . \quad . \quad (8'')$$

The values of these expressions are therefore also invariant.

We also meet with expressions in which ∇ occurs more than once; and these again are analogous to those considered in Chapter I. Thus from the equations (7) and (8) it is easy to prove the identities

$$\nabla \times \nabla \mathbf{V} \equiv 0 \quad . \quad . \quad . \quad . \quad (9)$$

$$\nabla \cdot \nabla \times \Phi \equiv 0 \quad . \quad . \quad . \quad . \quad (10)$$

which are analogous to (20) of Art. 9. Further,

$$\begin{aligned} \nabla \cdot \nabla \mathbf{V} &= \nabla \cdot \left(\mathbf{i} \frac{\partial \mathbf{V}}{\partial x} + \mathbf{j} \frac{\partial \mathbf{V}}{\partial y} + \mathbf{k} \frac{\partial \mathbf{V}}{\partial z} \right) \\ &= \frac{\partial^2 \mathbf{V}}{\partial x^2} + \frac{\partial^2 \mathbf{V}}{\partial y^2} + \frac{\partial^2 \mathbf{V}}{\partial z^2} \\ &= \nabla^2 \mathbf{V} \quad . \quad . \quad . \quad . \quad . \quad . \quad (11) \end{aligned}$$

as defined in Art. 9. Similarly

$$\begin{aligned} \nabla \cdot (\mathbf{V} \nabla) &= \Sigma \mathbf{i} \cdot \frac{\partial}{\partial x} \left(\frac{\partial \mathbf{V}}{\partial x} \mathbf{i} + \frac{\partial \mathbf{V}}{\partial y} \mathbf{j} + \frac{\partial \mathbf{V}}{\partial z} \mathbf{k} \right) \\ &= \Sigma \mathbf{i} \frac{\partial}{\partial x} \left(\Sigma \mathbf{i} \cdot \frac{\partial \mathbf{V}}{\partial x} \right) \\ &= \nabla \nabla \cdot \mathbf{V} = \text{grad div } \mathbf{V} \quad . \quad . \quad . \quad (11') \\ &= \nabla (\mathbf{V} \cdot \nabla). \end{aligned}$$

Lastly, it can be shown, as in proving (22) Art. 9, that

$$\nabla \times (\nabla \times \Phi) = \nabla \nabla \cdot \Phi - \nabla^2 \Phi \quad . \quad . \quad . \quad (12)$$

each term of this equation being a dyadic.

85. Formulæ of expansion. Various formulæ in some degree analogous to those of Art. 8 will now be proved, and will be found useful in the following chapters. Consider first the formulæ

$$\nabla (\mathbf{u} \cdot \mathbf{v}) = \nabla \mathbf{u} \cdot \mathbf{v} + \nabla \mathbf{v} \cdot \mathbf{u} \quad . \quad . \quad . \quad . \quad (13)$$

$$\nabla (\mathbf{u} \times \mathbf{v}) = \nabla \mathbf{u} \times \mathbf{v} - \nabla \mathbf{v} \times \mathbf{u} \quad . \quad . \quad . \quad (14)$$

in which the operator ∇ applies only to the vector next following it, unless brackets are used to indicate the contrary. This convention will henceforth be adhered to. The equation (13) is one of vectors, while (14) is one of dyadics. They may both be proved by the same method ; for example

$$\nabla(\mathbf{u}\times\mathbf{v}) = \Sigma\mathbf{i}\left(\frac{\partial\mathbf{u}}{\partial x}\times\mathbf{v} + \mathbf{u}\times\frac{\partial\mathbf{v}}{\partial x}\right)$$
$$= \left(\Sigma\mathbf{i}\frac{\partial\mathbf{u}}{\partial x}\right)\times\mathbf{v} - \left(\Sigma\mathbf{i}\frac{\partial\mathbf{v}}{\partial x}\right)\times\mathbf{u}$$
$$= \nabla\mathbf{u}\times\mathbf{v} - \nabla\mathbf{v}\times\mathbf{u},$$

which proves (14). The expansion (13), which may be proved in the same way, is alternative to (19) of Art. 8.

Similarly if u, $\mathbf{v}$ are scalar and vector point-functions, and Φ a variable dyadic, the following formulæ hold :

$$\nabla(u\mathbf{v}) = \nabla u\,\mathbf{v} + u\nabla\mathbf{v} \quad . \quad . \quad . \quad . \quad (15)$$
$$\nabla\cdot(u\Phi) = \nabla u\cdot\Phi + u\nabla\cdot\Phi \quad . \quad . \quad . \quad (16)$$
$$\nabla\times(u\Phi) = \nabla u\times\Phi + u\nabla\times\Phi \quad . \quad . \quad . \quad (17)$$

the last two of which correspond to (15) and (16) of Art. 8, and the first to (7) of Art. 4. To remember one set is to remember both. To prove (17) we have

$$\nabla\times(u\Phi) = \Sigma\mathbf{i}\times\left(\frac{\partial u}{\partial x}\Phi + u\frac{\partial\Phi}{\partial x}\right)$$
$$= \left(\Sigma\mathbf{i}\frac{\partial u}{\partial x}\right)\times\Phi + u\Sigma\mathbf{i}\times\frac{\partial\Phi}{\partial x}$$
$$= \nabla u\times\Phi + u\nabla\times\Phi,$$

and the other two may be similarly established. In particular, if Φ is equal to the idemfactor I, so that $\dfrac{\partial\Phi}{\partial x} = \text{etc.} = 0$, the equations (16), (17) become

$$\nabla\cdot(u\mathrm{I}) = \nabla u \quad . \quad . \quad . \quad . \quad (16')$$
$$\nabla\times(u\mathrm{I}) = \nabla u\times\mathrm{I} \quad . \quad . \quad . \quad . \quad (17')$$

Expansions might be investigated for

$$\nabla(\Phi\cdot\mathbf{V}), \quad \nabla\cdot(\Phi\cdot\mathbf{V}), \quad \nabla\times(\Phi\cdot\mathbf{V}),$$

and also for

$$\nabla\cdot(\Phi\times\mathbf{V}) \quad \text{and} \quad \nabla\times(\Phi\times\mathbf{V})$$

(see Exercises 18–19 at the end of this chapter). But in the following we shall need only the particular cases in which Φ is equal to the idemfactor. We can then prove that

$$\nabla\cdot(\mathrm{I}\times\mathbf{V}) = \nabla\times\mathbf{V}. \quad . \quad . \quad . \quad . \quad (18)$$
$$\nabla\times(\mathrm{I}\times\mathbf{V}) = \mathbf{V}\nabla - \mathrm{I}\nabla\cdot\mathbf{V} \quad . \quad . \quad . \quad (19)$$

For by definition

$$\nabla\cdot(\mathrm{I}\times\mathbf{V}) = \Sigma\mathbf{i}\cdot\frac{\partial}{\partial x}(\mathrm{I}\times\mathbf{V})$$
$$= \Sigma\mathbf{i}\cdot\mathrm{I}\times\frac{\partial\mathbf{V}}{\partial x} = \Sigma\mathbf{i}\times\frac{\partial\mathbf{V}}{\partial x}$$
$$= \nabla\times\mathbf{V},$$

which proves (18). Similarly for the other formula we may proceed, remembering $\mathrm{I}\times\mathbf{V}=\mathbf{V}\times\mathrm{I}$ (Art. 63),

$$\begin{aligned}\nabla\times(\mathrm{I}\times\mathbf{V}) &= \nabla\times(\mathbf{V}\times\mathrm{I}) = \Sigma\mathbf{i}\times\left(\frac{\partial\mathbf{V}}{\partial x}\times\mathrm{I}\right)\\ &= \Sigma\left[\mathbf{i}\times\left(\frac{\partial\mathbf{V}}{\partial x}\times\mathbf{i}\right)\mathbf{i}+\mathbf{i}\times\left(\frac{\partial\mathbf{V}}{\partial x}\times\mathbf{j}\right)\mathbf{j}+\ldots\right]\\ &= \Sigma\left[\frac{\partial\mathbf{V}}{\partial x}\mathbf{i}-\left(\mathbf{i}\cdot\frac{\partial\mathbf{V}}{\partial x}\right)(\mathbf{i}\,\mathbf{i}+\mathbf{j}\,\mathbf{j}+\mathbf{k}\,\mathbf{k})\right]\\ &= \mathbf{V}\nabla-\mathrm{I}\nabla\cdot\mathbf{V},\end{aligned}$$

as was to be proved.

Just one other formula will be needed in the chapter on elastic bodies. Remembering that the dyadic $\nabla u\times\mathrm{I}=\mathrm{I}\times\nabla u$ is anti-self-conjugate (Art. 63), we find from the above formula (17′)

$$\begin{aligned}(\nabla\times u\mathrm{I})\times\nabla &= (\nabla u\times\mathrm{I})\times\nabla\\ &= -\left[\nabla\times(\nabla u\times\mathrm{I})_c\right]_c && \text{by } (8'')\\ &= [\nabla\times(\mathrm{I}\times\nabla u)]_c\\ &= [(\nabla u)\nabla-\mathrm{I}\nabla\cdot\nabla u]_c && \text{by } (19)\\ &= \nabla\nabla u-\mathrm{I}\nabla^2 u.\end{aligned}$$

The same result is clearly got by treating $\nabla\times(u\mathrm{I}\times\nabla)$, so that the brackets are unnecessary and we may write the formula simply

$$\nabla\times u\mathrm{I}\times\nabla=\nabla\nabla u-\mathrm{I}\nabla^2 u \quad . \quad . \quad . \quad (20)$$

This dyadic is self-conjugate. The last term is clearly so, and the first term was shown to be so at the end of Art. 83.

Transformation of Integrals.

86. Line and surface integrals. Consider a curve C joining the points A, B. Let P, P' (Fig. 25) be the neighbouring points $\mathbf{r}$, $\mathbf{r}+d\mathbf{r}$ on this curve, and $\mathbf{V}$, $\mathbf{V}+d\mathbf{V}$ the values at these points of a certain vector function. Then by (3) the increment $d\mathbf{V}$ in the function from P to P' is given by

$$d\mathbf{V}=d\mathbf{r}\cdot\nabla\mathbf{V}.$$

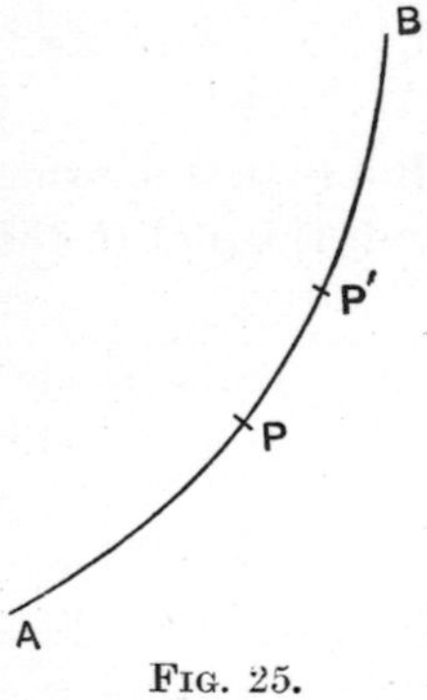

FIG. 25.

Summing for all the elements of arc from A to B we have

$$\mathbf{V}_B-\mathbf{V}_A=\int_A^B d\mathbf{r}\cdot\nabla\mathbf{V} \quad . \quad (21)$$

corresponding to (1) of Art. 13. If $\mathbf{V}$ is a uniform function and C

a closed curve, this formula becomes

$$\int_0 d\mathbf{r}\cdot\nabla\mathbf{V} = 0 \quad . \quad . \quad . \quad . \quad (21')$$

In the case of a closed curve C and an open surface S bounded by it, various theorems may be established by the same transformation as in the proof of Stokes's theorem, viz. that between i and ii of Art. 16. The argument there is equally true if we replace curl **F** by

$$\nabla\times\Phi = \mathbf{l}\times\frac{\partial\Phi}{\partial s_1} + \mathbf{m}\times\frac{\partial\Phi}{\partial s_2} + \mathbf{n}\times\frac{\partial\Phi}{\partial n}$$

where Φ is a dyadic, leading to the corresponding theorem

$$\int \mathbf{n}\cdot\nabla\times\Phi dS = \int_0 d\mathbf{r}\cdot\Phi \quad . \quad . \quad . \quad (22)$$

In the proof of Art. 16 the order of the factors in the scalar products was immaterial ; but in the present instance Φ and its derivatives are always postfactors.*

With the same notation, if **V** is a vector point-function,

$$\nabla\mathbf{V} = \mathbf{l}\frac{\partial\mathbf{V}}{\partial s_1} + \mathbf{m}\frac{\partial\mathbf{V}}{\partial s_2} + \mathbf{n}\frac{\partial\mathbf{V}}{\partial n},$$

and therefore

$$\mathbf{n}\times\nabla\mathbf{V} = \mathbf{m}\frac{\partial\mathbf{V}}{h_1\partial u} - \mathbf{l}\frac{\partial\mathbf{V}}{h_2\partial v},$$

which corresponds to i of Art. 16. With the omission of the dot for the scalar product the transformation of that Art. then leads to the theorem *

$$\int \mathbf{n}\times\nabla\mathbf{V}dS = \int_0 d\mathbf{r}\,\mathbf{V}. \quad . \quad . \quad . \quad (23)$$

Lastly, the argument of Art. 16 is equally true if the scalar products from i to ii are replaced by vector products, provided the order of the factors is maintained. We therefore have for the vector function **V** (in place of **F**)

$$\int_0 d\mathbf{r}\times\mathbf{V} = \int\left(\mathbf{m}\times\frac{\partial\mathbf{V}}{h_1\partial u} - \mathbf{l}\times\frac{\partial\mathbf{V}}{h_2\partial v}\right)dS$$

$$= \int\left[(\mathbf{n}\times\mathbf{l})\times\frac{\partial\mathbf{V}}{h_1\partial u} + (\mathbf{n}\times\mathbf{m})\frac{\partial\mathbf{V}}{h_2\partial v} + (\mathbf{n}\times\mathbf{n})\times\frac{\partial\mathbf{V}}{\partial n}\right]dS$$

Expanding the vector triple products we may write the integrand

$$\mathbf{l}\,\mathbf{n}\cdot\frac{\partial\mathbf{V}}{\partial s_1} + \mathbf{m}\,\mathbf{n}\cdot\frac{\partial\mathbf{V}}{\partial s_2} + \mathbf{n}\,\mathbf{n}\cdot\frac{\partial\mathbf{V}}{\partial n}$$

$$- \mathbf{n}\left(\mathbf{l}\cdot\frac{\partial\mathbf{V}}{\partial s_1} + \mathbf{m}\cdot\frac{\partial\mathbf{V}}{\partial s_2} + \mathbf{n}\cdot\frac{\partial\mathbf{V}}{\partial n}\right)$$

$$= \mathbf{n}\cdot(\mathbf{V}\nabla) - \mathbf{n}\nabla\cdot\mathbf{V}.$$

* For other proofs see Exercises 5–6 below.

Hence the theorem

$$\int_0 d\mathbf{r}\times\mathbf{V} = \int[\mathbf{n}\cdot(\mathbf{V}\nabla) - \mathbf{n}\nabla\cdot\mathbf{V}]dS \quad . \quad . \quad . \quad (24)$$

which will be found useful. We gather together the theorems of Arts. 16–17 and the present one for the purpose of reference, and to emphasise that they are but variations of the one transformation. Thus

$$\int\mathbf{n}\times\nabla V dS = \int_0 d\mathbf{r} V,$$

$$\int\mathbf{n}\times\nabla\mathbf{V} dS = \int_0 d\mathbf{r}\,\mathbf{V},$$

$$\int\mathbf{n}\cdot\nabla\times\mathbf{V} dS = \int_0 d\mathbf{r}\cdot\mathbf{V},$$

$$\int\mathbf{n}\cdot\nabla\times\Phi dS = \int_0 d\mathbf{r}\cdot\Phi,$$

and also (24), whose relation to these is not so apparent.

87. Surface and space integrals. The theorems (8) of Chapter II. will now be extended to apply when V and $\mathbf{F}$ have other meanings than in that chapter. If S is a closed surface bounding a certain region, the argument of Art. 14 from i to (3) is equally true of a vector function. That is to say,

$$\int\frac{\partial\mathbf{V}}{\partial x}dv = \int\mathbf{n}\cdot\mathbf{i}\,\mathbf{V}dS \quad . \quad . \quad . \quad . \quad . \quad \text{i}$$

where $\mathbf{V}$ is a vector point-function. By means of this and two similar relations that might be written down, we have

$$\int\Sigma\mathbf{i}\frac{\partial\mathbf{V}}{\partial x}dv = \int\mathbf{n}\cdot(\mathbf{i}\,\mathbf{i}+\mathbf{j}\,\mathbf{j}+\mathbf{k}\,\mathbf{k})\mathbf{V}dS;$$

that is,

$$\int\nabla\mathbf{V}dv = \int\mathbf{n}\mathbf{V}dS \quad . \quad . \quad . \quad . \quad . \quad . \quad (25)$$

which corresponds to (5) of Art. 15.

In a similar manner the divergence theorem may be deduced from i. For then

$$\int\Sigma\mathbf{i}\cdot\frac{\partial\mathbf{V}}{\partial x}dv = \int\Sigma\mathbf{n}\cdot\mathbf{i}\,\mathbf{i}\cdot\mathbf{V}dS$$

$$= \int\mathbf{n}\cdot\mathrm{I}\cdot\mathbf{V}dS;$$

that is,

$$\int\nabla\cdot\mathbf{V}dv = \int\mathbf{n}\cdot\mathbf{V}dS \quad . \quad . \quad . \quad . \quad . \quad (26)$$

which is the divergence theorem. In the same way

$$\int \Sigma \mathbf{i} \times \frac{\partial \mathbf{V}}{\partial x} dv = \int \Sigma \mathbf{n} \cdot \mathbf{i} \, \mathbf{i} \times \mathbf{V} dS$$
$$= \int \mathbf{n} \cdot \mathrm{I} \times \mathbf{V} dS ;$$

that is,

$$\int \nabla \times \mathbf{V} dv = \int \mathbf{n} \times \mathbf{V} dS \quad . \quad . \quad . \quad . \quad (27)$$

which is formula (6) of Art. 15.

Lastly, any dyadic Φ may by Art. 55 be put in the form

$$\Phi = \mathbf{i} \, \mathbf{U} + \mathbf{j} \, \mathbf{V} + \mathbf{k} \, \mathbf{W}$$

where **U**, **V**, **W** are vector point-functions. Then

$$\nabla \cdot \Phi = \Sigma \mathbf{i} \cdot \frac{\partial \Phi}{\partial x} = \frac{\partial \mathbf{U}}{\partial x} + \frac{\partial \mathbf{V}}{\partial y} + \frac{\partial \mathbf{W}}{\partial z}.$$

Hence the formula

$$\int \nabla \cdot \Phi dv = \int \left(\frac{\partial \mathbf{U}}{\partial x} + \frac{\partial \mathbf{V}}{\partial y} + \frac{\partial \mathbf{W}}{\partial z} \right) dv$$
$$= \int \mathbf{n} \cdot (\mathbf{i} \, \mathbf{U} + \mathbf{j} \, \mathbf{V} + \mathbf{k} \, \mathbf{W}) dS$$
$$= \int \mathbf{n} \cdot \Phi dS \quad . \quad . \quad . \quad . \quad . \quad (28)$$

which corresponds to the divergence theorem. Similarly

$$\nabla \times \Phi = \Sigma \mathbf{i} \times \frac{\partial \Phi}{\partial x} = \Sigma \left(\mathbf{k} \frac{\partial \mathbf{V}}{\partial x} - \mathbf{j} \frac{\partial \mathbf{W}}{\partial x} \right),$$

and therefore

$$\int \nabla \times \Phi dv = \int \Sigma \left(\mathbf{k} \frac{\partial \mathbf{V}}{\partial x} - \mathbf{j} \frac{\partial \mathbf{W}}{\partial x} \right) dv$$
$$= \int \Sigma (\mathbf{n} \cdot \mathbf{i} \, \mathbf{k} \, \mathbf{V} - \mathbf{n} \cdot \mathbf{i} \, \mathbf{j} \, \mathbf{W}) dS$$
$$= \int \mathbf{n} \cdot \mathrm{I} \times \Phi dS$$
$$= \int \mathbf{n} \times \Phi dS. \quad . \quad . \quad . \quad . \quad . \quad (29)$$

which corresponds to (27) above. These theorems are therefore all deducible from the transformation i of the present Art., with the corresponding formulæ in y and z. Their close connection is apparent from the following list, which we make for the purpose of reference, and to assist the student's memory. The theorems of Arts. 14, 15, 87 may be written

$$\int \nabla V dv = \int \mathbf{n} V dS,$$

$$\int \nabla \mathbf{V} dv = \int \mathbf{n}\, \mathbf{V} dS,$$

$$\int \nabla \cdot \mathbf{V} dv = \int \mathbf{n} \cdot \mathbf{V} dS,$$

$$\int \nabla \cdot \Phi dv = \int \mathbf{n} \cdot \Phi dS,$$

$$\int \nabla \times \mathbf{V} dv = \int \mathbf{n} \times \mathbf{V} dS,$$

$$\int \nabla \times \Phi dv = \int \mathbf{n} \times \Phi dS.$$

EXERCISES ON CHAPTER VII.

1. As an alternative to (18) of Art. 8 prove the formula

$$\nabla \times (\mathbf{u} \times \mathbf{v}) = \nabla \cdot (\mathbf{v}\, \mathbf{u} - \mathbf{u}\, \mathbf{v}),$$

which is sometimes convenient.

2. Prove the formulæ

$$\nabla \cdot (\mathbf{u}\, \mathbf{v}) = \nabla \cdot \mathbf{u}\, \mathbf{v} + \mathbf{u} \cdot \nabla \mathbf{v},$$
$$\nabla \times (\mathbf{u}\, \mathbf{v}) = \nabla \times \mathbf{u}\, \mathbf{v} - \mathbf{u} \times \nabla \mathbf{v}.$$

3. If Φ is a constant dyadic, and $\mathbf{r}$ the position vector of the current point, show that

$$\nabla (\mathbf{r} \cdot \Phi) = \Phi,$$

and for any function $\mathbf{v}$,

$$\nabla (\mathbf{v} \cdot \Phi) = (\nabla \mathbf{v}) \cdot \Phi.$$

4. If $\mathbf{v}$ is constant and $\mathbf{E}$ a point-function, show that

$$\text{div}\ (\mathbf{v} \cdot \mathbf{E}\, \mathbf{v}) = \mathbf{v} \cdot \nabla \mathbf{E} \cdot \mathbf{v},$$

and also that

$$\begin{aligned} &\text{curl}\ (\mathbf{v} \cdot \mathbf{E}\, \mathbf{v} - \mathbf{v}^2 \mathbf{E}) + \mathbf{v}\, \mathbf{v} \cdot \text{curl}\ \mathbf{E} \\ &= \text{curl}\ [\mathbf{v} \times (\mathbf{v} \times \mathbf{E})] - \mathbf{v}\ \text{div}\ (\mathbf{v} \times \mathbf{E}) \\ &= -\mathbf{v} \cdot \nabla (\mathbf{v} \times \mathbf{E}) = \mathbf{v} \cdot \nabla \mathbf{E} \times \mathbf{v}. \end{aligned}$$

5. By the substitution $V = \mathbf{V} \cdot \mathbf{d}$ in (10) of Art. 17, $\mathbf{d}$ being a constant vector, deduce formula (23) of the present chapter.

6. Apply Stokes's theorem to the vector $\Phi \cdot \mathbf{d}$, where $\mathbf{d}$ is constant, and deduce formula (22) of the present chapter.

7. Apply Stokes's theorem to the vector $\mathbf{V} \times \mathbf{d}$, where $\mathbf{d}$ is constant, and deduce theorem (24) of the present chapter.

8. In (5) of Art. 15 put $V = \mathbf{V} \cdot \mathbf{d}$ ($\mathbf{d}$ constant), and deduce (25) of this chapter.

9. Apply the divergence theorem to the vector $\mathbf{\Phi}\cdot\mathbf{d}$ ($\mathbf{d}$ constant), and deduce (28) of this chapter.

10. In (6) of Art. 15 put $\mathbf{F} = \mathbf{\Phi}\cdot\mathbf{d}$ ($\mathbf{d}$ constant), and deduce (29) of the present chapter.

11. Show that

$$\nabla\mathbf{s} = \tfrac{1}{2}(\nabla\mathbf{s} + \mathbf{s}\nabla) - \tfrac{1}{2}\mathrm{I}\times(\nabla\times\mathbf{s}).$$

12. If $\nabla\mathbf{s}$ is small, show that $(\mathrm{I} + \nabla\mathbf{s})$ and $(\mathrm{I} - \nabla\mathbf{s})$ are reciprocal.

13. If $\nabla\mathbf{s}$ is small, and $\mathbf{r}' = \mathbf{r}\cdot(\mathrm{I} + \nabla\mathbf{s})$, prove that

$$\mathbf{r}'^2 = \mathbf{r}\cdot(\mathrm{I} + \nabla\mathbf{s} + \mathbf{s}\nabla)\cdot\mathbf{r}$$

and

$$\mathbf{r}^2 = \mathbf{r}'\cdot(\mathrm{I} - \nabla\mathbf{s} - \mathbf{s}\nabla)\cdot\mathbf{r}'.$$

14. In Exercise 11 apply $\nabla\times$ to both sides, and show that

$$\nabla\times\mathbf{\Phi} = \mathbf{w}\nabla$$

where

$$\mathbf{\Phi} = \tfrac{1}{2}(\nabla\mathbf{s} + \mathbf{s}\nabla) \quad \text{and} \quad \mathbf{w} = \tfrac{1}{2}\,\mathrm{curl}\,\mathbf{s}.$$

Hence show that

$$\nabla\times\mathbf{\Phi}\times\nabla = 0.$$

15. If

$$\nabla\cdot\Psi' + \mu\mathbf{F} = 0$$

and

$$\mu\mathbf{r}\times\mathbf{F} - \nabla\cdot(\Psi'\times\mathbf{r})' = 0$$

where $\mathbf{r}$ is the position vector of the current point, show that Ψ' is self-conjugate.

16. If $\theta = \mathrm{div}\,\mathbf{s}$, and λ, μ are constants, show that

$$\nabla\cdot(\lambda\theta\mathrm{I} + \mu\nabla\mathbf{s} + \mu\mathbf{s}\nabla) = (\lambda + \mu)\nabla\theta + \mu\nabla^2\mathbf{s}.$$

17. If $\mathbf{r}$, r have their usual meanings, show that

$$\nabla\nabla\left(\frac{1}{r}\right) = \frac{3}{r^5}\mathbf{r}\,\mathbf{r} - \frac{1}{r^3}\mathrm{I}.$$

Hence prove that, if $\mathbf{a}$ is a constant vector,

$$\nabla\left[\mathbf{a}\cdot\nabla\nabla\frac{1}{r}\right] = \frac{3}{r^5}(\mathbf{a}\,\mathbf{r} + \mathbf{r}\,\mathbf{a} + \mathbf{a}\cdot\mathbf{r}\mathrm{I}) - \frac{15\mathbf{a}\cdot\mathbf{r}}{r^7}(\mathbf{r}\,\mathbf{r}),$$

and therefore

$$\mathbf{a}\cdot\nabla\left[\mathbf{a}\cdot\nabla\nabla\frac{1}{r}\right] = \frac{3}{r^5}(\mathbf{a}^2\mathbf{r} + 2\mathbf{a}\cdot\mathbf{r}\,\mathbf{a}) - \frac{15}{r^7}(\mathbf{a}\cdot\mathbf{r})^2\mathbf{r}.$$

The **notation of double multiplication** of dyads and dyadics is sometimes convenient. The double multiplication of dyads is defined by

$$(\mathbf{a}\,\mathbf{b}) : (\mathbf{c}\,\mathbf{d}) = \mathbf{a}\cdot\mathbf{c}\;\mathbf{b}\cdot\mathbf{d},$$
$$(\mathbf{a}\,\mathbf{b}) \overset{\cdot}{\times} (\mathbf{c}\,\mathbf{d}) = \mathbf{a}\cdot\mathbf{c}\;\mathbf{b}\times\mathbf{d},$$
$$(\mathbf{a}\,\mathbf{b}) \underset{\cdot}{\times} (\mathbf{c}\,\mathbf{d}) = \mathbf{a}\times\mathbf{c}\;\mathbf{b}\cdot\mathbf{d},$$
$$(\mathbf{a}\,\mathbf{b}) \overset{\times}{\times} (\mathbf{c}\,\mathbf{d}) = \mathbf{a}\times\mathbf{c}\;\mathbf{b}\times\mathbf{d}.$$

The double product of two dyadics is the sum of the double products of dyads obtained by formal expansion according to the distributive law. We employ this notation in the next few exercises.

18. We may expand $\nabla\cdot(\Phi\cdot\mathbf{v})$ as follows:

$$\begin{aligned}\nabla\cdot(\Phi\cdot\mathbf{v}) &= \Sigma\mathbf{i}\cdot\left[\frac{\partial\Phi}{\partial x}\cdot\mathbf{v} + \Phi\cdot\frac{\partial\mathbf{v}}{\partial x}\right] \\ &= (\nabla\cdot\Phi)\cdot\mathbf{v} + \Phi : \nabla\mathbf{v}.\end{aligned}$$

19. In the same way show that

$$\begin{aligned}\nabla\times(\Phi\cdot\mathbf{v}) &= (\nabla\times\Phi)\cdot\mathbf{v} + \nabla\mathbf{v} \overset{\times}{\cdot} \Phi, \\ \nabla\cdot(\Phi\times\mathbf{v}) &= (\nabla\cdot\Phi)\times\mathbf{v} + \Phi \overset{\cdot}{\times} \nabla\mathbf{v}, \\ \nabla\times(\Phi\times\mathbf{v}) &= (\nabla\times\Phi)\times\mathbf{v} - \nabla\mathbf{v} \overset{\times}{\times} \Phi.\end{aligned}$$

20. Prove that

$$\mathrm{I}:\nabla\mathbf{v} = \operatorname{div}\mathbf{v}, \quad \nabla\mathbf{v} \overset{\times}{\cdot} \mathrm{I} = \operatorname{curl}\mathbf{v} = \mathrm{I} \overset{\cdot}{\times} \nabla\mathbf{v}$$

and

$$\nabla\mathbf{v} \overset{\times}{\times} \mathrm{I} = \mathrm{I}\operatorname{div}\mathbf{v} - \mathbf{v}\nabla.$$

From this and the previous exercise deduce the formulæ (18) and (19) of Art. 85.

21. If $\mathbf{F}$ is a point-function and $\Phi = \mathrm{I} + k\mathbf{v}\,\mathbf{v}$, where k and $\mathbf{v}$ are constant, show that

$$\nabla\cdot(\Phi\cdot\mathbf{F}) = \nabla\cdot\mathbf{F} + k\mathbf{v}\cdot\nabla\mathbf{F}\cdot\mathbf{v}$$

and

$$\nabla\cdot(\Phi\times\mathbf{F}) = \nabla\times\mathbf{F} - k\mathbf{v}\cdot\nabla\mathbf{F}\times\mathbf{v}.$$

22. Prove that, for any dyadic Φ,

$$\Phi \overset{\times}{\cdot} \mathrm{I} = \mathrm{I} \overset{\cdot}{\times} \Phi = \Phi_v$$

and

$$\Phi : \mathrm{I} = \mathrm{I} : \Phi = \Phi_s.$$

23. Prove that if the position vector $\mathbf{r}$ of the point x, y, z is a function of the position vector $\mathbf{r}'$ of the point x', y', z', then for a scalar (or vector) point-function V

$$\nabla' V = (\nabla'\mathbf{r})\cdot\nabla V$$

where

$$\nabla' = \mathbf{i}\frac{\partial}{\partial x'} + \mathbf{j}\frac{\partial}{\partial y'} + \mathbf{k}\frac{\partial}{\partial z'}.$$

24. Lagrange's hydrodynamical equations. In Lagrange's method we fix our attention upon a definite particle of the fluid. If $\mathbf{r}'$ is its initial position vector, and $\mathbf{r}$ its position vector at a time t, then the value of $\mathbf{r}$ in terms of $\mathbf{r}'$ and t gives the history of every particle of the fluid. Let ∇' have the same meaning as in the previous exercise.

The acceleration of the particle is $\frac{d^2\mathbf{r}}{dt^2}$, and the equation of motion is then by Art. 37

$$\frac{d^2\mathbf{r}}{dt^2} = \mathbf{F} - \frac{1}{\rho}\nabla p \quad . \quad . \quad . \quad . \quad \text{(i)}$$

Multiply both sides by $\nabla'\mathbf{r}$ as a prefactor Then, on the assumption of a force potential, and a relation between p and ρ only, we have

$$\nabla'\mathbf{r}\cdot\frac{d^2\mathbf{r}}{dt^2} = -\nabla'\mathbf{r}\cdot\nabla V - \nabla'\mathbf{r}\cdot\nabla P.$$

In virtue of the previous exercise this may be written

$$\frac{d}{dt}\left(\nabla'\mathbf{r}\cdot\frac{d\mathbf{r}}{dt}\right) - \nabla'\frac{d\mathbf{r}}{dt}\cdot\frac{d\mathbf{r}}{dt} + \nabla'(V+P) = 0.$$

Then since the velocity is $\mathbf{v} = \frac{d\mathbf{r}}{dt}$ this relation is by (13) of the present chapter

$$\frac{d}{dt}(\nabla'\mathbf{r}\cdot\mathbf{v}) + \nabla'(V + P - \tfrac{1}{2}\mathbf{v}^2) = 0.$$

If now we put

$$W = \int_0^t (V + P - \tfrac{1}{2}\mathbf{v}^2)dt,$$

our equation becomes

$$\frac{d}{dt}(\nabla'\mathbf{r}\cdot\mathbf{v}) = -\nabla'\frac{dW}{dt},$$

which on integration gives

$$\nabla'\mathbf{r}\cdot\mathbf{v} = \mathbf{v}_0 - \nabla' W \quad . \quad . \quad . \quad . \quad \text{ii}$$

where $\mathbf{v}_0$ is the initial velocity, because initially $\nabla'\mathbf{r} = \mathrm{I}$. The equation ii, together with

$$\frac{dW}{dt} = V + P - \tfrac{1}{2}\mathbf{v}^2 \quad . \quad . \quad . \quad . \quad \text{iii}$$

and the equation of continuity, are the differential equations to be satisfied by $\mathbf{r}$, p, and W. The initial conditions are $\mathbf{r} = \mathbf{r}'$, $\mathbf{v} = \mathbf{v}_0$, and $W = 0$.

CHAPTER VIII.

EQUILIBRIUM OF DEFORMABLE BODIES. MOTION OF VISCOUS FLUIDS.

I. Strain Relations.

88. Homogeneous strain. A deformable body, as opposed to a perfectly rigid body, is one whose particles are capable of displacement relative to each other. The assemblage of such relative displacements constitutes a *strain*. Owing to the strain, the particle of the body originally at the point $\mathbf{r}$ moves to another point $\mathbf{r}'$. The vector $\mathbf{r}'$ is a continuous function of $\mathbf{r}$; for a discontinuity would mean a rupture of the body. The displacement $\mathbf{s}$ of the particle originally at $\mathbf{r}$ is its change of position $\mathbf{r}' - \mathbf{r}$, and is therefore also a continuous function of $\mathbf{r}$. Since the strain depends only on the *relative* displacement of the particles, we may regard any one particle as fixed, and take the position of that particle as origin of position vectors.

The simplest kind of strain, called a *homogeneous strain*, is that for which $\mathbf{r}'$ is a linear vector function of $\mathbf{r}$. In this case the coordinates x', y', z' of the point $\mathbf{r}'$ are expressible linearly with finite constant coefficients in terms of x, y, z, the coordinates of $\mathbf{r}$. Or, as shown in Art. 53, $\mathbf{r}'$ is then expressible in the form

$$\mathbf{r}' = \Phi\cdot\mathbf{r}\,. \qquad . \quad . \quad . \quad . \quad (1)$$

where Φ is a certain dyadic, which has the same value for all points and depends on the constant coefficients in the linear relations between x', y', z' and x, y, z. The displacement $\mathbf{s}$ of the particle at $\mathbf{r}$ is

$$\mathbf{s} = \mathbf{r}' - \mathbf{r} = (\Phi - \mathrm{I})\cdot\mathbf{r} \qquad . \quad . \quad . \quad (1')$$

and is therefore also a linear vector function of $\mathbf{r}$.

Consider a particle lying originally at the point $\mathbf{r}$ on the plane $\mathbf{r}\cdot\mathbf{n} = q$. Since by (1) $\mathbf{r} = \Phi^{-1}\cdot\mathbf{r}'$, its position vector $\mathbf{r}'$ after displacement satisfies the relation

$$\mathbf{n}\cdot(\Phi^{-1}\cdot\mathbf{r}') = q\,;$$

that is,

$$(\mathbf{n} \cdot \Phi^{-1}) \cdot \mathbf{r}' = q.$$

Thus particles originally on a plane perpendicular to $\mathbf{n}$ lie after displacement on a plane perpendicular to $\mathbf{n} \cdot \Phi^{-1}$. Briefly we may say that in a homogeneous strain a plane remains a plane; and parallel planes remain parallel. Similarly particles originally in the straight line $\mathbf{r} = \mathbf{b} + t\hat{\mathbf{a}}$ are displaced so as to lie in the straight line

$$\mathbf{r}' = \Phi \cdot (\mathbf{b} + t\hat{\mathbf{a}}) = \Phi \cdot \mathbf{b} + t\Phi \cdot \hat{\mathbf{a}},$$

showing that parallel straight lines remain parallel. A line of unit length parallel to $\hat{\mathbf{a}}$ becomes a line with the length and direction of $\Phi \cdot \hat{\mathbf{a}}$. The fractional extension, that is, the elongation per unit length of such a line, is mod $(\Phi \cdot \hat{\mathbf{a}}) - 1$. This is the same for all parallel lines, and may be called briefly the *extension* or *elongation* for the direction $\hat{\mathbf{a}}$.

The equation (1) may also be written

$$\mathbf{r} = \Phi^{-1} \cdot \mathbf{r}' = \mathbf{r}' \cdot \Phi^{-1}{}_c,$$

so that

$$\mathbf{r}^2 = \mathbf{r}' \cdot (\Phi^{-1}{}_c \cdot \Phi^{-1}) \cdot \mathbf{r}'.$$

Thus particles originally on the sphere

$$\mathbf{r}^2 = \epsilon^2 \quad . \quad . \quad . \quad . \quad . \quad (2)$$

are displaced so as to lie on the ellipsoid

$$\mathbf{r}' \cdot (\Phi^{-1}{}_c \cdot \Phi^{-1}) \cdot \mathbf{r}' = \epsilon^2. \quad . \quad . \quad . \quad (3)$$

which is called the *strain ellipsoid*. Thus a sphere is transformed into an ellipsoid; and a set of straight lines originally equal in length transform into others whose lengths are proportional to the radii of the strain ellipsoid parallel to them. If, further, $\mathbf{r}_1$ and $\mathbf{r}_2$ are points at the ends of perpendicular radii of the sphere (2), the relation $\mathbf{r}_1 \cdot \mathbf{r}_2 = 0$ is equivalent to

$$\mathbf{r}'_1 \cdot \Phi^{-1}{}_c \cdot \Phi^{-1} \cdot \mathbf{r}'_2 = 0,$$

so that $\mathbf{r}'_1$ and $\mathbf{r}'_2$ are parallel to conjugate diameters of the strain ellipsoid. Thus perpendicular radii of the sphere are transformed into conjugate semi-diameters of the ellipsoid. In particular the axes of the ellipsoid correspond to orthogonal radii of the sphere; showing that there are three mutually perpendicular straight lines which remain orthogonal after the strain. The original directions of these lines are called the *principal axes of strain*.

Similarly from (1) it follows that

$$\mathbf{r}'^2 = \mathbf{r} \cdot \Phi_c \cdot \Phi \cdot \mathbf{r},$$

so that particles originally on the ellipsoid

$$\mathbf{r}\cdot(\Phi_c\cdot\Phi)\cdot\mathbf{r} = \epsilon^2 \quad . \quad . \quad . \quad . \quad (4)$$

lie after displacement on the sphere

$$\mathbf{r}'^2 = \epsilon^2 \, . \quad . \quad . \quad . \quad . \quad . \quad (5)$$

and any set of conjugate diameters of the ellipsoid (4) are transformed into orthogonal diameters of the sphere. The ellipsoid (4), being the reciprocal of (3) with respect to the sphere (2), is called the *reciprocal strain ellipsoid.* In particular the axes of this ellipsoid remain orthogonal after displacement, and are therefore the principal axes of strain.

If the dyadic Φ is *self-conjugate* it may be expressed in the form (Art. 64)

$$\Phi = a\mathbf{i}\,\mathbf{i} + b\mathbf{j}\,\mathbf{j} + c\mathbf{k}\,\mathbf{k}.$$

Then

$$\Phi^{-1} = \frac{1}{a}\mathbf{i}\,\mathbf{i} + \frac{1}{b}\mathbf{j}\,\mathbf{j} + \frac{1}{c}\mathbf{k}\,\mathbf{k}$$

is also self-conjugate. The equation of the strain ellipsoid is now

$$\frac{x^2}{a^2} + \frac{y^2}{b^2} + \frac{z^2}{c^2} = \epsilon^2,$$

and that of the reciprocal strain ellipsoid

$$a^2x^2 + b^2y^2 + c^2z^2 = \epsilon^2,$$

their axes being parallel to **i**, **j**, **k**. The orthogonal diameters of the sphere (2) in these directions become the axes of the strain ellipsoid, unchanged in direction but stretched in the ratios $a:1$, $b:1$, $c:1$ respectively. These are therefore the principal axes of strain; and the displacement of the particles constitutes what is called a *pure strain.*

89. Small homogeneous strain. Suppose that the displacement **s** of each particle relative to the origin is small. Then, being a linear vector function of **r**, it may be written

$$\mathbf{s} = \Psi\cdot\mathbf{r} \; . \quad . \quad . \quad . \quad . \quad . \quad (6)$$

where Ψ is small; that is to say, has one vector in each dyad small. Now by Art. 62 this relation may be expressed

$$\mathbf{s} = \Phi\cdot\mathbf{r} - \mathbf{c}\times\mathbf{r} \quad . \quad . \quad . \quad . \quad . \quad (7)$$

where

$$\Phi = \tfrac{1}{2}(\Psi + \Psi_c), \quad \mathbf{c} = \tfrac{1}{2}\Psi_v.$$

The small dyadic Φ is self-conjugate, and the small vector **c** is half the vector of Ψ. Hence the position vector of the particle after displacement is

$$\begin{aligned}\mathbf{r}' &= \mathbf{r} + \mathbf{s}\\ &= (\mathrm{I} + \Phi)\cdot\mathbf{r} - \mathbf{c}\times\mathbf{r}. \quad . \quad . \quad . \quad (8)\end{aligned}$$

Now the term $-\mathbf{c}\times\mathbf{r}$ is the displacement of the particle due to a rotation of the body as a whole about an axis through the origin parallel to $\mathbf{c}$, by a small angle whose circular measure is $-\text{mod}\ \mathbf{c}$. This term therefore represents no deformation of the body. The relation

$$\mathbf{r}' = (\mathrm{I} + \Phi)\cdot\mathbf{r}$$

represents a pure strain since the dyadic is self-conjugate. Thus the general displacement given by (7) consists of a pure strain and a rotation of the body as rigid. The two may be taken in any order; for a rotation after the pure strain brings about a displacement

$$-\mathbf{c}\times(\mathrm{I} + \Phi)\cdot\mathbf{r} = -\mathbf{c}\times\mathbf{r},$$

since both $\mathbf{c}$ and Φ are small, and their product is negligible.

Referring the self-conjugate dyadic Φ to its principal directions (Art. 64) we may write

$$\begin{aligned} \mathrm{I} + \Phi &= \mathrm{I} + a_1\mathbf{i}\,\mathbf{i} + a_2\mathbf{j}\,\mathbf{j} + a_3\mathbf{k}\,\mathbf{k} \\ &= (1 + a_1)\mathbf{i}\,\mathbf{i} + (1 + a_2)\mathbf{j}\,\mathbf{j} + (1 + a_3)\mathbf{k}\,\mathbf{k}. \end{aligned}$$

Then the pure strain transforms the sphere $\mathbf{r}^2 = \epsilon^2$ into the strain ellipsoid

$$\frac{x'^2}{(1 + a_1)^2} + \frac{y'^2}{(1 + a_2)^2} + \frac{z'^2}{(1 + a_3)^2} = \epsilon^2.$$

The ratio of the volume of the ellipsoid to that of the sphere is

$$(1 + a_1)(1 + a_2)(1 + a_3) = 1 + (a_1 + a_2 + a_3),$$

since a_1, a_2, a_3 are small. Hence the increase in volume per unit volume, or the *dilation*, as it is generally called, is given by

$$\theta = a_1 + a_2 + a_3.$$

This is the scalar of the dyadic Φ, and is therefore equal to the scalar of Ψ because the scalar of the anti-self-conjugate part is zero. The rotation represented by the last term of (7) produces no change in volume. Hence Ψ_s is the dilation for the general small strain represented by (6).

Suppose that the body is subject to *several small strains* successively, corresponding to displacements

$$\Psi_1\cdot\mathbf{r}, \quad \Psi_2\cdot\mathbf{r}, \ \ldots$$

Owing to the first strain the particle at $\mathbf{r}$ shifts to

$$\mathbf{r}' = (\mathrm{I} + \Psi_1)\cdot\mathbf{r}.$$

The next strain moves it to

$$\mathbf{r}'' = (\mathrm{I} + \Psi_2)\cdot\mathbf{r}' = (\mathrm{I} + \Psi_2)\cdot(\mathrm{I} + \Psi_1)\cdot\mathbf{r},$$

and so on. Now the dyadics Ψ are all small. Hence on neglecting small quantities of the second and higher orders we have for the final position of the particle originally at $\mathbf{r}$

$$(\mathrm{I} + \Psi_1 + \Psi_2 + \ldots)\cdot\mathbf{r} = \mathbf{r} + \Psi_1\cdot\mathbf{r} + \Psi_2\cdot\mathbf{r} + \ldots$$

that is to say, the total displacement is the vector sum of the displacements due to the several small strains separately.

From this point of view a small pure strain may be expressed as the sum of six small strains—three stretches and three shears. For in a pure strain the displacement $\mathbf{s} = \Psi\cdot\mathbf{r}$ is such that Ψ is self-conjugate, and its nonion form is therefore

$$\Psi = a_{11}\mathbf{i}\,\mathbf{i} + a_{22}\mathbf{j}\,\mathbf{j} + a_{33}\mathbf{k}\,\mathbf{k} + a_{12}(\mathbf{i}\,\mathbf{j} + \mathbf{j}\,\mathbf{i}) + \ldots + \ldots$$

Henee the particle at $\mathbf{r}$ goes to $\mathbf{r}'$, which is given by

$$\begin{aligned} \mathbf{r}' &= (\mathrm{I} + \Psi)\cdot\mathbf{r} \\ &= (\mathrm{I} + a_{11}\mathbf{i}\,\mathbf{i})\cdot(\mathrm{I} + a_{22}\mathbf{j}\,\mathbf{j})\cdot \ldots \cdot(\mathrm{I} + a_{12}\mathbf{i}\,\mathbf{j} + a_{12}\mathbf{j}\,\mathbf{i})\cdot \ldots \cdot\mathbf{r}, \end{aligned}$$

since the small quantities of higher order than the first are negligible. The first factor represents a strain in which lines parallel to $\mathbf{i}$ are stretched in the ratio $1 + a_{11} : 1$, so that a_{11} is the extension for that direction ; while lines parallel to $\mathbf{j}$ and $\mathbf{k}$ are unaltered in length Such a strain is called a *stretch*, and involves a dilation a_{11}. The next two factors represent stretches parallel to $\mathbf{j}$ and $\mathbf{k}$ respectively. The factor $(\mathrm{I} + a_{12}\mathbf{i}\,\mathbf{j} + a_{12}\mathbf{j}\,\mathbf{i})$ represents what is called a *simple shear* whose plane is parallel to $\mathbf{i}, \mathbf{j}$. It involves no dilation, since the scalar of $a_{12}(\mathbf{i}\,\mathbf{j} + \mathbf{j}\,\mathbf{i})$ is zero. The principal axes of the shear are parallel to $\mathbf{i} + \mathbf{j}$ and $\mathbf{i} - \mathbf{j}$, the elongations in these directions being a_{12} and $-a_{12}$ respectively. A square whose sides are parallel to $\mathbf{i}$ and $\mathbf{j}$ is transformed into a rhombus, whose diagonals have their original directions, but whose angles are each altered by $2a_{12}$ radians. The reader can easily verify these statements for himself.

90. Heterogeneous strain. Considering now the general case in which the strain is not necessarily homogeneous, let $\mathbf{s}$ be the displacement of the particle originally at the point P whose position vector is $\mathbf{r}$. Then after the strain the position vector of the particle is

$$\mathbf{r}' = \mathbf{r} + \mathbf{s}.$$

Let $d\mathbf{r}$ be the elementary vector $\overrightarrow{PQ}$ determined by two neighbouring particles P, Q before the strain, and $d\mathbf{r}'$ that determined by the same two after the strain. Then

$$d\mathbf{r}' = d\mathbf{r} + d\mathbf{s}.$$

But since $\mathbf{s}$ is a vector point-function,

$$d\mathbf{s} = d\mathbf{r}\cdot\nabla\mathbf{s} \qquad . \quad . \quad . \quad . \quad \text{i}$$

by Art. 83. Hence

$$d\mathbf{r}' = d\mathbf{r} + d\mathbf{r}\cdot\nabla\mathbf{s}$$
$$= d\mathbf{r}\cdot(\mathrm{I} + \nabla\mathbf{s}) \quad . \quad . \quad . \quad . \quad (9)$$

Now $d\mathbf{s}$ is the relative displacement of the particles Q and P; and in a sufficiently small neighbourhood round P the dyadic $\nabla\mathbf{s}$ is constant. Thus in the neighbourhood of P the relative displacement is, by i, a linear vector function of their relative position. The strain round that point is therefore sensibly homogeneous, and the properties proved above for homogeneous strain are true of this also, the finite vectors $\mathbf{r}$, $\mathbf{r}'$ being replaced by the infinitesimal $d\mathbf{r}$, $d\mathbf{r}'$.

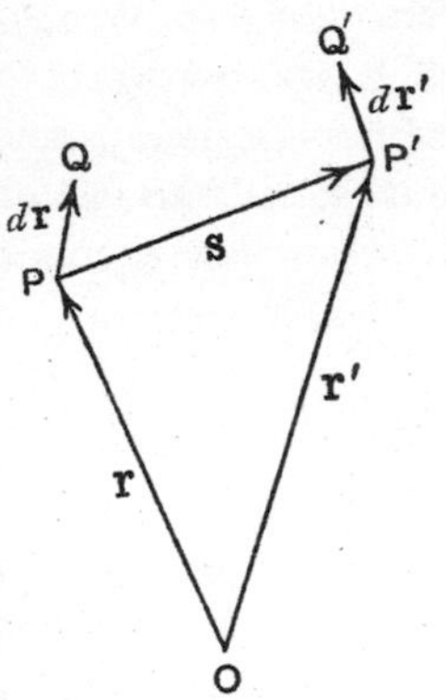

FIG. 26.

Considering only *small strains* the dyadic $\nabla\mathbf{s}$ is small, as is also its conjugate $\mathbf{s}\nabla$. The reciprocal of $(\mathrm{I} + \nabla\mathbf{s})$ is $(\mathrm{I} - \nabla\mathbf{s})$, for their product differs from the idemfactor only by the square of the small $\nabla\mathbf{s}$. Similarly the reciprocal of $(\mathrm{I} + \mathbf{s}\nabla)$ is $(\mathrm{I} - \mathbf{s}\nabla)$. The equation (9) is therefore equivalent to

$$d\mathbf{r} = d\mathbf{r}'\cdot(\mathrm{I} - \nabla\mathbf{s}) = (\mathrm{I} - \mathbf{s}\nabla)\cdot d\mathbf{r}'.$$

Hence, neglecting small quantities of the second order,

$$(d\mathbf{r})^2 = d\mathbf{r}'\cdot(\mathrm{I} - \nabla\mathbf{s})\cdot(\mathrm{I} - \mathbf{s}\nabla)\cdot d\mathbf{r}'$$
$$= d\mathbf{r}'\cdot(\mathrm{I} - \nabla\mathbf{s} - \mathbf{s}\nabla)\cdot d\mathbf{r}'.$$

Thus particles on a sphere with centre at P and radius ϵ are displaced so as to lie on the ellipsoid whose equation relative to its centre P' is

$$d\mathbf{r}'\cdot(\mathrm{I} - \nabla\mathbf{s} - \mathbf{s}\nabla)\cdot d\mathbf{r}' = \epsilon^2 \quad . \quad . \quad . \quad (10)$$

This is the *strain ellipsoid* for the point P. In the same way we have

$$d\mathbf{r}' = d\mathbf{r}\cdot(\mathrm{I} + \nabla\mathbf{s}) = (\mathrm{I} + \mathbf{s}\nabla)\cdot d\mathbf{r},$$

and therefore

$$(d\mathbf{r}')^2 = d\mathbf{r}\cdot(\mathrm{I} + \nabla\mathbf{s})\cdot(\mathrm{I} + \mathbf{s}\nabla)\cdot d\mathbf{r}$$
$$= d\mathbf{r}\cdot(\mathrm{I} + \nabla\mathbf{s} + \mathbf{s}\nabla)\cdot d\mathbf{r}$$

to the first order. Hence the ellipsoid

$$d\mathbf{r}\cdot(\mathrm{I} + \nabla\mathbf{s} + \mathbf{s}\nabla)\cdot d\mathbf{r} = \epsilon^2 \quad . \quad . \quad . \quad . \quad (11)$$

deforms into the sphere $(d\mathbf{r}')^2 = \epsilon^2$. This ellipsoid is the *reciprocal strain ellipsoid*, and is the reciprocal of (10) with respect to a sphere of radius ϵ.

Separating the dyadic $\nabla\mathbf{s}$ into self-conjugate and anti-self-conjugate parts, we may write (9) in virtue of (21′), Art. 62,

$$d\mathbf{r}' = d\mathbf{r}\cdot(\mathrm{I} + \Phi) - d\mathbf{r}\times\mathbf{w} \quad . \quad . \quad . \quad (12)$$

where $\Phi = \frac{1}{2}(\nabla\mathbf{s} + \mathbf{s}\nabla)$

and $\mathbf{w} = \frac{1}{2}(\nabla\mathbf{s})_v = \frac{1}{2}\text{ curl }\mathbf{s}.$

The first part of the expression (12) represents a pure strain, because Φ is self-conjugate. The second part represents a small rotation of the particles round P as a rigid body, about an axis parallel to curl **s**, and through an angle whose circular measure is mod **w**. The rotation causes no dilation; but the dilation due to the pure strain is, by the previous Art.,

$$\theta = (\nabla\mathbf{s})_s = \text{div }\mathbf{s} \quad . \quad . \quad . \quad . \quad (13)$$

The same value for the dilation also follows by the divergence theorem. For, considering any portion of the body bounded by a closed surface S, its increase in volume owing to the strain is

$$\int \mathbf{s}\cdot\mathbf{n}dS = \int \text{div }\mathbf{s}\, dv.$$

And since this is true for any surface S, it is true for the infinitesimal surface surrounding an element of the body of volume dv. The increase in the volume of this element is therefore (div **s**)dv, and the dilation consequently div **s**.

If curl $\mathbf{s} = 0$, the rotation part of the strain is everywhere zero, and only the pure strain remains. A pure strain is therefore said to be irrotational. And since curl $\mathbf{s} = 0$, we may put

$$\mathbf{s} = \nabla\phi$$

where ϕ is a scalar point-function called the *strain potential*. In terms of this the dilation is

$$\theta = \text{div }\mathbf{s} = \nabla^2\phi.$$

If the dilation vanishes in an irrotational strain, the potential ϕ is harmonic.

91. Explicit expressions. Components of strain. If we express the displacement **s** as the sum of rectangular components in the form

$$\mathbf{s} = u\mathbf{i} + v\mathbf{j} + w\mathbf{k}$$

and expand the dyadics

$$\nabla\mathbf{s} = \Sigma\mathbf{i}\frac{\partial\mathbf{s}}{\partial x}, \quad \mathbf{s}\nabla = \Sigma\frac{\partial\mathbf{s}}{\partial x}\mathbf{i},$$

we have

$$2\Phi = \nabla\mathbf{s} + \mathbf{s}\nabla = 2\left(\frac{\partial u}{\partial x}\mathbf{i}\,\mathbf{i} + \frac{\partial v}{\partial y}\mathbf{j}\,\mathbf{j} + \frac{\partial w}{\partial z}\mathbf{k}\,\mathbf{k}\right)$$
$$+\left(\frac{\partial w}{\partial y} + \frac{\partial v}{\partial z}\right)(\mathbf{j}\,\mathbf{k} + \mathbf{k}\,\mathbf{j}) + \ldots + \ldots$$

which may be written more briefly

$$2\Phi = 2(e_{11}\mathbf{i\,i} + e_{22}\mathbf{j\,j} + \ldots) + e_{23}(\mathbf{j\,k} + \mathbf{k\,j}) + \ldots + \ldots,$$

the coefficients e_{mn} being called the six *components of strain*. If

$$d\mathbf{r} = dr(l\mathbf{i} + m\mathbf{j} + n\mathbf{k})$$

of length dr and direction cosines l, m, n, is the relative position vector of two neighbouring particles in the unstrained body, then by (11) it is strained to one of length dr' given by

$$(dr')^2 = (dr)^2[1 + 2(e_{11}l^2 + e_{22}m^2 + \ldots + e_{23}mn + \ldots + \ldots)]$$

or

$$dr' = dr[1 + (e_{11}l^2 + e_{22}m^2 + \ldots + e_{23}mn + \ldots + \ldots)]$$

if we neglect small quantities of the second order. The *extension* for this element is therefore

$$e = \frac{dr' - dr}{dr} = e_{11}l^2 + e_{22}m^2 + \ldots + e_{23}mn + \ldots + \ldots$$

In particular e_{11}, e_{22}, e_{33} are the extensions for elements which in the unstrained body are parallel to **i**, **j**, **k** respectively.

Let $d\mathbf{r}_1$ and $d\mathbf{r}_2$ be a pair of elements whose direction cosines are l_1, m_1, n_1, and l_2, m_2, n_2, and whose extensions are e_1 and e_2. Then if θ is their mutual inclination before the strain, and dashes indicate corresponding quantities after the strain, we have as above

$$d\mathbf{r}'_1 \cdot d\mathbf{r}'_2 = d\mathbf{r}_1 \cdot [\mathrm{I} + \nabla\mathbf{s} + \mathbf{s}\nabla] \cdot d\mathbf{r}_2\,;$$

that is,

$$(1 + e_1)(1 + e_2)\cos\theta' = \cos\theta + 2(e_{11}l_1l_2 + e_{22}m_1m_2 + \ldots) \\ + e_{23}(m_1n_2 + m_2n_1) + \ldots + \ldots$$

If the elements are perpendicular in the unstrained body, $\theta = \frac{\pi}{2}$ and $\left(\frac{\pi}{2} - \theta'\right)$ is a small angle. Hence, neglecting quantities of higher order than the first, we have

$$\frac{\pi}{2} - \theta' = 2(e_{11}l_1l_2 + e_{22}m_1m_2 + \ldots) + e_{23}(m_1n_2 + m_2n_1) + \ldots$$

This is the small change of inclination of two elements initially perpendicular. In particular e_{23} is the change of inclination between elements initially parallel to **j** and **k**. Similarly for e_{31} and e_{12} Hence the name " components of strain " given to the quantities e_{mn}.

As remarked above, the small heterogeneous strain represented by (12) is equivalent to a pure strain followed by a rotation of the rigid element. The dyadic involved in the pure strain is

$$\mathrm{I} + \Phi = \mathrm{I} + e_{11}\mathbf{i\,i} + e_{22}\mathbf{j\,j} + \ldots + \tfrac{1}{2}e_{23}(\mathbf{j\,k} + \mathbf{k\,j}) + \ldots$$

And since the components of strain are small, this may be written as the product of six factors,

$$(\mathrm{I} + e_{11}\mathbf{i}\,\mathbf{i})\cdot(\mathrm{I} + e_{22}\mathbf{j}\,\mathbf{j})\cdot\ \ldots\ \cdot[\mathrm{I} + \tfrac{1}{2}e_{23}(\mathbf{j}\,\mathbf{k} + \mathbf{k}\,\mathbf{j})]\cdot\ \ldots$$

The first three factors correspond to simple stretches e_{11}, e_{22}, e_{33} parallel to **i**, **j**, **k** respectively ; and the last three to simple shears whose planes are parallel to **j** and **k**, **k** and **i**, **i** and **j** respectively, with angular deformations e_{23}, e_{31}, e_{12}.

Certain *identical relations between the components of strain* may be derived as follows. We have seen that

$$\nabla\mathbf{s} = \Phi - \mathrm{I}\times\mathbf{w}$$

where Φ and **w** have the same meanings as above. Applying $\nabla\times$ to both sides, the first vanishes by (9) of Art. 84, and we obtain

$$\nabla\times\Phi = \nabla\times(\mathrm{I}\times\mathbf{w}) = \mathbf{w}\nabla$$

by (19) of Art. 85, since $\nabla\cdot\mathbf{w} = \frac{1}{2}\nabla\cdot\nabla\times\mathbf{s} = 0$. Again, operating on both members with $\times\nabla$, the second vanishes, showing that

$$\nabla\times\Phi\times\nabla = 0 \quad . \quad . \quad . \quad . \quad (14)$$

If we introduce the nonion form found above for the self-conjugate dyadic Φ, this equation gives *six* identical relations between the components of strain.

II. Stress Relations.

92. Stress across a plane at a point. We have already considered the stress at a point in a fluid across a plane through that point, and the intensity of stress as the force per unit area at that point. In the case of frictionless fluids the stress was seen to be normal to the surface considered, and always of the nature of a pressure. With a solid body or a viscous fluid the stress is not in general normal to the surface, the cohesion between particles rendering tangential action possible.

Consider any surface through a point P of the body. Let **n** be the unit normal at that point and δS the area of an element of the surface at P. Further, let $\delta\mathbf{T}$ be the force across this element acting on the particles *at the back of the plane*; that is, those lying in a direction from the surface opposite to that of **n**. Then the limiting value of the quotient $\delta\mathbf{T}/\delta S$ as δS tends to zero will be spoken of as the (intensity of) *stress* or *traction* at the point P across the surface whose normal is **n**. In this way there is no question of whether the normal resolute of the stress is of the nature of a pressure or a tension. But in specifying the plane it is necessary to specify the sense of the normal. If $\mathbf{T}_n$ is the stress at P across the surface whose normal is $\mathbf{n}$, the force across the element of surface whose area is dS is then $\mathbf{T}_n dS$ acting on the material at the back of the element.

To find the relation between the tractions at a point across different surfaces, consider an element of the body bounded by an infinitesimal tetrahedron $PLMN$ (Fig. 16) whose edges PL, PM, PN are parallel to $\mathbf{i}$, $\mathbf{j}$, $\mathbf{k}$ respectively and whose face LMN is normal to the unit vector $\mathbf{n}$ directed outward from the tetrahedron. If A is the area of this face, the areas of the other faces are $\mathbf{n}\cdot\mathbf{i}A$, $\mathbf{n}\cdot\mathbf{j}A$, and $\mathbf{n}\cdot\mathbf{k}A$. Let $\mathbf{T}_1$, $\mathbf{T}_2$, $\mathbf{T}_3$ be the average stresses at P across the faces whose normals are $\mathbf{i}$, $\mathbf{j}$, $\mathbf{k}$. Then the force across the face PMN is $\mathbf{n}\cdot\mathbf{i}A\mathbf{T}_1$ acting on the material to the back of the plane, and therefore $-\mathbf{n}\cdot\mathbf{i}A\mathbf{T}_1$ on the material inside the tetrahedron. Similarly for the other two perpendicular faces. If $\mathbf{T}_n$ is the average stress across the face LMN, the force across this face acting on the material within the tetrahedron is $A\mathbf{T}_n$. Lastly, if h is the perpendicular distance of P from the plane LMN, ρ the average density of the material in the figure, and $\mathbf{F}$ the average external force per unit mass acting on it, the total external force on the material within the tetrahedron is $\frac{1}{3}hA\rho\mathbf{F}$. Combining all these forces, we have for the equation of equilibrium of the element of the body

$$A\mathbf{T}_n - \mathbf{n}\cdot\mathbf{i}A\mathbf{T}_1 - \mathbf{n}\cdot\mathbf{j}A\mathbf{T}_2 - \mathbf{n}\cdot\mathbf{k}A\mathbf{T}_3 + \tfrac{1}{3}hA\rho\mathbf{F} = 0.$$

If now the volume of the element tends to zero, the plane LMN moving normally to itself toward P, h tends to zero, and therefore also the last term. In the limit the stresses all become stresses at P, and the equation gives

$$\begin{aligned}\mathbf{T}_n &= \mathbf{n}\cdot\mathbf{i}\,\mathbf{T}_1 + \mathbf{n}\cdot\mathbf{j}\,\mathbf{T}_2 + \mathbf{n}\cdot\mathbf{k}\,\mathbf{T}_3 \\ &= \mathbf{n}\cdot\Psi \qquad \qquad (15)\end{aligned}$$

where the *stress dyadic* Ψ is defined by

$$\Psi = \mathbf{i}\,\mathbf{T}_1 + \mathbf{j}\,\mathbf{T}_2 + \mathbf{k}\,\mathbf{T}_3 \qquad (16)$$

And since the traction across a plane at P is independent of any choice of axes, the dyadic Ψ defined by (16) is invariant with respect to the choice of rectangular axes.

93. The stress equations of equilibrium. Take a body at rest in its strained condition, and consider the portion of the body lying within a closed surface S not passing outside the body. The material within S is in equilibrium under the external force $\mathbf{F}$ per unit mass, and the total stress over S. If $\mathbf{n}$ is the outward normal at a point Q of this surface, the stress acting on the material within S across the element of surface at Q is $\mathbf{n}\cdot\Psi dS$, where dS is the area of the element and Ψ' the value of the stress dyadic at Q. Hence for the equilibrium of the portion of the body within S we must have

$$\int \mathbf{n}\cdot\Psi' dS + \int \rho\mathbf{F}dv = 0,$$

which by (28) of Art. 87 is equivalent to

$$\int (\nabla\cdot\Psi' + \rho\mathbf{F})dv = 0.$$

And since this is true for all such surfaces S, the integrand must vanish identically, so that

$$\nabla\cdot\Psi' + \rho\mathbf{F} = 0 \quad . \quad . \quad . \quad . \quad (17)$$

If the body is in motion, the acceleration of a particle, whose displacement is $\mathbf{s}$, is $\dfrac{d^2\mathbf{s}}{dt^2}$. The above argument then shows that the *equation of motion* corresponding to the equilibrium condition (17) is

$$\nabla\cdot\Psi' + \rho\left(\mathbf{F} - \frac{d^2\mathbf{s}}{dt^2}\right) = 0 \quad . \quad . \quad . \quad (17')$$

We have so far considered only the condition of equilibrium arising from the vanishing of the vector sum of the forces. The further condition, that the sum of their torques should also vanish, shows that the dyadic Ψ' is *self-conjugate*. For if $\mathbf{r}$ is the position vector of the variable point, the condition for zero moment about the origin gives

$$\int \mathbf{r}\times(\mathbf{n}\cdot\Psi')dS + \int \rho\mathbf{r}\times\mathbf{F}dv = 0;$$

that is,

$$-\int \mathbf{n}\cdot(\Psi'\times\mathbf{r})dS + \int \rho\mathbf{r}\times\mathbf{F}dv = 0,$$

which by (28) of Art. 87 is equivalent to

$$\int [\rho\mathbf{r}\times\mathbf{F} - \nabla\cdot(\Psi'\times\mathbf{r})]dv = 0.$$

And since this is true for every surface S, the integrand vanishes identically, giving

$$\rho\mathbf{r}\times\mathbf{F} - \nabla\cdot(\Psi'\times\mathbf{r}) = 0.$$

If now we expand the second term, the equation may be written

$$\rho\mathbf{r}\times\mathbf{F} - (\nabla\cdot\Psi')\times\mathbf{r} - \Sigma\mathbf{i}\cdot\Psi'\times\frac{\partial\mathbf{r}}{\partial x} = 0.$$

The sum of the first two terms is zero by (17). Hence by (8″), Art. 56,

$$\Psi'_v = -\Sigma\mathbf{i}\cdot\Psi'\times\mathbf{i} = 0 \quad . \quad . \quad . \quad (18)$$

and since the vector of the dyadic Ψ is zero, the dyadic is self-conjugate.

From this it follows that three mutually perpendicular unit vectors $\mathbf{i}', \mathbf{j}', \mathbf{k}'$ can be found such that

$$\Psi = T_1\mathbf{i}'\mathbf{i}' + T_2\mathbf{j}'\mathbf{j}' + T_3\mathbf{k}'\mathbf{k}'.$$

The stresses across planes perpendicular to these vectors are $T_1\mathbf{i}'$, $T_2\mathbf{j}'$, $T_3\mathbf{k}'$ respectively, being therefore normal to the planes. These normal stresses are called the *principal stresses* at the point considered, and the planes to which they are normal are the *principal planes of stress.*

The general nonion form of the self-conjugate dyadic Ψ is

$$\Psi = T_{11}\mathbf{i}\,\mathbf{i} + T_{22}\mathbf{j}\,\mathbf{j} + T_{33}\mathbf{k}\,\mathbf{k} + T_{23}(\mathbf{j}\,\mathbf{k} + \mathbf{k}\,\mathbf{j}) + \ldots + \ldots$$

The stress across a plane whose normal is $\mathbf{i}$ is

$$\mathbf{i}\cdot\Psi = T_{11}\mathbf{i} + T_{12}\mathbf{j} + T_{13}\mathbf{k}.$$

Hence the physical significance of the six quantities T_{mn}. For instance, T_{12} is the resolute in the direction of $\mathbf{j}$ of the stress across a plane normal to $\mathbf{i}$. Since $T_{12} = T_{21}$, this is equal to the resolute parallel to $\mathbf{i}$ of the stress across a plane normal to $\mathbf{j}$.

94. Geometrical representation of stress. The traction at the point P across the plane normal to the unit vector $\mathbf{n}$ is $\mathbf{n}\cdot\Psi$, and is therefore normal to the quadric surface

$$\mathbf{r}\cdot\Psi\cdot\mathbf{r} = \epsilon^2 \quad . \quad . \quad (19)$$

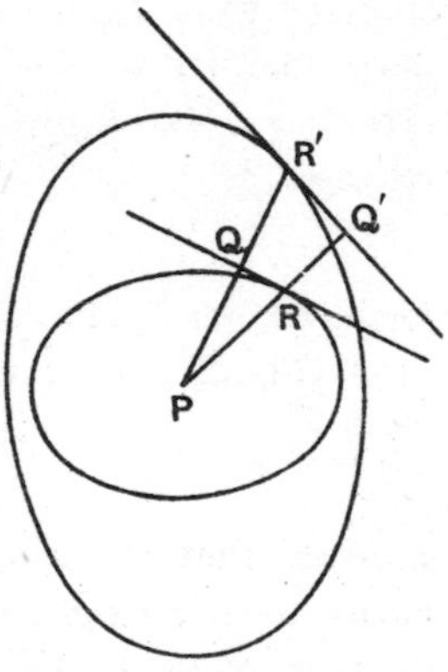

FIG. 27.

at the point R whose position vector relative to P is parallel to $\mathbf{n}$, and equal to $r\mathbf{n}$ (say). Hence across the principal planes of this quadric the stresses are normal to the planes, which are therefore the principal planes of stress at P. This surface is known as *Cauchy's stress quadric.* For any plane through P the resolute of the stress normal to the plane is

$$\mathbf{T}_n\cdot\mathbf{n} = \mathbf{n}\cdot\Psi\cdot\mathbf{n} \quad \frac{\epsilon^2}{r^2},$$

and therefore varies inversely as the square of the radius of the stress quadric which is normal to the plane. If we introduce the quadric which is reciprocal to the above in a sphere of radius ϵ, viz.

$$\mathbf{r}\cdot\Psi^{-1}\cdot\mathbf{r} \quad \epsilon^2 \quad . \quad . \quad . \quad (20)$$

the direction of the stress across the plane at P normal to PR is parallel to PR'; and the normal resolute of this stress as found above is

$$\frac{\epsilon^2}{r^2} = \frac{p'^2}{\epsilon^2}$$

where $p' = PQ'$ is the length of the perpendicular from P to the tangent plane at R'. Thus the normal stress across any plane at P varies as the square of the perpendicular from P to the parallel tangent plane to the quadric (20). This surface is known as *Lamé's stress-director quadric.*

Further, the magnitude T_n of the stress at P across a plane perpendicular to $\mathbf{n}$ is given by

$$T_n{}^2 = \mathbf{n}\cdot\Psi\cdot\Psi\cdot\mathbf{n}.$$

Hence introducing the ellipsoid

$$\mathbf{r}\cdot\Psi^2\cdot\mathbf{r} = \epsilon^2 \quad . \quad . \quad . \quad . \quad (21)$$

whose radius vector $\overrightarrow{PR} = r\mathbf{n}$, we have

$$T_n{}^2 = \frac{\epsilon^2}{r^2},$$

showing that T_n varies inversely as the radius of the surface (21) perpendicular to the plane considered. This surface is known as *Cauchy's stress ellipsoid.* The reciprocal surface, called *Lamé's stress ellipsoid,* is

$$\mathbf{r}\cdot(\Psi^{-1})^2\cdot\mathbf{r} = \epsilon^2 \quad . \quad . \quad . \quad . \quad (22)$$

If the tangent plane to this surface perpendicular to $\mathbf{n}$ is cut by PR in Q' (Fig. 27), the length of PQ' is $p' = \epsilon^2/r$. Hence

$$T_n = \frac{\epsilon}{r} = \frac{p'}{\epsilon},$$

showing that the magnitude of the stress at P across any plane varies as the length of the perpendicular from P to the parallel tangent plane to the ellipsoid (22). In particular the principal stresses at P are proportional to the axes of Lamé's stress ellipsoid.

III. Isotropic Bodies.

95. Stress-strain relations. A body is said to be *isotropic* when its physical properties at any point are independent of direction. Bodies for which this is not true are termed *anisotropic.*

For all the small elastic strains that are met with, experiment proves that the intensity of the deforming stress on a given body varies as the strain produced by it. This relation is known as

Hooke's Law. We assume the generalisation of this law, and define a *perfectly elastic body* by the property that the six components of stress at any point are linear functions of the six components of strain. Consider an elementary parallelepiped whose edges are parallel to the principal axes of strain at the point. Let e_1, e_2, e_3 be the principal extensions. Then, if the body is isotropic, the stresses across the faces of the parallelepiped will be normal to the faces, because the elastic properties are independent of direction. Thus the principal planes of stress are normal to the principal axes of strain. Let T_1, T_2, T_3 be the magnitudes of the principal stresses at the point. Then, by the generalised form of Hooke's law,

$$T_1 = \lambda_1 e_1 + \lambda_2 e_2 + \lambda_3 e_3,$$

the values of the constants λ_n depending on the nature of the material. But $\lambda_2 = \lambda_3$ because the properties of the body are independent of direction. Hence

$$T_1 = \lambda_2(e_1 + e_2 + e_3) + (\lambda_1 - \lambda_2)e_1,$$

which may be more conveniently expressed

$$T_1 = \lambda(e_1 + e_2 + e_3) + 2\mu e_1.$$

Similarly

$$T_2 = \lambda(e_1 + e_2 + e_3) + 2\mu e_2$$

and

$$T_3 = \lambda(e_1 + e_2 + e_3) + 2\mu e_3.$$

where the constants λ, μ depend on the elastic properties of the material. The coefficient of λ in these expressions is the sum of the principal extensions, which by Art. 91 is equal to Φ_s or the dilation θ at the point.

If $\mathbf{i}$, $\mathbf{j}$, $\mathbf{k}$ are the unit vectors parallel to the principal stresses, we have for the stress dyadic

$$\begin{aligned} \Psi &= T_1\mathbf{i}\,\mathbf{i} + T_2\mathbf{j}\,\mathbf{j} + T_3\mathbf{k}\,\mathbf{k} \\ &= \lambda(e_1 + e_2 + e_3)\mathrm{I} + 2\mu(e_1\mathbf{i}\,\mathbf{i} + e_2\mathbf{j}\,\mathbf{j} + e_3\mathbf{k}\,\mathbf{k}) \\ &= \lambda\theta\mathrm{I} + 2\mu\Phi. \qquad (23) \end{aligned}$$

by Art. 91, since the strain dyadic Φ is here referred to its principal directions. This is the required relation between the stress and strain dyadics. Since both sides are invariant, the relation holds for any rectangular axes of reference. If we introduce the general nonion forms of Φ and Ψ given in Arts. 91 and 93, the equation (23) is equivalent to six scalar relations between the components of stress and strain, of the forms

$$T_{11} = \lambda\theta + 2\mu e_{11}, \quad T_{23} = \mu e_{23}.$$

Also, equating the scalars of the two sides of (23), we obtain, since $\Phi_s = \theta$,

$$\Theta = (3\lambda + 2\mu)\theta \quad . \quad . \quad . \quad . \quad (24)$$

where Θ is the scalar of Ψ, and is equal to $T_{11} + T_{22} + T_{33}$, or to the sum of the principal stresses $T_1 + T_2 + T_3$. It is of course invariant.

96. The equations of equilibrium in terms of displacement. In the equation of equilibrium

$$\rho\mathbf{F} + \nabla\cdot\Psi = 0,$$

substitute the value of Ψ given by (23). Then

$$\rho\mathbf{F} + \nabla\cdot(\lambda\theta\mathrm{I} + \mu\nabla\mathbf{s} + \mu\mathbf{s}\nabla) = 0$$

by the definition of Φ. Now

$$\nabla\cdot(\theta\mathrm{I}) = \nabla\theta \quad . \quad . \quad \text{by (16') of Art. 85}$$

and

$$\nabla\cdot(\mathbf{s}\nabla) = \nabla\nabla\cdot\mathbf{s} = \nabla\theta \ . \quad \text{by (11') of Art. 84}$$

Hence our equation is equivalent to

$$\rho\mathbf{F} + (\lambda + \mu)\nabla\theta + \mu\nabla^2\mathbf{s} = 0 \quad . \quad . \quad . \quad (25)$$

This is the required equation of equilibrium in terms of the displacement $\mathbf{s}$, since $\theta = \operatorname{div} \mathbf{s}$. It may be written in the alternative form

$$\rho\mathbf{F} + (\lambda + 2\mu)\nabla\theta - 2\mu\nabla\times\mathbf{w} = 0 \ . \quad . \quad . \quad (25')$$

where $\mathbf{w} = \frac{1}{2}\nabla\times\mathbf{s}$ is the rotation of the element at the point considered. On taking the divergence of both sides we obtain the relation

$$\nabla\cdot(\rho\mathbf{F}) + (\lambda + 2\mu)\nabla^2\theta = 0 \quad . \quad . \quad . \quad (26)$$

so that if there are no impressed forces $\mathbf{F}$, the body being in equilibrium under surface traction only, the dilation θ is an harmonic function. By (24) the same is then true of Θ.

The *stress at a point*, across a plane perpendicular to the unit vector $\mathbf{n}$, is

$$\begin{aligned} \mathbf{T}_n = \mathbf{n}\cdot\Psi &= \mathbf{n}\cdot(\lambda\theta\mathrm{I} + \mu\nabla\mathbf{s} + \mu\mathbf{s}\nabla) \\ &= \mathbf{n}\cdot(\lambda\theta\mathrm{I} + 2\mu\nabla\mathbf{s} + \mu\mathrm{I}\times\nabla\times\mathbf{s}) \end{aligned}$$

by (21') of Art. 62. Putting $\mathbf{w} = \frac{1}{2}\operatorname{curl}\mathbf{s}$ we may write this equation

$$\mathbf{T}_n = \lambda\theta\mathbf{n} + 2\mu\frac{\partial\mathbf{s}}{\partial n} + 2\mu\mathbf{n}\times\mathbf{w} \quad . \quad . \quad . \quad (27)$$

97.* The strain-energy-function. Imagine that the displacement $\mathbf{s}$ at each point of the body is increased by an infinitesimal amount $\delta\mathbf{s}$. The work done on the material within a closed surface S drawn

* This Art. may be omitted by the reader if he so desires.

in the body, by the impressed force **F** and the stress over S, is

$$\delta W = \int \mathbf{n}\cdot\Psi\cdot\delta\mathbf{s}dS + \int \rho\mathbf{F}\cdot\delta\mathbf{s}dv$$
$$= \int [\nabla\cdot(\Psi\cdot\delta\mathbf{s}) + \rho\mathbf{F}\cdot\delta\mathbf{s}]dv$$

by the divergence theorem. The first term of the integrand may be expanded by Exercise 18 of Chapter VII., and the result written

$$\delta W = \int (\nabla\cdot\Psi + \rho\mathbf{F})\cdot\delta\mathbf{s}dv + \int \Psi : \nabla(\delta\mathbf{s})dv.$$

Now the first integral is zero by (17). And remembering that Ψ is self-conjugate we may write

$$\Psi : \nabla(\delta\mathbf{s}) = \Psi : \delta\nabla\mathbf{s} = \Psi : \tfrac{1}{2}\delta(\nabla\mathbf{s} + \mathbf{s}\nabla)$$
$$= \Psi : \delta\Phi$$
$$= (\lambda\theta\mathrm{I} + 2\mu\Phi) : \delta\Phi.$$

Then because $\theta = \Phi_s$ and $\mathrm{I} : \delta\Phi = (\delta\Phi)_s = \delta\Phi_s$ by Exercise 22, Chapter VII., this expression is equal to

$$\lambda\Phi_s\delta\Phi_s + 2\mu\Phi : \delta\Phi = \tfrac{1}{2}\delta(\lambda\Phi_s^2 + 2\mu\Phi : \Phi) = \tfrac{1}{2}\delta(\Psi : \Phi).$$

Hence the work done by the forces during the infinitesimal displacement is

$$\delta W = \int \tfrac{1}{2}\delta(\Psi : \Phi)dv = \delta\int \tfrac{1}{2}(\Psi : \Phi)dv.$$

Summing for the whole displacement of the body from its unstrained state to the final displacement **s**, we have for the work of the impressed forces and the stress over S upon the enclosed portion of the body

$$W = \int \tfrac{1}{2}(\Psi : \Phi)dv \quad . \quad . \quad . \quad . \quad (28)$$

The function $\frac{1}{2}(\Psi : \Phi)$ is called the *strain-energy-function*, and represents the potential energy per unit volume of the strained body. If we use the value of Φ from Art. 91 in terms of the components of strain, and then the value of Ψ given by (23), we easily calculate the energy-function in the form

$$\tfrac{1}{2}(\Psi : \Phi) = \tfrac{1}{2}[\lambda\theta^2 + 2\mu(e_{11}^2 + e_{22}^2 + e_{33}^2) + \mu(e_{23}^2 + e_{31}^2 + e_{12}^2)] \quad (29)$$

IV. **Motion of Viscous Fluids.**

98. Stress. The discussion given in Part II. of this chapter, of the stresses in a deformable body at rest, is immediately extended to the case of motion by equating the vector sum of the forces on any portion of the body to the rate of increase of its linear momentum. In this way, if $\mathbf{v}$ is the velocity of the fluid at any point, and therefore $\frac{d\mathbf{v}}{dt}$ the acceleration of the particle there, we have only to replace the impressed force $\mathbf{F}$ in that discussion by $\left(\mathbf{F} - \frac{d\mathbf{v}}{dt}\right)$. The argument, moreover, is equally true for solids and fluids. In the case of a perfect fluid we have seen that the stress across a plane is always normal to it, and hence that the magnitude of the stress-intensity at a point is independent of the direction. For a viscous fluid in motion, however, this is not the case.

With the notation of Art. 92, if $\mathbf{T}_1$, $\mathbf{T}_2$, $\mathbf{T}_3$ are the intensities of stress across planes perpendicular to $\mathbf{i}$, $\mathbf{j}$, $\mathbf{k}$ through the point P in the viscous fluid, the stress $\mathbf{T}_n$ across a plane perpendicular to $\mathbf{n}$ is given by

$$\mathbf{T}_n = \mathbf{n}\cdot\Psi$$

where Ψ is the stress dyadic

$$\Psi = \mathbf{i}\,\mathbf{T}_1 + \mathbf{j}\,\mathbf{T}_2 + \mathbf{k}\,\mathbf{T}_3,$$

which has been proved self-conjugate. And in place of the stress equation of equilibrium (17) we now have the *equation of motion* for the fluid

$$\nabla\cdot\Psi + \rho\mathbf{F} = \rho\frac{d\mathbf{v}}{dt} \quad . \quad . \quad . \quad . \quad (30)$$

And since Ψ is self-conjugate, there are three mutually perpendicular unit vectors $\mathbf{i}'$, $\mathbf{j}'$, $\mathbf{k}'$ such that

$$\Psi = T_1\mathbf{i}'\mathbf{i}' + T_2\mathbf{j}'\mathbf{j}' + T_3\mathbf{k}'\mathbf{k}'.$$

The stresses across planes perpendicular to these vectors are normal to the planes, which therefore constitute the *principal planes* of stress at the point. The corresponding stresses are the *principal stresses* at the point.

The scalar Ψ_s of the stress dyadic is an invariant. If, with the usual notation, we write

$$\mathbf{T}_1 = T_{11}\mathbf{i} + T_{12}\mathbf{j} + T_{13}\mathbf{k},$$

and so on, this scalar has the value $T_{11} + T_{22} + T_{33}$, which is the sum of the normal intensities of stress across three mutually perpendicular planes. It is also represented by $T_1 + T_2 + T_3$, the sum of the magnitudes of the principal stresses at the point. We shall denote its value by $-\,3p$. Thus

$$\Psi_s = -\,3p \quad . \quad . \quad . \quad . \quad (31)$$

p being the average value of the normal intensity of *pressure* for three perpendicular planes through P. In the case of a fluid at rest, p is simply the pressure at that point.

99. Rate of strain. Let $\mathbf{v} = u\mathbf{i} + v\mathbf{j} + w\mathbf{k}$ be the velocity of the particle at P. The rate of change (per unit length) of the linear element of the fluid at P in the direction of $\hat{\mathbf{a}}$ is $\hat{\mathbf{a}}\cdot\nabla\mathbf{v}$, and is therefore a linear vector function of $\hat{\mathbf{a}}$. The dyadic $\nabla\mathbf{v}$ here involved may be written

$$\begin{aligned}\nabla\mathbf{v} &= \tfrac{1}{2}(\nabla\mathbf{v} + \mathbf{v}\nabla) - \tfrac{1}{2}\mathrm{I}\times(\nabla\mathbf{v})_v \\ &= \Phi - \mathrm{I}\times\mathbf{w} \qquad . \quad . \quad . \quad . \quad . \quad (32)\end{aligned}$$

where $\mathbf{w} = \frac{1}{2}$ curl $\mathbf{v}$ is the *vorticity* or molecular rotation of the fluid at P, and Φ is the self-conjugate dyadic

$$\begin{aligned}\Phi &= \tfrac{1}{2}(\nabla\mathbf{v} + \mathbf{v}\nabla) \\ &= \frac{\partial u}{\partial x}\mathbf{i}\,\mathbf{i} + \frac{\partial v}{\partial y}\mathbf{j}\,\mathbf{j} + \ldots + \tfrac{1}{2}\left(\frac{\partial w}{\partial y} + \frac{\partial v}{\partial z}\right)(\mathbf{j}\,\mathbf{k} + \mathbf{k}\,\mathbf{j}) + \ldots,\end{aligned}$$

which we may write

$$\Phi = e_{11}\mathbf{i}\,\mathbf{i} + e_{22}\mathbf{j}\,\mathbf{j} + \ldots + \tfrac{1}{2}e_{23}(\mathbf{j}\,\mathbf{k} + \mathbf{k}\,\mathbf{j}) + \ldots + \ldots \quad . \quad (33)$$

The coefficient $e_{11} = (\mathbf{i}\cdot\Phi)\cdot\mathbf{i}$ is the resolute parallel to $\mathbf{i}$ of the rate of change of a linear element in the direction of $\mathbf{i}$. We call this briefly the "rate of extension parallel to $\mathbf{i}$." Similarly e_{22} and e_{33} are the rates of extension parallel to $\mathbf{j}$ and $\mathbf{k}$; while e_{23} is the rate of decrease of the angle between elements parallel to $\mathbf{j}$ and $\mathbf{k}$. And since Φ is self-conjugate, there are three mutually perpendicular unit vectors $\mathbf{i}'$, $\mathbf{j}'$, $\mathbf{k}'$ such that

$$\Phi = e_1\mathbf{i}'\mathbf{i}' + e_2\mathbf{j}'\mathbf{j}' + e_3\mathbf{k}'\mathbf{k}' \quad . \quad . \quad . \quad (33')$$

The directions of these are the principal axes of the rate of strain, the rates of shear for the perpendicular planes being now zero. The dyadic Φ may be called the *rate of strain dyadic*.

The scalar of Φ is an invariant relative to coordinate axes, having the value

$$\Phi_s = \tfrac{1}{2}(\nabla\mathbf{v} + \mathbf{v}\nabla)_s = (\nabla\mathbf{v})_s = \nabla\cdot\mathbf{v}$$

by Art. 83. And it was shown in Art. 35 that the divergence of the velocity is the rate of dilation of the fluid at P. We shall denote it by θ. In terms of the principal rates of strain,

$$\theta = \Phi_s = e_1 + e_2 + e_3 \quad . \quad . \quad . \quad . \quad (34)$$

100. Relation between stress and rate of strain. By considerations of symmetry, if the fluid is isotropic the principal axes of the rate of strain will be parallel to the directions of the principal stresses. For a fluid at rest the principal stresses will be equal to each other, and to the negative of the pressure p at that point. We assume that, for a fluid in motion, the differences between the principal stresses and the value of $-p$ given by (31) are linear functions of the principal rates of strain, so that we may write

$$T_1 = -p + \lambda(e_1 + e_2 + e_3) + 2\mu e_1,$$
$$T_2 = -p + \lambda(e_1 + e_2 + e_3) + 2\mu e_2,$$
$$T_3 = -p + \lambda(e_1 + e_2 + e_3) + 2\mu e_3,$$

where λ, μ are constants depending on the physical properties of the fluid. Adding these equations we have, in virtue of (31) and (34),

$$-3p = -3p + 3\lambda\theta + 2\mu\theta;$$

that is,

$$\lambda = -\tfrac{2}{3}\mu.$$

The stress dyadic may now be expressed

$$\begin{aligned}\Psi &= T_1\mathbf{i}'\mathbf{i}' + T_2\mathbf{j}'\mathbf{j}' + T_3\mathbf{k}'\mathbf{k}' \\ &= -p\mathrm{I} - \tfrac{2}{3}\mu\theta\mathrm{I} + 2\mu\Phi \quad . \quad . \quad . \quad . \quad (35)\end{aligned}$$

in virtue of (33′). This relation is independent of the axes chosen; so that, for axes that are not principal, we have the relations

$$T_{11} = -p - \tfrac{2}{3}\mu\theta + 2\mu e_{11}, \text{ etc.},$$
$$T_{23} = \mu e_{23}, \text{ etc.}$$

The constant μ is called the *coefficient of viscosity*. Its physical meaning may be illustrated by the case of "laminar" motion, in which the particles move in one direction in a system of parallel planes, the velocity in any plane being proportional to the distance from one of the parallel planes. Taking **i** parallel to the velocity, **k** perpendicular to the planes, and the origin on the plane of zero velocity, we have

$$\mathbf{v} = cz\mathbf{i}, \qquad \theta = \operatorname{div}\mathbf{v} = 0,$$
$$\nabla\mathbf{v} = c\mathbf{k}\,\mathbf{i}, \qquad \mathbf{v}\nabla = c\mathbf{i}\,\mathbf{k},$$

and therefore

$$\Psi = -p\mathrm{I} + c\mu(\mathbf{i}\,\mathbf{k} + \mathbf{k}\,\mathbf{i}).$$

The stress across a plane perpendicular to **k** is then

$$\mathbf{k}\cdot\Psi = -p\mathbf{k} + c\mu\mathbf{i}.$$

Thus the tangential stress between two consecutive strata parallel to the velocity is $c\mu$ per unit area, that is, μ times the (scalar) gradient of v in the direction of **k**.

101. Equation of motion. The stress equation of motion (30) can be transformed by using the value of Ψ given in (35). It then becomes

$$\rho\left(\frac{d\mathbf{v}}{dt} - \mathbf{F}\right) = \nabla\cdot[-p\mathrm{I} - \tfrac{2}{3}\mu\theta\mathrm{I} + \mu(\nabla\mathbf{v} + \mathbf{v}\nabla)],$$

which, in virtue of (11′) and (16′) of Chapter VII., is equivalent to

$$\rho\left(\frac{d\mathbf{v}}{dt} - \mathbf{F}\right) = -\nabla p + \frac{\mu}{3}\nabla\theta + \mu\nabla^2\mathbf{v} \quad . \quad . \quad (36)$$

The quantity $\nu = \mu/\rho$ was called by Maxwell the "kinematical coefficient of viscosity." In terms of this we may write the equation of motion

$$\frac{d\mathbf{v}}{dt} = \mathbf{F} - \frac{1}{\rho}\nabla p + \frac{\nu}{3}\nabla\theta + \nu\nabla^2\mathbf{v} \quad . \quad . \quad . \quad (36')$$

which, as in Art. 37, may be given the alternative form

$$\frac{\partial\mathbf{v}}{\partial t} - 2\mathbf{v}\times\mathbf{w} = \mathbf{F} - \frac{1}{\rho}\nabla p + \frac{\nu}{3}\nabla\theta + \nu\nabla^2\mathbf{v} - \tfrac{1}{2}\nabla\mathbf{v}^2 \quad . \quad (37)$$

Or again, since

$$\nabla^2\mathbf{v} = \nabla\nabla\cdot\mathbf{v} - \nabla\times\nabla\times\mathbf{v},$$

we may also write the equation

$$\frac{\partial\mathbf{v}}{\partial t} - 2\mathbf{v}\times\mathbf{w} + 2\nu\nabla\times\mathbf{w} = \mathbf{F} - \frac{1}{\rho}\nabla p + \frac{4}{3}\nu\nabla\theta - \tfrac{1}{2}\nabla\mathbf{v}^2 \quad . \quad (37')$$

If the impressed force $\mathbf{F}$ is derivable from a potential V, so that $\mathbf{F} = -\nabla V$, and if, further, ρ is uniform or else a function of p only, we may define a function P such that $\nabla P = \frac{1}{\rho}\nabla p$, and the second member of (37′) is then the gradient of a function U given by

$$U = -\left(V + P - \frac{4}{3}\nu\theta + \tfrac{1}{2}\mathbf{v}^2\right).$$

The equation of motion then takes the simple form

$$\frac{\partial\mathbf{v}}{\partial t} - 2\mathbf{v}\times\mathbf{w} + 2\nu\nabla\times\mathbf{w} = \nabla U \quad . \quad . \quad . \quad (38)$$

The *equation of continuity* is the same as in the case of a frictionless fluid, viz.

$$\frac{\partial\rho}{\partial t} + \nabla\cdot(\rho\mathbf{v}) = 0 \quad . \quad . \quad . \quad . \quad (39)$$

or

$$\frac{d\rho}{dt} + \rho\nabla\cdot\mathbf{v} = 0 \quad . \quad . \quad . \quad . \quad (39')$$

In the case of a *liquid* ρ is invariable in time, and the last equation is simply $\theta = 0$.

The definitions given in Art. 38 of line of flow, vortex line, vortex tube, and circulation apply to the viscous fluid also. The strength of a vortex tube is constant along the tube, and is equal to half the circulation round any closed path drawn on the surface of the tube, and encircling the tube once only. The case of a viscous fluid in equilibrium is the same as that of a frictionless fluid, since the tangential stress vanishes with the velocity.

102.* Loss of kinetic energy due to viscosity. Consider the body of fluid contained within a closed surface S moving with the fluid. Let dv be the volume of an element containing always the same particles, so that $\frac{d}{dt}(\rho dv) = 0$. The rate of increase of the kinetic energy of the fluid within S is

$$\frac{dT}{dt} = \frac{d}{dt}\tfrac{1}{2}\int \rho \mathbf{v}^2 dv = \int \rho \mathbf{v} \cdot \frac{d\mathbf{v}}{dt} dv$$
$$= \int (\nabla \cdot \Psi + \rho \mathbf{F}) \cdot \mathbf{v} dv \quad . \quad . \quad . \quad . \quad (40)$$

by (30). Now the rate at which work is done on this body of fluid by the impressed force $\mathbf{F}$ and the stress over S is

$$\int \rho \mathbf{F} \cdot \mathbf{v} dv + \int (\mathbf{n} \cdot \Psi) \cdot \mathbf{v} dS = \int [\rho \mathbf{F} \cdot \mathbf{v} + \nabla \cdot (\Psi \cdot \mathbf{v})] dv$$

by the divergence theorem; and by Exercise 18 of Chapter VII. this may be expressed

$$\int (\rho \mathbf{F} + \nabla \cdot \Psi) \cdot \mathbf{v} dv + \int \Psi : \nabla \mathbf{v} dv.$$

Hence the excess of the rate of work over the rate of increase of the kinetic energy is

$$\int \Psi : \nabla \mathbf{v} dv = \int \Psi : \Phi dv \quad . \quad . \quad . \quad (41)$$

since Ψ is self-conjugate. The integrand $\Psi : \Phi$ then represents this expenditure of energy per unit volume. By (35) the value of this is

$$(-p\mathrm{I} - \tfrac{2}{3}\mu\theta\mathrm{I} + 2\mu\Phi) : \Phi.$$

And since $\mathrm{I} : \Phi = \Phi_s = \theta$, we have, on using the expression (33) for Φ,

$$\Psi : \Phi = -p\theta - \tfrac{2}{3}\mu\theta^2 + 2\mu(e_{11}{}^2 + e_{22}{}^2 + e_{33}{}^2) + \mu(e_{23}{}^2 + e_{31}{}^2 + e_{12}{}^2).$$

The term $-p\theta$ is the rate of expenditure of energy in compressing the fluid; the remaining terms give the rate of expenditure in overcoming viscous resistance.

103. Vortex-motion of a liquid. For a liquid let ρ be uniform and invariable. Then $\theta = 0$ by the equation of continuity, and

$$P = \int \frac{dp}{\rho} = \frac{p}{\rho}.$$

On the assumption of a force potential the equation of motion is (38). Taking the curl of both sides, and using the formulæ (18) and (22)

* The reader may omit this Art. if he so desires.

of Chapter I., it follows because div $\mathbf{v} = 0$ that

$$\frac{\partial \mathbf{w}}{\partial t} + \mathbf{v}\cdot\nabla\mathbf{w} - \mathbf{w}\cdot\nabla\mathbf{v} - \nu\nabla^2\mathbf{w} = 0,$$

which is equivalent to

$$\frac{d\mathbf{w}}{dt} = \mathbf{w}\cdot\nabla\mathbf{v} + \nu\nabla^2\mathbf{w} \quad . \quad . \quad . \quad . \quad (42)$$

The last term is that part of the rate of increase of **w** which is due to viscosity; and the form of the equation (42) shows that this variation follows the law of thermal conduction. By analogy, then, it follows that vortex-motion cannot originate in the interior of the liquid, but must be communicated inward from the boundary.

Kelvin's circulation theorem does not apply to a viscous fluid, owing to the term $\mu\nabla^2\mathbf{v}$ in (36).

EXERCISES ON CHAPTER VIII.

1. Simple dilation. For a strain given by $\mathbf{s} = a\mathbf{r}$, where a is a (small) constant, show that the dilation θ is constant and equal to $3a$. Also $\nabla\mathbf{s} = a\mathrm{I}$. Hence, for an isotropic body, prove that

$$\Psi = (3\lambda + 2\mu)a\mathrm{I}$$

and

$$\mathbf{T}_n = (3\lambda + 2\mu)a\mathbf{n}.$$

The stress is therefore always normal to the surface, and the stress intensity constant in magnitude and equal to T, say. Then

$$\frac{T}{\theta} = \lambda + \tfrac{2}{3}\mu = k,$$

where k is called the *bulk-modulus* of the material.

2. Simple shear. Consider the strain defined by $\mathbf{s} = ay\mathbf{i}$. Show that θ is identically zero, and $\nabla\mathbf{s} = a\mathbf{j}\,\mathbf{i}$. For an isotropic body,

$$\Psi = a\mu(\mathbf{j}\,\mathbf{i} + \mathbf{i}\,\mathbf{j}).$$

Show that the stresses across planes normal to **i** and **j** are $\mathbf{T}_1 = a\mu\mathbf{j}$ and $\mathbf{T}_2 = a\mu\mathbf{i}$, being therefore tangential in both cases. The magnitude of either stress is $T = a\mu$. The change in angle for a square with sides parallel to **i** and **j** is a radians. And $T/a = \mu$ is called the *simple rigidity* of the material. Generally denoted by n; so that $n = \mu$. *Cor.* In terms of n and k the constant λ is

$$\lambda = k - \tfrac{2}{3}\mu = k - \tfrac{2}{3}n.$$

3. Stretch-squeeze corresponds to $\mathbf{s} = ax\mathbf{i} - by\mathbf{j} - bz\mathbf{k}$. Show that $\theta = a - 2b$ and $\nabla\mathbf{s} = a\mathbf{i}\,\mathbf{i} - b(\mathbf{j}\,\mathbf{j} + \mathbf{k}\,\mathbf{k})$. For an isotropic body,

$$\Psi = \lambda(a - 2b)\mathrm{I} + 2\mu(a\mathbf{i}\,\mathbf{i} - b\mathbf{j}\,\mathbf{j} - b\mathbf{k}\,\mathbf{k}).$$

Hence find $\mathbf{T}_1, \mathbf{T}_2, \mathbf{T}_3 = \mathbf{i}\cdot\Psi, \mathbf{j}\cdot\Psi, \mathbf{k}\cdot\Psi$ respectively. If

$$\frac{b}{a} = \frac{\lambda}{2(\lambda+\mu)},$$

$\mathbf{T}_2$ and $\mathbf{T}_3$ both vanish, while

$$\mathbf{T}_1 = 2\mu(a+b)\mathbf{i} = \frac{\mu(3\lambda+2\mu)a\mathbf{i}}{\lambda+\mu}.$$

If T is the magnitude of this stress, a being the corresponding extension,

$$E = \frac{T}{a} = \frac{\mu(3\lambda+2\mu)}{\lambda+\mu} = \frac{9nk}{n+3k}$$

is called the *Young's modulus* of the material. The ratio of the lateral contraction to the longitudinal extension

$$\eta = \frac{b}{a} = \frac{\lambda}{2(\lambda+\mu)} = \frac{3k-2n}{2(n+3k)}$$

is called *Poisson's ratio* for the material. Since n is positive, η is clearly less than $\frac{1}{2}$.

4. Show that, when there are no impressed forces, the displacement $\mathbf{s}$ for an isotropic body satisfies the equation $\nabla^4\mathbf{s} = 0$.

5. Referred to orthogonal curvilinear coordinates ξ, η, ζ with arcual parameters $h_1; h_2, h_3$ (Art. 11), let the displacement have the value $\mathbf{s} = u\mathbf{a} + v\mathbf{b} + w\mathbf{c}$ where $\mathbf{a}, \mathbf{b}, \mathbf{c}$ are unit vectors parallel to the coordinate axes at the point. Prove that the six components of strain are given by

$$e_{11} = \frac{1}{h_1}\frac{\partial u}{\partial \xi} + \frac{v}{h_1 h_2}\frac{\partial h_1}{\partial \eta} + \frac{w}{h_1 h_3}\frac{\partial h_1}{\partial \zeta},$$

$$e_{23} = \frac{h_3}{h_2}\frac{\partial}{\partial \eta}\left(\frac{w}{h_3}\right) + \frac{h_2}{h_3}\frac{\partial}{\partial \zeta}\left(\frac{v}{h_2}\right),$$

and similar equations. The values of the dilation θ and the rotation $\mathbf{w}$ may be written down by Arts. 12 and 18.

6. Find the Cartesian equivalents of the identical relation $\nabla\times\Phi\times\nabla = 0$ of Art. 91.

7. If an elastic body is subjected successively to two systems of forces, the work that would be done by the forces of the first system if the displacement were that due to the second, is equal to the work that would be done by the forces of the second system if the displacement were that due to the first; or

$$\int \rho\mathbf{F}\cdot\mathbf{s}'dv + \int \mathbf{T}_n\cdot\mathbf{s}'dS = \int \rho\mathbf{F}'\cdot\mathbf{s}dv + \int \mathbf{T}'_n\cdot\mathbf{s}dS.$$

This is *Betti's reciprocal theorem*. (Use the method of Art. 97.)

8. An isotropic body is subjected to a hydrostatic pressure $\mathbf{T}_n = -p\mathbf{n}$ uniform over the surface, the impressed force being zero. Show that

$$(3\lambda + 2\mu)\int \theta dv = -3pV$$

where V is the volume of the body.

9. An isotropic body is subjected to an impressed force $\mathbf{F}$ per unit mass, and a surface traction $\mathbf{T}_n$. Prove that

$$(3\lambda + 2\mu)\int \theta dv = \int \rho \mathbf{r}\cdot\mathbf{F} dv + \int \mathbf{r}\cdot\mathbf{T}_n dS,$$

$\mathbf{r}$ being the position vector of the point considered.

10. Show that the equation (14) of the present chapter is also true for the rate of strain dyadic in the motion of viscous fluids.

11. Prove that the equation for impulsive generation of motion in a viscous liquid is the same as that for a frictionless liquid.

12. Express the equation of motion (36′) for a viscous fluid by three scalar equations in i, cylindrical coordinates; ii, spherical polar coordinates; iii, general curvilinear coordinates.

13. In the slow steady motion of a viscous fluid under no impressed forces, show that

$$\int \mathbf{n}\cdot\Psi dS = 0$$

where the integral is taken over any closed surface drawn in the fluid.

14. Viscous liquid fills the space within a closed fixed boundary at which there is no slipping. Show that the rate of dissipation of energy due to viscosity (Art. 102) is

$$4\mu\int \mathbf{w}^2 dv.$$

In the general case, when the above boundary conditions are removed, show that the rate is

$$4\mu\int \mathbf{w}^2 dv + \mu\int (\mathbf{n}\cdot\nabla\mathbf{v}^2 - 4\mathbf{n}\cdot\mathbf{v}\times\mathbf{w}) dS.$$

15. Express the components of rate of strain in curvilinear coordinates (*cf.* Ex. 5), and hence also by Art. 100 the components of stress for a viscous fluid.

16. In the slow steady motion of a viscous liquid through a fine circular tube of radius a and length l, show that the velocity at a distance r from the axis, on the assumption of no slipping at the surface of the tube, is

$$v = \frac{p_1 - p_2}{4\mu l}(a^2 - r^2),$$

where p_1, p_2 are the pressures at the ends of the tube. Hence the volume of liquid that flows through per unit time is

$$V = \frac{\pi a^4}{8\mu} \cdot \frac{(p_1 - p_2)}{l}.$$

17. The space between two concentric cylinders of radii a and $b(<a)$ is filled with a viscous liquid. The outer cylinder is kept fixed, and the inner is rotated with angular velocity ω about their common axis. On the assumption of no slipping of the fluid at the surface of the cylinders, show that the torque necessary to hold the outer one stationary is $4\pi\mu\omega a^2 b^2/(a^2 - b^2)$ per unit length of the cylinder.

CHAPTER IX.

ELEMENTARY THEORY OF ELECTRICITY AND MAGNETISM.*

In the present chapter we shall assume that the reader possesses an elementary practical knowledge of electrical and magnetic phenomena, such as is acquired by most students in a first year's course in Physics at any university. It is our purpose to give a mathematical setting for such knowledge, and to show how this leads up to the more advanced parts of the subject, built upon the electromagnetic equations of Maxwell and Lorentz.

Intensity and Potential.

104. Point charges and poles. The force of attraction or repulsion between two small bodies charged with electricity, or between two magnetic poles, is along the straight line joining them and is jointly proportional directly to the charges e, e', or the pole strengths m, m', and inversely to the square of their distance r apart. We write this

$$F \propto \frac{ee'}{r^2}, \quad \text{or} \quad F \propto \frac{mm'}{r^2}.$$

The electrostatic (E.S.) unit of charge and the unit magnetic pole are chosen so that, when air is the medium between the bodies, the constant of proportion is unity in each case. Thus in the case of air,

$$F = \frac{ee'}{r^2}, \quad \text{or} \quad F = \frac{mm'}{r^2}.$$

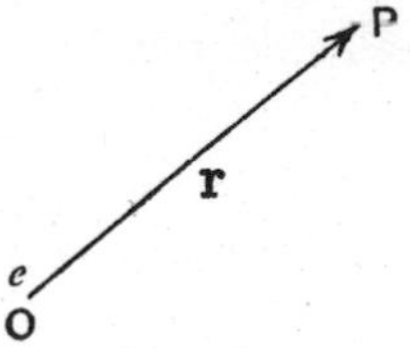

Fig. 28.

The *intensity* of the electric force, or the *electric intensity* at a point P, is measured by the force that would act on a unit positive charge placed at P This is a vector quantity. If the electric field is due to a single charge e at the point O, the intensity at the point P, whose position

* The whole of this chapter, except Arts. 107 and 116, is independent of the theory of dyadics, and can be read if desired immediately after Art. 28.

vector is $\mathbf{r}$ relative to O, is

$$\mathbf{E} = \frac{e\hat{\mathbf{r}}}{r^2} = -\nabla\left(\frac{e}{r}\right).$$

The same argument, as in the case of the gravitational force (Art. 22), shows that e/r measures the work done against the electric intensity in bringing a unit positive charge from infinity up to the point P. This is called the *electric potential* at P, and will be denoted by V. Thus the electric intensity and potential at a point are connected by the relation

$$\mathbf{E} = -\nabla V.$$

Similarly the *magnetic intensity* at a point is measured by the force that would act on a unit positive pole placed there. The intensity $\mathbf{H}$ at P due to a pole of strength m at O is

$$\mathbf{H} = -\nabla\left(\frac{m}{r}\right) = -\nabla U,$$

where $U = m/r$ is the *magnetic potential* at P due to the pole at O.

Suppose that the electric field is that due to several charges $e_1, e_2, \ldots$ at the points $O_1, O_2, \ldots$ from which the distances to P are $r_1, r_2, \ldots$ respectively. Then the intensity at P is the vector sum of the intensities due to each; that is,

$$\mathbf{E} = -\nabla\left(\frac{e_1}{r_1}\right) - \nabla\left(\frac{e_2}{r_2}\right) - \ldots = -\nabla\Sigma\frac{e}{r}.$$

The work done in bringing a unit positive charge by any path from infinity up to the point P is

$$V = \int_P^\infty \mathbf{E}\cdot d\mathbf{r} = -\left[\Sigma\frac{e}{r}\right]_P^\infty = \Sigma\frac{e}{r}.$$

Thus the potential at P due to the system of charges is the sum of the potentials due to each; and $\mathbf{E} = -\nabla V$. Also, as in Art. 22, the potential satisfies Laplace's equation

$$\nabla^2 V = 0,$$

except at the points occupied by the charges. This equation may also be written

$$\operatorname{div} \mathbf{E} = 0.$$

Similarly in the magnetic field due to poles of strengths $m_1, m_2, \ldots$ at the points $O_1, O_2, \ldots$ the potential at P is

$$U = \Sigma\frac{m}{r},$$

and the intensity is

$$\mathbf{H} = -\nabla\Sigma\frac{m}{r} = -\nabla U.$$

The equation

$$\nabla^2 U = 0 \quad \text{or} \quad \operatorname{div} \mathbf{H} = 0$$

is satisfied except at the points occupied by the magnetic poles.

105. Continuous distributions. If the field is due to a *volume distribution* of charge of density ρ, or of magnetism of pole strength ρ per unit volume throughout a certain region, the potential due to such a distribution is

$$V \text{ or } U = \int \frac{\rho}{r} dv.$$

The integration is to be extended throughout the region occupied by electricity or magnetism, or throughout the whole of space since ρ is identically zero elsewhere. As in Art. 23, the potential and intensity due to such a volume distribution are finite and continuous at all points.

If the field is due to a *surface distribution* of charge of density σ per unit area, or of magnetism of pole strength σ per unit area, the potential at a point P is

$$V \text{ or } U = \int \frac{\sigma}{r} dS.$$

This integral is of the same type as that which expresses the potential due to a simple stratum of matter over S (Art. 27). Hence its value is finite and continuous everywhere, and possesses a continuous gradient except at the surface S, where the normal derivative possesses a discontinuity of $-4\pi\sigma$.

Gauss's theorem of *total normal intensity* (Art. 24) is equally true for the electrical and magnetic cases. Thus the total normal intensity over any closed surface drawn in the field is equal to 4π times the sum of the enclosed charges, or 4π times the sum of the strengths of the enclosed poles. We may write this

$$\int \mathbf{E}\cdot\mathbf{n} dS = 4\pi \Sigma e = 4\pi \int \rho dv,$$

or

$$\int \mathbf{H}\cdot\mathbf{n} dS = 4\pi \Sigma m = 4\pi \int \rho dv.$$

It follows, as in Art. 25, that at a point P where the density of the volume distribution is ρ, the potentials V, U satisfy Poisson's equation

$$\nabla^2 V = -4\pi\rho$$
$$\nabla^2 U = -4\pi\rho.$$

This is true for all points except those occupied by a surface distribution, for the derivatives of V or U are discontinuous at such a surface. Laplace's equation of the preceding Art. is a particular case of Poisson's, for which $\rho = 0$.

The *equipotential surfaces* for an electric or magnetic field are the level-surfaces of the potential function V or U. A *line of force* is one whose tangent at any point is parallel to the intensity there. Hence the lines of force are orthogonal to the equipotential surfaces. A *tube of force* is the region bounded by the assemblage of lines of force passing through a closed curve in the field. It follows from Gauss's theorem that the normal surface integral of the intensity, taken over a section of a tube of force (Fig. 18), is the same for all sections along a portion of the tube not enclosing any charge or poles. This constant value is called the *strength of the tube.*

Magnetism.

106. Magnetic moment. Short magnet. The action of a *bar magnet* is equivalent to that of two opposite poles of equal strength situated near the ends of the magnet. The line joining the poles is called the *axis* of the magnet, their distance l apart the *length* of the magnet. The *moment* of the magnet is a vector quantity whose direction is that of the axis from the negative pole to the positive, and whose magnitude is jointly proportional to the length of the magnet and the pole strength m. Thus, with the obvious choice of unit moment, we have for the moment of the magnet

$$\mathbf{M} = ml\hat{\mathbf{a}}$$

where $\hat{\mathbf{a}}$ is a unit vector parallel to the axis of the magnet, in the direction S to N.

A *short magnet* is one whose length is small compared with its distance from the various points considered. Suppose a short magnet of length ds and pole-strength m *placed in a magnetic field* whose potential is U. The moment of the magnet is $\mathbf{M} = mds\hat{\mathbf{a}}$. If U is the value of the potential at the negative pole, the value at the positive pole is $U + ds\hat{\mathbf{a}}\cdot\nabla U$. Hence the potential energy of the magnet placed in the field is

$$\left.\begin{aligned} -mU + m(U + ds\hat{\mathbf{a}}\cdot\nabla U) &= \mathbf{M}\cdot\nabla U \\ &= -\mathbf{M}\cdot\mathbf{H} \end{aligned}\right\} \quad . \quad . \quad (1)$$

where $\mathbf{H}$ is the intensity of the field in the neighbourhood of the small magnet. The forces on the magnet are $-m\mathbf{H}$ at the negative pole and $m(\mathbf{H} + ds\hat{\mathbf{a}}\cdot\nabla\mathbf{H}) = m\mathbf{H} + \mathbf{M}\cdot\nabla\mathbf{H}$ at the positive pole. These are equivalent to a *force* $\mathbf{M}\cdot\nabla\mathbf{H}$ together with a *torque*

$$ds\hat{\mathbf{a}}\times m\mathbf{H} = \mathbf{M}\times\mathbf{H} \quad . \quad . \quad . \quad . \quad (2)$$

Suppose that we require to find the *magnetic field due to a short magnet.* Let r be the distance measured from a point P of the field. The potential at P due to the negative pole is then $-\frac{m}{r}$, and that due to the positive pole $m\left(\frac{1}{r} + ds\hat{\mathbf{a}}\cdot\nabla\frac{1}{r}\right)$. Hence the potential at P due to the magnet is $mds\hat{\mathbf{a}}\cdot\nabla\frac{1}{r} = \mathbf{M}\cdot\nabla\frac{1}{r}$, where it is to be understood that the operator ∇ refers to a variable point in the neighbourhood of the magnet, P being the pole from which r is measured. If, however, we take P as the variable point and the centre of the magnet O as pole, since

FIG. 29.

$$\nabla_P \frac{1}{r} = -\nabla_0 \frac{1}{r},$$

we may more conveniently express the potential due to a short magnet, at a point P distant r from it, as

$$U = -\mathbf{M}\cdot\nabla\frac{1}{r} \quad . \quad . \quad . \quad . \quad (3)$$

The magnetic intensity at P due to the magnet is

$$\begin{aligned}\mathbf{H} &= -\nabla U \\ &= \left(\nabla\nabla\frac{1}{r}\right)\cdot\mathbf{M} \quad . \quad . \quad . \quad . \quad (4)\end{aligned}$$

by (13) of Chapter VII., $\mathbf{M}$ being a constant vector.

107. Two short magnets. If there are two short magnets of moments $\mathbf{M}$, $\mathbf{M}'$ at the points P, P' respectively, their mutual action is easily found by the preceding Art. Let r be their distance apart, P being regarded as the pole from which r is measured. The intensity due to the first magnet is $\mathbf{H} = \left(\nabla\nabla\frac{1}{r}\right)\cdot\mathbf{M}$. Hence the *potential energy of the system*, being the potential energy of the second magnet in the field due to the first, is by (1)

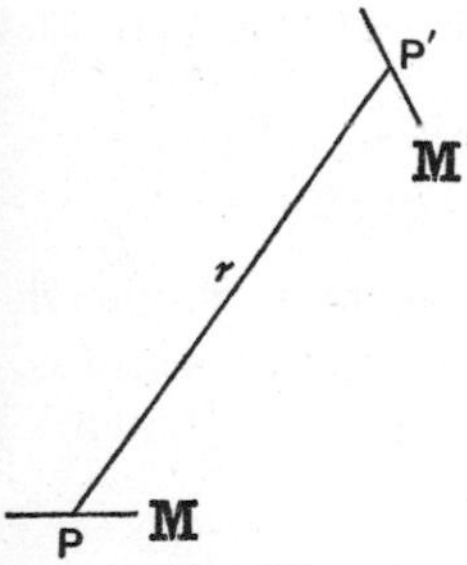

FIG. 30.

$$-\mathbf{M}'\cdot\mathbf{H} = -\mathbf{M}'\cdot\left(\nabla\nabla\frac{1}{r}\right)\cdot\mathbf{M}.$$

The dyadic in this expression is self-conjugate. Its value is easily shown to be

$$\nabla\nabla\frac{1}{r} = \frac{3}{r^5}\mathbf{r}\,\mathbf{r} - \frac{1}{r^3}\mathrm{I}.$$

The *action on the second magnet* is equivalent to a force and a torque. The value of the force is

$$\mathbf{M}'\cdot\nabla\mathbf{H} = \mathbf{M}'\cdot\nabla\left(\mathbf{M}\cdot\nabla\nabla\frac{1}{r}\right),$$

whose value is easily found in terms of r and $\mathbf{r}$ (*cf.* Ex. 17, Chap. VII.); and the value of the torque is

$$\mathbf{M}'\times\mathbf{H} = \mathbf{M}'\times\left(\nabla\nabla\frac{1}{r}\right)\cdot\mathbf{M}$$

$$= \frac{3}{r^5}\mathbf{M}'\times\mathbf{r}\;\mathbf{M}\cdot\mathbf{r} - \frac{1}{r^3}\mathbf{M}'\times\mathbf{M}.$$

The force and torque on the first magnet differ only in sign from those on the second.

108. Poisson's theory of magnetisation. It is found that the magnetism of a permanent magnet does not reside only at the so-called poles. Every portion of the body, however small, is magnetised, and has a magnetic field identical with that of a certain bar magnet. The moment of this equivalent magnet is called the magnetic moment of the portion considered. Let dv be the volume and $d\mathbf{M}$ the moment of an element of the body in the neighbourhood of P. As dv tends to zero the quotient $d\mathbf{M}/dv$ tends to a definite finite limiting value $\mathbf{I}$,* called the *intensity of magnetisation* of the body at P. In other words, the intensity of magnetisation at a point is the magnetic moment per unit volume in the neighbourhood of that point. The moment of an element of volume dv is then

$$d\mathbf{M} = \mathbf{I}dv.$$

Consider now the field due to a magnetised body bounded by a closed surface S. The potential at a point P is the sum of the potentials due to all the elements of the body. If r is the distance of P from an element at Q whose moment is $d\mathbf{M} = \mathbf{I}dv$, the potential at P due to the element is, by Art. 106,

$$dU = d\mathbf{M}\cdot\nabla_Q\frac{1}{r} = \mathbf{I}\cdot\nabla_Q\frac{1}{r}dv,$$

the operator ∇_Q having reference to a variable point in the neighbourhood of Q, and P being the pole from which r is measured. With this understanding we may drop the suffix Q. The potential due to the whole body is then

$$U = \int\mathbf{I}\cdot\nabla\frac{1}{r}dv.$$

* This will not be confused with the Idemfactor.

Transforming the integrand and using the divergence theorem, we may write for the value of the potential

$$U = \int\left[\operatorname{div}\left(\frac{\mathbf{I}}{r}\right) - \frac{1}{r}\operatorname{div}\mathbf{I}\right]dv$$

$$= \int\frac{\mathbf{n}\cdot\mathbf{I}}{r}dS - \int\frac{\operatorname{div}\mathbf{I}}{r}dv \quad . \quad . \quad . \quad . \quad (5)$$

Hence the potential is the same as that due to a volume distribution of magnetism of pole strength $\rho = -\operatorname{div}\mathbf{I}$ per unit volume, and a surface distribution of pole strength $\sigma = \mathbf{n}\cdot\mathbf{I}$ per unit area. This potential is continuous even at the surface of the body; but the normal derivative of the part due to the surface distribution has at the surface a discontinuity of $4\pi\sigma = 4\pi\mathbf{n}\cdot\mathbf{I}$.

When the intensity of magetisation is uniform, $\rho = \operatorname{div}\mathbf{I} = 0$, and the potential is that due to a surface distribution only, viz.

$$U = \mathbf{I}\cdot\int\frac{\mathbf{n}}{r}dS.$$

In the case of a straight bar magnet uniformly magnetised in the direction of its length, σ is zero over the sides, and at the flat ends has the value

$$\sigma = \mathbf{I}\cdot\mathbf{n} = I.$$

This justifies the practice of regarding the magnetism as localised at the poles, the pole strength per unit area being the (scalar) intensity of magnetisation.

109. Action on a magnetised body in a non-homogeneous magnetic field. Consider a body whose intensity of magnetisation is $\mathbf{I}$, in a magnetic field of potential U and intensity $\mathbf{H} = -\nabla U$. An element of the body of volume dv is equivalent to a short magnet of moment $\mathbf{I}dv$. The action of the field on the element is therefore (Art. 106) equivalent to a force $\mathbf{I}\cdot\nabla\mathbf{H}dv$ and a torque $\mathbf{I}\times\mathbf{H}dv$. Take any point O of the body as origin, and let $\mathbf{r}$ be the position vector of this element relative to O. Then, considering all the elements of the body, we find the action of the field on it to be equivalent to a force

$$\mathbf{F} = \int\mathbf{I}\cdot\nabla\mathbf{H}dv$$

through the origin, and a torque

$$\mathbf{L} = \int[\mathbf{r}\times(\mathbf{I}\cdot\nabla\mathbf{H}) + \mathbf{I}\times\mathbf{H}]dv.$$

110. Magnetic induction. Consider a body B magnetised by induction, under the influence of other magnetic bodies. Let U_1 be the potential due to the other bodies, U_2 that due to the induced magnetism in B, and $\mathbf{I}$ the intensity of magnetisation of B. By Art. 108 the value of U_2 is the same as the potential due to a certain volume distribution of magnetism through B of density $\rho = -\operatorname{div}\mathbf{I}$, and a surface distribution of density $\sigma = \mathbf{n}\cdot\mathbf{I}$. The potential U_2 due to these distributions has a definite finite value for points within B; and we define the total magnetic force $\mathbf{H}$ for a point inside B as the vector sum of the intensity $\mathbf{H}_1 = -\nabla U_1$ due to the external bodies, and $\mathbf{H}_2 = -\nabla U_2$ due to the volume distribution ρ and the surface distribution σ. Thus $\mathbf{H} = \mathbf{H}_1 + \mathbf{H}_2$.

Now by Poisson's equation

$$4\pi\rho = -\nabla^2 U_2 = \operatorname{div}\mathbf{H}_2,$$

and by Art. 105

$$0 = -\nabla^2 U_1 = \operatorname{div}\mathbf{H}_1.$$

From these results it follows that

$$\operatorname{div}(\mathbf{H}_1 + \mathbf{H}_2) = 4\pi\rho,$$

or

$$\operatorname{div}\mathbf{H} = -4\pi\operatorname{div}\mathbf{I} \quad . \quad . \quad . \quad (6)$$

The vector

$$\mathbf{B} = \mathbf{H} + 4\pi\mathbf{I} \quad . \quad . \quad . \quad . \quad (7)$$

is called the *magnetic induction*; and the last equation shows that

$$\operatorname{div}\mathbf{B} = 0 \quad . \quad . \quad . \quad . \quad (8)$$

Hence, by the divergence theorem, the integral of the normal induction $\mathbf{n}\cdot\mathbf{B}$ is zero over any closed surface which encloses only induced magnetism.

In the case of an isotropic body magnetised by induction (influence), the intensity of magnetisation $\mathbf{I}$ has the same direction as the magnetic force $\mathbf{H}$, and the quotient $\mathbf{I}/\mathbf{H}$ is called the *susceptibility* of the material, being denoted by k. The magnetic induction is then

$$\mathbf{B} = (1 + 4\pi k)\mathbf{H} = \mu\mathbf{H} \text{ (say)},$$

and has the same direction as $\mathbf{H}$. The quantity

$$\mu = 1 + 4\pi k$$

is called the magnetic *permeability* of the material.

The *boundary conditions* that are satisfied at the surface of separation of two different media of permeabilities μ_1 and μ_2 will be discussed in Art. 114.

111. Magnetic shell. By a "magnetic shell" we understand a shell of infinitesimal thickness, magnetised at each point in the direction of the normal, and in such a way that if $d\mathbf{M}$ is the moment of an element of the shell of area dS, the quotient $d\mathbf{M}/dS$ tends to a definite finite limit $M\mathbf{n}$ as dS tends to zero, $\mathbf{n}$ being the unit normal directed from the negative to the positive face of the shell. The quantity M is called the *strength* or (scalar) moment of the shell at the point considered. The moment of an element of area dS is then

$$d\mathbf{M} = MdS\mathbf{n}.$$

The shell is said to be " uniform " when the strength M is the same for all points.

We may calculate the potential of the field due to a *uniform magnetic shell*, not necessarily closed. Take an element of the shell at Q, distant r from P. The moment of the element is $MdS\mathbf{n}$; and the potential at P due to it is

$$dU = M\mathbf{n}\cdot\nabla_Q\frac{1}{r}dS$$
$$= M\frac{\partial}{\partial n}\left(\frac{1}{r}\right)dS = \frac{M\cos\theta}{r^2}dS$$

where θ is the inclination of QP to $\mathbf{n}$. This may also be written

$$dU = Md\phi$$

where $d\phi$ is the solid angle subtended at P by the element of

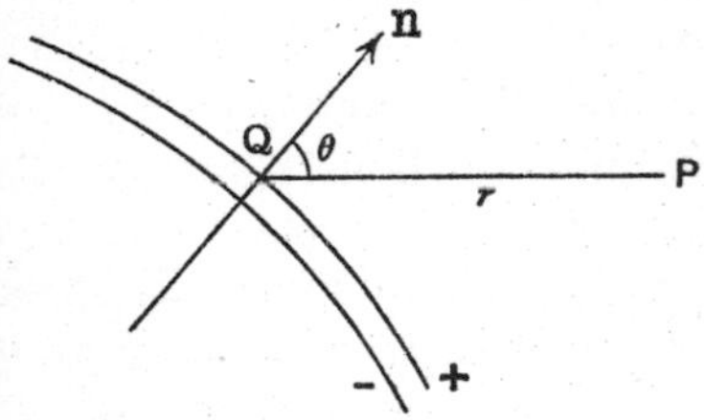

FIG. 31.

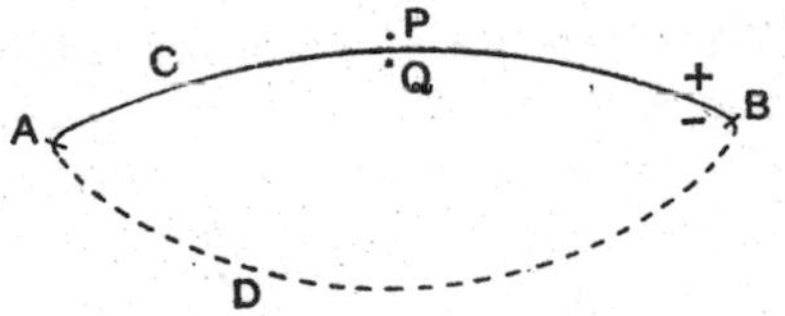

FIG. 32.

the shell, being reckoned positive when θ is acute. Summing for all the elements of the shell, we have for the potential at P due to the whole shell

$$U = M\phi \quad . \quad . \quad . \quad . \quad (9)$$

that is, M times the solid angle subtended at P by the shell. In the case of a closed shell magnetised in the direction of the outward normal, the potential is $-4\pi M$ for points within the shell, and zero for all external points.

If P is a point adjacent to the shell on the positive side, and Q a similar point on the negative side, their distance apart being infinitesimal, the potential at P exceeds that at Q by $4\pi M$. To prove this consider the closed uniform shell consisting of the original part

ACB and another part ADB; so that Q is within the closed shell and on the negative side. If U, U' are the potentials due to the original shell and the part ADB respectively, it follows that

$$U_Q + U_Q' = -4\pi M$$

and

$$U_P + U_P' = 0,$$

since Q is inside, and P outside, the uniform closed shell. But $U_Q' = U_P'$, since P, Q are adjacent points at a finite distance from the part ADB. Hence on subtraction of the above results we have the required relation

$$U_P - U_Q = 4\pi M \quad . \quad . \quad . \quad . \quad (10)$$

Electrostatics.

112. Theory of dielectrics. In Arts. 104 and 105 the medium in which the electric force was considered was assumed to be air. For other insulating media the potential due to given charges has different values. The behaviour of the insulating medium or dielectric is best explained by analogy with magnetic induction in a magnetisable body, along the lines of Poisson's theory of Art. 108. Each particle of the dielectric under electrical influence is assumed to become polarised, the small positive and negative charges on the particle separating slightly from each other, and forming an elementary electric doublet with a definite small electric moment, analogous to the moment of a small magnet. The value $\mathbf{P}$ of the electric moment per unit volume at a point is called the *polarisation* of the medium at that point, and is analogous to the intensity of magnetisation.

The polarisation of the dielectric produces an electric field whose potential V_2 is equal to that due to a volume distribution of charge of density $\rho' = -\operatorname{div} \mathbf{P}$ throughout the dielectric, and a surface distribution of density $\sigma = \mathbf{n} \cdot \mathbf{P}$ over the boundary of the dielectric. The electric force $\mathbf{E}_2$ due to the polarisation is defined for all points as the negative gradient $-\nabla V_2$ of the potential V_2 due to these distributions. In addition, the charges in the field of volume density ρ produce a potential V_1 and an intensity $\mathbf{E}_1 = -\nabla V_1$. The total electric force $\mathbf{E}$ at any point is the vector sum of $\mathbf{E}_1$ and $\mathbf{E}_2$.

Now by Poisson's theorem

$$4\pi\rho' = -\nabla^2 V_2 = \operatorname{div} \mathbf{E}_2$$

and

$$4\pi\rho = -\nabla^2 V_1 = \operatorname{div} \mathbf{E}_1.$$

Hence by addition

$$\text{div}\ (\mathbf{E}_1 + \mathbf{E}_2) = 4\pi\rho + 4\pi\rho',$$

which is equivalent to

$$\text{div}\ (\mathbf{E} + 4\pi\mathbf{P}) = 4\pi\rho.$$

The vector $\mathbf{E} + 4\pi\mathbf{P}$ is called the *electric induction*, and is denoted by $\mathbf{D}$. Thus

$$\text{div}\ \mathbf{D} = 4\pi\rho \quad . \quad . \quad . \quad . \quad (11)$$

If then we take any closed surface S, the divergence theorem shows that

$$\int \mathbf{n}\cdot\mathbf{D}dS = \int \text{div}\ \mathbf{D}dv = 4\pi\int \rho dv \qquad (12)$$

or the total normal induction over the surface is equal to 4π times the total charge enclosed. This is the *theorem of total normal induction.*

If the dielectric is isotropic, $\mathbf{P}$ is parallel to $\mathbf{E}$ and proportional to it. Writing $\mathbf{P}/\mathbf{E} = k$ we have

$$\mathbf{D} = (1 + 4\pi k)\mathbf{E}.$$

The quantity $1 + 4\pi k$ is denoted by K, and is called the *dielectric constant*, or "specific inductive capacity." It is analogous to the permeability μ of Art. 110, but differs from it in that, while μ depends on the value of $\mathbf{H}$ when the latter is not small, K is practically independent of the value of $\mathbf{E}$. Thus, when the dielectric is isotropic,

$$\mathbf{D} = K\mathbf{E} \quad . \quad . \quad . \quad . \quad (13)$$

and the equation (11) may be written

$$\text{div}\ (K\nabla V) = -4\pi\rho \quad . \quad . \quad . \quad (11')$$

113. Coulomb's theorem. We may find the value of the electric intensity $\mathbf{E}$ at a point just off the surface of a charged conductor, by applying the theorem of total normal induction as follows. Take a small closed cylindrical surface, as in Art. 27, enclosing an element of the surface of the conductor of area dS. The plane ends PQ, RS (Fig. 15) of the cylindrical surface are parallel to the tangent plane at the element, one just inside the conductor and the other just outside. The generating lines are normal to the surface of the conductor; so that the area of each of the plane faces is dS, and that of the curved cylindrical part is negligible compared with dS.

If σ is the surface density of the charge on the conductor in the neighbourhood of the element, the charge enclosed by the above surface is σdS. The normal induction over the cylindrical surface is zero, for the double reason that the area of this part is negligible, and the intensity is parallel to this surface, being perpendicular to the equipotential surface of the conductor. Within the material of the conductor the potential is constant, and the intensity is therefore zero over the face PQ. Hence it is only the face RS which contributes anything to the normal induction over the closed surface. If K is the dielectric constant for the medium adjoining the conductor, the theorem of total normal induction gives

$$K\mathbf{E}\cdot\mathbf{n}dS = 4\pi\sigma dS.$$

And, since $\mathbf{E}$ is parallel to $\mathbf{n}$, it follows that

$$\mathbf{E} = \frac{4\pi\sigma}{K}\mathbf{n} \quad . \quad . \quad . \quad . \quad (14)$$

while the induction is

$$\mathbf{D} = 4\pi\sigma\mathbf{n} \quad . \quad . \quad . \quad . \quad (14')$$

This result is due to Coulomb.

114. Boundary conditions. Suppose that, at a certain surface in the field, the value of K possesses a discontinuity, changing abruptly from K_1 on one side to K_2 on the other. Then the induction itself will in general be discontinuous, the following relations holding at the boundary:

i. The normal resolute of the induction has a discontinuity $4\pi\sigma$, where σ is the surface density of the charge (if any) at the surface of discontinuity.
ii. The tangential resolute of the intensity is continuous at the surface.

We may prove the first of these by applying the theorem of total normal induction to the same small cylindrical surface $PQRS$ as in the previous Art., with plane ends PQ, RS in the media K_1, K_2 respectively. The theorem then gives

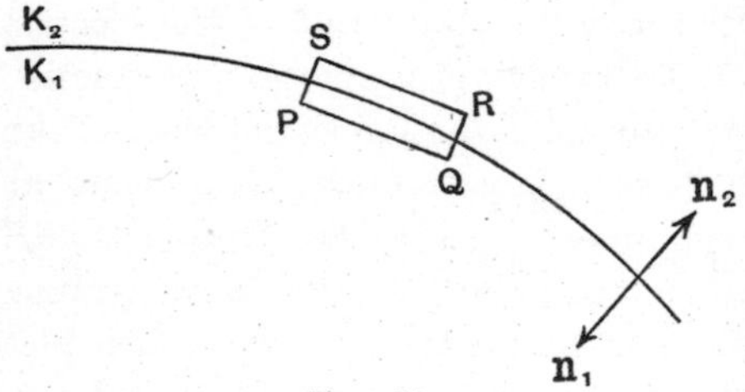

FIG. 33.

$$(\mathbf{D}_1\cdot\mathbf{n}_1 + \mathbf{D}_2\cdot\mathbf{n}_2)dS = 4\pi\sigma dS$$

where $\mathbf{D}_1$, $\mathbf{D}_2$ are the values of the induction on the two sides of the surface, and $\mathbf{n}_1$, $\mathbf{n}_2$ the unit normals directed from the bounding surface in each case. Putting $\mathbf{n} = \mathbf{n}_2 = -\mathbf{n}_1$ we have the required relation

$$\mathbf{D}_2\cdot\mathbf{n} - \mathbf{D}_1\cdot\mathbf{n} = 4\pi\sigma \quad . \quad . \quad . \quad . \quad (15)$$

or

$$(K_2\mathbf{E}_2 - K_1\mathbf{E}_1)\cdot\mathbf{n} = 4\pi\sigma.$$

If, as is usually the case, there is no charge on the surface of discontinuity, the normal induction is continuous there.

The second relation may be proved by considering a rectangular circuit $PQRS$ whose sides PQ, RS of length ds are parallel to the surface, while QR, SP are normal to it, and have lengths of the second order only. From the principle of energy the work done in taking a unit charge round this circuit is zero. Hence if F_1, F_2 are the resolutes of the intensity in the two media in the direction PQ or SR, we have

$$F_1 ds - F_2 ds = 0,$$

and therefore $F_1 = F_2$ as stated.

Similarly it may be shown for the *magnetic field* that at a surface of discontinuity where the permeability changes abruptly from μ_1 to μ_2, the tangential resolute of the magnetic force and the normal resolute of the magnetic induction are continuous.

115. Electrical energy. Let the field be that due to any distribution of charges. The potential energy due to the charges is equal to the work spent in establishing the distribution from an original condition of zero charge everywhere. To find its value imagine that the system is charged by successive small increments, so that at each instant the potentials of all the parts are proportional to their final potentials. In this way the small increment of charge dQ on any portion of the system is to its final charge Q, as the small increment dV in the potential of that portion is to its final potential V. Thus

$$\frac{dQ}{dV} = \frac{Q}{V} = C \text{ (say)}.$$

Hence the work done on the system during the small change is

$$\Sigma V dQ = \Sigma C V dV$$

where the summation refers to all the portions of the system. By integration we have the value of the total work from the condition of zero charge everywhere to the final condition, as

$$\int_0^V \Sigma C V dV = \tfrac{1}{2}\Sigma C V^2 = \tfrac{1}{2}\Sigma Q V$$

where Q is the charge on any portion, and V the final potential of that portion. Thus if the system of charges consists of a space distribution of density ρ, and a surface distribution of density σ, the energy of the system is

$$W = \tfrac{1}{2}\int \sigma V dS + \tfrac{1}{2}\int \rho V dv \quad . \quad . \quad . \quad (16)$$

Let the surface distribution lie on one or more conductors. Consider the region external to these conductors, bounded by their surfaces and a sphere of very large radius R. If $\mathbf{n}$ is the unit normal directed outward from this region, then, by Coulomb's theorem,

$$\sigma = -\frac{K}{4\pi}\mathbf{n}\cdot\mathbf{E} = \frac{K}{4\pi}\mathbf{n}\cdot\nabla V,$$

while, for any point in the region,

$$\rho = -\frac{1}{4\pi}\operatorname{div}(K\nabla V).$$

In the above expression for W the surface integral may be taken over the infinite sphere also ; for at infinity $V\mathbf{n}\cdot\nabla V$ is of the order $1/R^3$, and the area of the sphere of the order R^2. Hence the energy of the system may be expressed

$$W = \frac{1}{8\pi}\int KV\mathbf{n}\cdot\nabla V dS - \frac{1}{8\pi}\int V \operatorname{div}(K\nabla V)dv$$
$$= \frac{1}{8\pi}\int[\operatorname{div}(KV\nabla V) - V\operatorname{div}(K\nabla V)]dv.$$

Expanding the first term of the integrand by (15) of Art. 8 we may write this

$$W = \frac{1}{8\pi}\int\nabla V\cdot(K\nabla V)dv$$
$$= \frac{1}{8\pi}\int\mathbf{E}\cdot\mathbf{D}dv = \frac{1}{8\pi}\int K\mathbf{E}^2 dv \quad . \quad . \quad . \quad (17)$$

For this reason the dielectric is often regarded as the seat of the energy ; and the energy per unit volume is then

$$\frac{1}{8\pi}\mathbf{E}\cdot\mathbf{D} = \frac{1}{8\pi}K\mathbf{E}^2.$$

A similar argument shows that, in the case of the *magnetic field*, the potential energy of the distribution of magnetism is

$$W = \frac{1}{8\pi}\int\nabla U\cdot(\mu\nabla U)dv$$
$$= \frac{1}{8\pi}\int\mathbf{H}\cdot\mathbf{B}dv = \frac{1}{8\pi}\int\mu\mathbf{H}^2 dv \quad . \quad . \quad . \quad (18)$$

and the density of the magnetic energy in the medium is

$$\frac{1}{8\pi}\mathbf{H}\cdot\mathbf{B} = \frac{1}{8\pi}\mu\mathbf{H}^2$$

per unit volume.

Electric Currents.

116. Magnetic field associated with a current. Oersted discovered that a circuit carrying an electric current has associated with it a magnetic field whose intensity is proportional to the strength of the current. To Ampère is due the enunciation of the law from which the magnetic intensity at any point may be determined. This law may be stated: The magnetic field due to the current in a closed circuit is identical with that produced by a certain magnetic shell, whose bounding edge coincides with the position of the circuit, and whose strength is proportional to the current. The direction **n** of magnetisation of the shell is positive relative to the sense in which the current travels round the circuit. The *electromagnetic* (E.M.) *unit of current* is chosen so that the constant of proportion in the above relation is unity when the medium is the ether; that is, so that a current of strength i is equivalent to a magnetic shell of strength i. Then the potential of the magnetic field due to the current is

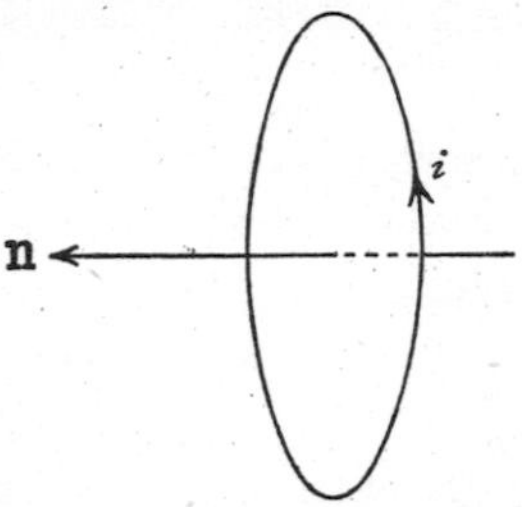

FIG. 34.

$$U = i\phi \quad . \quad . \quad . \quad . \quad . \quad (19)$$

at a point P, at which ϕ is the solid angle subtended by an open surface bounded by the circuit, ϕ being reckoned as positive when the current as viewed from P describes the circuit anti-clockwise.

In a medium other than the ether, the magnetic field due to the current i is equal to that due to a magnetic shell of strength μi, μ being the permeability of the medium. The value of μ for air is practically unity; so that the equivalent shell for air may be taken as of strength i.

The electromagnetic (E.M.) unit of charge is the quantity of electricity conveyed by an E.M. unit current in one second past any point of the circuit. This is very much larger than the electrostatic (E.S.) unit defined in Art. 104. The ratio of the E.M. to the E.S. unit is denoted by c; and experiment shows that its value is approximately 3×10^{10}, a number which also measures the velocity of light in the ether in cm./sec. Also since, in either system, unit current conveys unit charge in unit time past any point of the circuit, c is also the ratio of the E.M. to the E.S. unit of current. Lastly, in each system, unit work (the erg) is done when unit charge is moved against unit electric intensity through unit distance (the cm.). That is to say, the units of electric intensity in the two systems are in the inverse ratio of the units of charge ; so that $\frac{1}{c}$ is the ratio of the E.M. to the E.S. unit of intensity. These relations will be used in the next chapter.

From the above value of the magnetic potential U due to a current flowing round a circuit we may deduce an expression for the magnetic intensity $\mathbf{H}$ in terms of the circuit itself. Inserting the value of the solid angle ϕ subtended at P we have

$$U = i\phi = i\int \mathbf{n}\cdot\nabla_Q \frac{1}{r} dS$$

where dS is the area of an element at Q of the open surface bounded by the circuit, and r is the distance PQ. Hence the magnetic intensity at P is

$$\begin{aligned} \mathbf{H} &= -\nabla_P U = -i\nabla_P \int \mathbf{n}\cdot\nabla_Q \frac{1}{r} dS \\ &= i\int \mathbf{n}\cdot\nabla_Q \nabla_Q \frac{1}{r} dS \quad . \quad . \quad . \quad . \quad . \quad (20) \end{aligned}$$

the dyadic $\nabla\nabla\frac{1}{r}$ being self-conjugate. If now in formula (24) of Chapter VII. we put $\mathbf{V} = \nabla\frac{1}{r}$, so that div $\mathbf{V} = 0$ and $(\nabla\mathbf{V})\cdot\mathbf{n} = \mathbf{n}\cdot\nabla\mathbf{V}$, that formula becomes

$$\int \nabla\left(\frac{1}{r}\right)\times d\mathbf{r} = -\int \mathbf{n}\cdot\nabla\nabla\frac{1}{r} dS$$

where $d\mathbf{r}$ is an element of the circuit whose sense is that of the current in the element. Hence (20) is equivalent to

$$\left.\begin{aligned} \mathbf{H} &= -i\int \nabla_Q\left(\frac{1}{r}\right)\times d\mathbf{r} \\ &= i\int \nabla_P\left(\frac{1}{r}\right)\times d\mathbf{r} \end{aligned}\right\} \quad . \quad . \quad . \quad (21)$$

Q being the variable point and P the fixed pole in the first expression, while in the second Q is the pole and $\nabla_P\frac{1}{r}$ is calculated relative to P as variable point. Thus the magnetic intensity may be calculated as though the element $d\mathbf{r}$ of the circuit at Q contributed to the intensity at P an amount $i\nabla_P\frac{1}{r}\times d\mathbf{r}$, which is perpendicular both to the element and to QP, and is of magnitude $ids \sin\theta/r^2$, ds being the length of $d\mathbf{r}$ and θ its inclination to $\overrightarrow{QP}$.

117. Circuital theorem. *The tangential line integral of the* *magnetic intensity due to a current, taken round any closed path threading the circuit once, is equal to* $4\pi i$.

Let the closed path be $PRQP$. The line integral round this path is equal to that along PRQ if P, Q are adjacent points, because the intensity in the neighbourhood of these points is finite. Now replace the electric current by an equivalent magnetic shell, chosen so as to pass between Q and P. In this way the path PRQ is right outside the material of the shell; and the line integral of the intensity along it is equal to the fall of potential in passing from P to Q. But, since these are adjacent points on opposite sides of the shell, this difference of potential is equal to $4\pi i$ by (18). Hence the theorem.

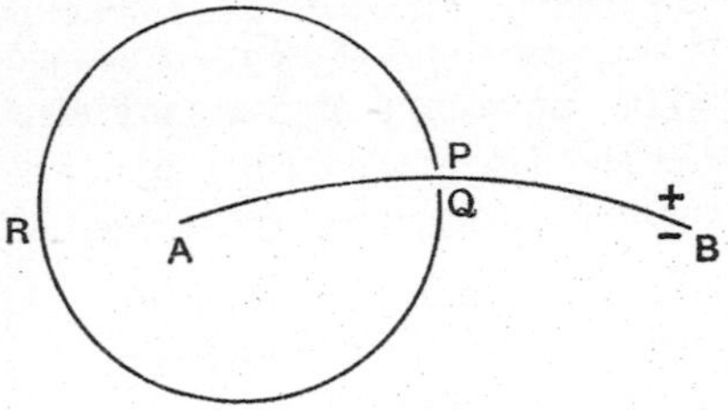

FIG. 35.

If the closed path does not thread the circuit, it does not cut the magnetic shell. In this case there is no fall of potential from P to Q, and the line integral of the intensity is zero.

Cor. The work done in taking a unit positive pole round the closed path QRP embracing the current once is equal to $4\pi i$. If the path QRP is threaded by the current circuit n times in the same direction, the work done is $4\pi ni$.

118. Potential energy of a current. Mutual inductance. The magnetic potential at a point P due to the current i in the circuit is $U = i\phi$. If a pole of strength m be placed at P, the potential energy of the system is mU or $mi\phi$. Further, the normal surface integral of the intensity due to this pole, over an open surface S bounded by the circuit, is

$$N = -\int \mathbf{n}\cdot\nabla_Q\left(\frac{m}{r}\right)dS = -m\int \mathbf{n}\cdot\nabla_Q\frac{1}{r}dS$$
$$= -m\phi.$$

This integral of the normal intensity over S is called the *magnetic flux* through the circuit, or sometimes the "number of lines of force threading the circuit." Thus if N is the magnetic flux through the circuit due to the pole, the potential energy of the system is $-Ni$. For any number of poles the magnetic flux through the circuit is the sum of those due to the separate poles; so that the potential energy of a system consisting of a current and any distribution of poles is equal to $-i$ times the total magnetic flux through the circuit.

Suppose there are two circuits A, B in the neighbourhood of each other. Let M be the magnetic flux through B due to a unit current in A. Then if i, i' are the currents in the two circuits, Mi is the flux through B due to the current in A, and the potential energy of the current i' due to the proximity of A is $-Mii'$. As this must depend symmetrically on the two circuits, it follows that M is also the magnetic flux through A due to a unit current in B. The quantity M is called the *mutual inductance* of the two circuits.

119. Equations of a steady electromagnetic field. Suppose now that the flow of electricity is not confined to one or more wires, but is distributed generally throughout the medium, which must therefore be a conducting medium. At any point P let $\hat{\mathbf{a}}$ be the unit vector in the direction of the flow, and let dq be the excess of the positive electricity over the negative that flows per second across an elementary surface through P of area dS and perpendicular to $\hat{\mathbf{a}}$. Then if f is the limiting value of dq/dS as dS tends to zero, the vector $f\hat{\mathbf{a}}$ defines the *current density* at P. We denote it by $\mathbf{j}$. It is the rate of flow of the electricity per unit area across a surface at P perpendicular to the direction of flow. The current across any surface drawn in the medium is

$$i = \int \mathbf{n}\cdot\mathbf{j}\,dS.$$

Now by Art. 117 the tangential line integral of the magnetic intensity round any closed path drawn in the medium is equal to 4π times the sum of the currents enclosed by the path. The sum of these currents is equal to the rate of flow of the electricity across an open surface bounded by the path. Hence

$$\int_0 \mathbf{H}\cdot d\mathbf{r} = 4\pi \int \mathbf{n}\cdot\mathbf{j}\,dS,$$

which, by Stokes's theorem, may be written

$$\int \mathbf{n}\cdot \operatorname{curl} \mathbf{H}\,dS = \int 4\pi\mathbf{n}\cdot\mathbf{j}\,dS.$$

And since this is true for any surface, we must have identically

$$\operatorname{curl} \mathbf{H} = 4\pi\mathbf{j} \quad . \quad . \quad . \quad . \quad (22)$$

from which it also follows that

$$\operatorname{div} \mathbf{j} = 0 \quad . \quad . \quad . \quad . \quad (23)$$

On the assumption that the medium is not magnetised, it follows from (6) that

$$\operatorname{div} \mathbf{H} = -4\pi \operatorname{div} \mathbf{I} = 0.$$

We may then, by Art. 26, express the solenoidal vector **H** as

$$\mathbf{H} = \frac{1}{4\pi}\operatorname{curl}\int\frac{\operatorname{curl}\mathbf{H}}{r}dv$$

or

$$\mathbf{H} = \operatorname{curl}\mathbf{A} \quad . \quad . \quad . \quad . \quad . \quad (24)$$

where the vector **A** has the value

$$\mathbf{A} = \frac{1}{4\pi}\int\frac{\operatorname{curl}\mathbf{H}}{r}dv = \int\frac{\mathbf{j}}{r}dv \quad . \quad . \quad . \quad (25)$$

and is called the *vector potential* of the magnetic force. If the current density **j** is zero, both **A** and **H** vanish identically as we require.

120. Field due to a linear current (*otherwise*). As an illustration of these results, we may show that the intensity of the magnetic field due to a linear current, calculated from the preceding Art., has the value already found in Art. 116.

Let A be the area of the cross-section of the circuit, **t** the unit tangent in the direction of the current, and i the strength of the current. Then on the circuit the current density is $\mathbf{j} = \mathbf{t}i/A$, but is zero elsewhere. The volume of an element of the circuit of length ds is Ads. Hence the vector potential of the magnetic force is

$$\mathbf{A} = \int\frac{\mathbf{j}}{r}dv = \int\frac{\mathbf{t}i}{A}\,\frac{Ads}{r} = i\int\frac{\mathbf{t}}{r}ds,$$

giving for the value of the magnetic intensity at P

$$\mathbf{H} = \operatorname{curl}\mathbf{A} = i\operatorname{curl}\int\frac{\mathbf{t}}{r}ds.$$

Using (16) of Art. 8, and remembering that **t** is not a function of the point P where the intensity **H** is considered, we find

$$\mathbf{H} = i\int\nabla_P\left(\frac{1}{r}\right)\times\mathbf{t}ds = i\int\nabla_P\left(\frac{1}{r}\right)\times d\mathbf{r},$$

which is the value already found in Art. 116 by a different method.

121. Neumann's formula for mutual inductance. Let A, B be two circuits in the neighbourhood of each other. The intensity of the magnetic field due to a unit current in A is

$$\mathbf{H} = \operatorname{curl}\mathbf{A}$$

where, by the preceding Art.,

$$\mathbf{A} = \int_A\frac{\mathbf{t}}{r}ds = \int_A\frac{1}{r}d\mathbf{r}$$

where the suffix A to the integral sign denotes integration round the closed circuit A, ds being the length of an element of that circuit, and r its distance from the point P where the intensity is considered. The mutual inductance of the two circuits is the magnetic flux through B due to unit current in A. If dS' is the area of an element of an open surface bounded by B, this flux has the value

$$M = \int \mathbf{n}\cdot\mathbf{H}dS' = \int \mathbf{n}\cdot \operatorname{curl} \mathbf{A}dS'$$

$$= \int_B \mathbf{A}\cdot d\mathbf{r}'$$

where $d\mathbf{r}'$ is the vector determined by an element of B (fig. 36). Introducing the above value of A, we have finally

$$M = \int_B\int_A \frac{1}{r}d\mathbf{r}\cdot d\mathbf{r}' \quad . \quad . \quad . \quad . \quad (26)$$

the integration being taken round both circuits. If θ is the inclination of the elementary vectors $d\mathbf{r}$ and $d\mathbf{r}'$, this is equivalent to

$$M = \int_B\int_A \frac{\cos\theta}{r}dsds' \quad . \quad . \quad . \quad . \quad (26')$$

which is Neumann's formula for the mutual inductance of the two circuits.

122. Action of a magnetic field on a circuit carrying a current. We have seen that the magnetic field due to a current may be calculated on the assumption that an element $d\mathbf{r}$ of the circuit at Q produces at P a magnetic intensity $i\nabla_P\left(\frac{1}{r}\right)\times d\mathbf{r}$, where r is the distance QP. A unit pole at P would then be acted on by this force; and we should therefore expect that the unit pole would act on the element of circuit with an equal and opposite force. Such a force would be $i\nabla_Q\left(\frac{1}{r}\right)\times d\mathbf{r}$. But $\nabla_Q\frac{1}{r} = -\mathbf{H}$, where $\mathbf{H}$ is the magnetic intensity at Q due to the pole at P. Thus the element of circuit in the magnetic field $\mathbf{H}$ due to the pole would be acted on by a force $id\mathbf{r}\times\mathbf{H}$. That this is true generally, whatever the cause of the magnetic field, may be verified as follows.

Let the element of circuit at Q be displaced by a small amount $d\mathbf{s}$ without rotation. The consequent increase in the vector area of an open surface bounded by the circuit is $d\mathbf{s}\times d\mathbf{r}$, and the increment in the magnetic flux through the circuit is

$$\mathbf{H}\cdot d\mathbf{s}\times d\mathbf{r} = d\mathbf{r}\times\mathbf{H}\cdot d\mathbf{s}.$$

Hence, by Art. 118, the consequent decrease in the potential energy of the current in the magnetic field is

$$id\mathbf{r}\times\mathbf{H}\cdot d\mathbf{s}.$$

This must be equal to the work done during the displacement $d\mathbf{s}$ by the force acting on the element $d\mathbf{r}$ of the circuit ; showing that the value of this force is $id\mathbf{r}\times\mathbf{H}$, as stated above.

123. Mutual action of two circuits. Consider the two circuits A and B of Art. 121. The magnetic intensity due to the current in A is

$$\mathbf{H} = i\int\nabla\left(\frac{1}{r}\right)\times\mathbf{t}ds$$

where $\mathbf{t}$ is the unit tangent at the element ds. Hence the force on an element $d\mathbf{r}' \equiv \mathbf{t}'ds'$ of B, carrying a current i', is

$$i'\mathbf{t}'\times\mathbf{H}ds' = ii'\mathbf{t}'\times\int\nabla\left(\frac{1}{r}\right)\times\mathbf{t}dsds'.$$

With any convenient point O as origin, let $\mathbf{r}'$ be the position vector of the element ds' of B. Then the forces on the different elements of B are equivalent to a rigid body resultant

$$\mathbf{F} = ii'\int_B\int_A \mathbf{t}'\times\left(\nabla\frac{1}{r}\times\mathbf{t}\right)dsds' \qquad (27)$$

acting through O, together with a torque

$$\mathbf{L} = ii'\int_B\int_A \mathbf{r}'\times[\mathbf{t}'\times(\nabla\frac{1}{r}\times\mathbf{t})]dsds' \qquad (28)$$

The integrand for the resultant force $\mathbf{F}$ may be written

$$\mathbf{t}'\cdot\mathbf{t}\,\nabla\frac{1}{r} - \mathbf{t}'\cdot\nabla\frac{1}{r}\,\mathbf{t} = \mathbf{t}'\cdot\mathbf{t}\,\nabla\frac{1}{r} - \frac{\partial}{\partial s'}\left(\frac{1}{r}\right)\mathbf{t}.$$

When this is integrated round the circuit B, $\mathbf{t}$ is a constant vector,

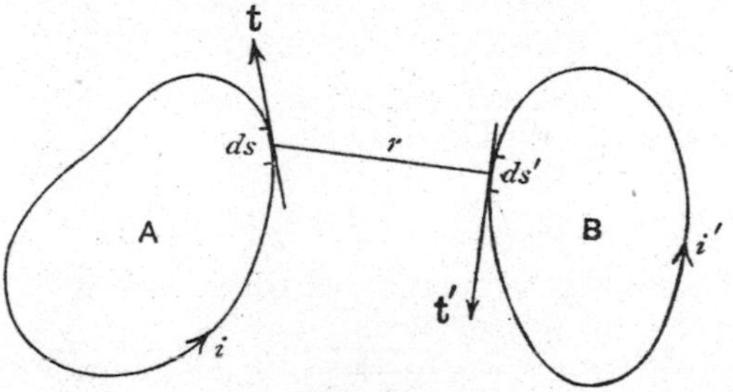

FIG. 36.

and the second term vanishes because $\frac{1}{r}$ is single-valued. Hence the vector sum of the forces on the circuit B is

$$\mathbf{F} = ii'\int_B\int_A \nabla\frac{1}{r}\,\mathbf{t}'\cdot\mathbf{t}dsds'$$

$$= ii'\iint\cos\epsilon\nabla\frac{1}{r}dsds' \qquad (27')$$

which may be looked upon as due to a force of attraction $ii' \cos \epsilon\, ds ds'/r^2$ between two elements of the circuits, of lengths ds and ds', and mutual inclination ϵ.

EXERCISES ON CHAPTER IX.

1. Show that the potential at P due to a uniformly magnetised body is

$$\int \text{div}\ \frac{\mathbf{I}}{r} dv = \mathbf{I}\cdot\int \nabla \frac{1}{r} dv$$

where r is the distance from P as pole to the element dv.

Hence prove that the potential due to a uniformly magnetised solid sphere of volume V is the same as that due to a short magnet at its centre, whose moment is $V\mathbf{I}$.

2. Find the mutual potential energy of two magnetic bodies.

If U is the potential due to the first, and $\mathbf{I}'$ the intensity of magnetisation of the second, their mutual potential energy is

$$\int \mathbf{I}'\cdot\nabla U dv' = \int [\text{div}\ U\mathbf{I}' - U\ \text{div}\ \mathbf{I}'] dv'$$

$$= \int U\mathbf{n}'\cdot\mathbf{I}' dS' - \int U\ \text{div}\ \mathbf{I}' dv',$$

the accented symbols referring to the second body.

3. The mutual potential energy of two magnetic shells of strengths M, M' is

$$-MM'\iint \frac{\mathbf{t}\cdot\mathbf{t}'}{r} ds ds' = -MM'\iint \frac{\cos\theta}{r} ds ds'$$

where the integrations are to be taken round the two rims.

4. The mutual potential energy of two magnetic molecules of (scalar) moments M, M' is

$$\frac{MM'}{r^3}(\cos\epsilon - 3\cos\theta\cos\theta')$$

where ϵ is the mutual inclination of their axes, and θ, θ' those of their axes to the line joining them.

Also show that the invariant $\mathbf{F}\cdot\mathbf{L}$ of the force and torque on either magnet (Art. 107) is equal to

$$3\left(\frac{MM'}{r^4}\right)^2(\cos\epsilon - 2\cos\theta\cos\theta')p\sin\epsilon$$

where p is the shortest distance between the axes.

Hence the torque on either magnet vanishes if

$$\cos\epsilon = 2\cos\theta\cos\theta'.$$

5. Show that the vector potential $\mathbf{A}$ (such that $\mathbf{H} = \text{curl}\ \mathbf{A}$) has the following values:

i. In the field due to a magnetic molecule of moment **M**,

$$\mathbf{A} = \nabla\frac{1}{r}\times\mathbf{M}.$$

ii. In the field due to a long straight current i parallel to $\hat{\mathbf{a}}$,

$$\mathbf{A} = -2i\log r\,\hat{\mathbf{a}}$$

where r is the perpendicular distance from the wire.

iii. For a uniform field of intensity $H\mathbf{k}$,

$$\mathbf{A} = \tfrac{1}{2}H(x\mathbf{j} - y\mathbf{i}).$$

iv. In the field due to a body whose intensity of magnetisation is **I**,

$$\mathbf{A} = \int\nabla\frac{1}{r}\times\mathbf{I}dv.$$

If **I** is uniform,

$$\mathbf{A} = -\mathbf{I}\times\int\nabla\frac{1}{r}dv = -\mathbf{I}\times\nabla U$$

where U is the gravitational potential due to a body of the same boundary and unit density.

6. If the law of force is the inverse k^{th} power of the distance, prove that the potential due to a short magnet of moment **M** is

$$U = -\frac{1}{k-1}\mathbf{M}\cdot\nabla\left(\frac{1}{r^{k-1}}\right),$$

and that the mutual potential energy of the two magnetic molecules of Exercise 4 is

$$\frac{MM'}{r^{k+1}}\left[\cos\epsilon - (k+1)\cos\theta\cos\theta'\right].$$

7. Find the mutual action between two magnetic molecules when the law of force between two poles is the inverse k^{th} power of the distance (*cf.* Art. 107).

8. If U is the potential of the earth's magnetic field and F the vertical component of the magnetic force at the Earth's surface, show that the field in outside space may be considered as due to a surface distribution of density

$$-\frac{F}{2\pi} - \frac{U}{4\pi a}$$

where a is the earth's radius. (St John's Coll.)

9. Find the magnetic intensity at a point in the plane $x = 0$ due to two magnetic molecules of equal moment $M\mathbf{k}$ at the points $\pm a\mathbf{i}$.

10. Determine the magnetic intensity due to a long straight steady current.

Hence find the force and the torque on a magnetic molecule in the neighbourhood of the current.

11. A direct current and the return current flow in long parallel wires. Show that the lines of magnetic force due to them are all circles. (St John's Coll.)

12. Regarding the earth as a uniformly and rigidly magnetised sphere of radius a, and denoting the intensity of the magnetic field on the equator by H, show that a wire surrounding the earth along the parallel of south latitude λ, and carrying a current i from west to east, would experience a resultant force towards the south pole of the heavens, equal to

$$6\pi aiH \sin \lambda \cos^2 \lambda.$$

13. Show that the magnetic intensity inside a long straight solenoid with n turns per unit length, carrying a current i, is $4\pi ni$ parallel to the axis of the solenoid.

14. Show that the mutual action of two circuits (Art. 123) may be calculated as though two elements ds, ds' of the circuits attracted each other with a force

$$ii'\frac{dsds'}{r^2}(2 \cos \epsilon - 3 \cos \theta \cos \theta')$$

where ϵ is their mutual inclination, and θ, θ' their inclinations to the line joining them. This is *Ampère's rule.*

15. Express the equation

$$\text{div}\,(K\nabla V) = -4\pi\rho$$

in i, general curvilinear coordinates; ii, spherical polar coordinates; iii, cylindrical coordinates.

CHAPTER X.

THE EQUATIONS OF MAXWELL AND LORENTZ. THE LORENTZ-EINSTEIN TRANSFORMATION.

I. The Electromagnetic Equations.

124. The total current. The current density $\mathbf{j}$ was defined in Art. 119 as the vector rate of flow of electricity per unit area across a surface perpendicular to the direction of flow. If ρ is the volume density of the electricity at a point P, and $\mathbf{v}$ the velocity of the charge there, the current density at P is given by

$$\mathbf{j} = \rho\mathbf{v}.$$

Or, more generally, on the assumption of several currents through the same point, of volume densities ρ_1, ρ_2, . . . and velocities $\mathbf{v}_1$, $\mathbf{v}_2$, . . ., the current density at P is

$$\mathbf{j} = \Sigma\rho\mathbf{v},$$

in which ρ is negative for currents of negative electricity. The total density of the electricity at P is then $\Sigma\rho$. We shall argue in terms of only a single current at each point; but to satisfy the more general assumption we have only to replace ρ in the following by $\Sigma\rho$, and $\rho\mathbf{v}$ by $\Sigma\rho\mathbf{v}$.

The fundamental electromagnetic laws, as proved by experiment, refer to closed circuits, and otherwise have no meaning. We follow Maxwell's line of reasoning, assuming that the laws are also applicable to open circuits, or making all circuits closed by counting as a current something which is not actually a flow of electricity. In Art. 119 we arrived at the equation

$$\text{curl } \mathbf{H} = 4\pi\mathbf{j} \quad . \quad . \quad . \quad . \quad \text{i}$$

on the assumption of a steady field This requires div $\mathbf{j} = 0$; and if $\mathbf{j}$ has the value $\rho\mathbf{v}$ with which we started, the equation div $(\rho\mathbf{v}) = 0$ is inconsistent with the equation of continuity (Art. 35)

$$\frac{\partial\rho}{\partial t} + \text{div } (\rho\mathbf{v}) = 0,$$

which is as true of electricity as of a material fluid.

To overcome this difficulty we assume that the theorem of total normal induction is true, not only for electrostatics, but universally. As shown in Art. 112, this theorem is equivalent to

$$\operatorname{div} \mathbf{D} = 4\pi\rho \quad . \quad . \quad . \quad . \quad \text{ii}$$

in virtue of which the equation of continuity becomes

$$\operatorname{div}\left(\frac{1}{4\pi}\frac{\partial \mathbf{D}}{\partial t} + \rho\mathbf{v}\right) = 0.$$

Hence the equation i may be taken to hold without affecting the laws for steady currents, if we give $\mathbf{j}$ the value $\left(\frac{1}{4\pi}\frac{\partial \mathbf{D}}{\partial t} + \rho\mathbf{v}\right)$ in electrostatic (E.S.) units; or in electromagnetic (E.M.) units

$$\mathbf{j} = \frac{1}{c}\left(\frac{1}{4\pi}\frac{\partial \mathbf{D}}{\partial t} + \rho\mathbf{v}\right) \quad . \quad . \quad . \quad . \quad \text{iii}$$

c being the ratio of the E.M. to the E.S. unit of charge as defined in Art. 116. The second term of this expression gives the actual rate of flow of electricity. The first term, involving the rate of change of the electric induction, is what Maxwell called the *displacement current*. It is also termed the *ether-current-density*.

125. The electromagnetic equations. Faraday's researches proved that when the flux of magnetic induction through a circuit is changing, there is an induced E.M.F. round the circuit, whose measure in E.M. units is equal to the rate of decrease of the flux. If $\mathbf{E}$ is the value of the electric intensity in E.S. units, $c\mathbf{E}$ is its value in E.M. units, since, by Art. 116, the E.M. unit of intensity is only $\frac{1}{c}$ times the E.S. unit. Hence since the E.M.F. round a circuit is the tangential line integral of the intensity, the above law of electromagnetic induction shows that

$$-\frac{\partial}{\partial t}\int \mathbf{n}\cdot\mathbf{B}\,dS = \int_0 c\mathbf{E}\cdot d\mathbf{r},$$

dS being the area of an element of an open surface bounded by the closed circuit. We assume, with Maxwell, that this relation is true for every closed circuit drawn in the field. In virtue of Stokes's theorem we may write it

$$-\int \mathbf{n}\cdot\frac{\partial \mathbf{B}}{\partial t}dS = \int c\mathbf{n}\cdot \operatorname{curl} \mathbf{E}\,dS,$$

and since this is true for every surface, we must have identically

$$\operatorname{curl} \mathbf{E} = -\frac{1}{c}\frac{\partial \mathbf{B}}{\partial t} \quad . \quad . \quad . \quad . \quad \text{iv}$$

Lastly, the magnetic induction was shown in Art. 110 to satisfy the equation div $\mathbf{B} = 0$. Hence, collecting the results of this Art. and the preceding, we may combine them in the system of equations

$$\text{curl } \mathbf{H} = \frac{1}{c}\left(\frac{\partial \mathbf{D}}{\partial t} + 4\pi\rho\mathbf{v}\right) \quad . \quad . \quad . \quad (1)$$

$$\text{curl } \mathbf{E} = -\frac{1}{c}\frac{\partial \mathbf{B}}{\partial t} \quad . \quad . \quad . \quad . \quad (2)$$

$$\text{div } \mathbf{D} = 4\pi\rho \quad . \quad . \quad . \quad . \quad . \quad (3)$$

$$\text{div } \mathbf{B} = 0 \; . \quad . \quad . \quad . \quad . \quad . \quad (4)$$

When the medium is non-magnetic the last equation is simply

$$\text{div } \mathbf{H} = 0 \quad . \quad . \quad . \quad . \quad (4')$$

The general form of the equations (1)–(4) is due to *Lorentz*. In the case of free ether $\rho = 0$, $\mathbf{B} = \mathbf{H}$, $\mathbf{D} = \mathbf{E}$, and the relations then become

$$\text{curl } \mathbf{H} = \frac{1}{c}\frac{\partial \mathbf{E}}{\partial t} \quad . \quad . \quad . \quad . \quad (5)$$

$$\text{curl } \mathbf{E} = -\frac{1}{c}\frac{\partial \mathbf{H}}{\partial t} \; . \quad . \quad . \quad . \quad (6)$$

$$\text{div } \mathbf{E} = 0 \; . \quad . \quad . \quad . \quad . \quad (7)$$

$$\text{div } \mathbf{H} = 0 \; . \quad . \quad . \quad . \quad . \quad (8)$$

These equations were first obtained by *Maxwell*, and are called after him.

From Maxwell's equations it follows that, in free ether,

$$\frac{1}{c^2}\frac{\partial^2 \mathbf{E}}{\partial t^2} = \frac{1}{c}\text{ curl }\frac{\partial \mathbf{H}}{\partial t} = -\text{ curl curl } \mathbf{E}$$
$$= \nabla^2\mathbf{E} - \nabla\nabla\cdot\mathbf{E}.$$

The last term is zero by (7), and we have

$$\nabla^2\mathbf{E} = \frac{1}{c^2}\frac{\partial^2 \mathbf{E}}{\partial t^2}.$$

Similarly we may show that

$$\nabla^2\mathbf{H} = \frac{1}{c^2}\frac{\partial^2 \mathbf{H}}{\partial t^2}.$$

Thus both **E** and **H** satisfy the differential equation of wave-propagation with velocity c; or, electromagnetic actions are propagated through the ether with a velocity 3×10^{10} cm./sec. Experiment shows that this is also the velocity of light in free space, thus giving considerable weight to the theory that light consists of electromagnetic vibrations. In the case of any non-magnetic dielectric we deduce in the same way from Lorentz's equations, putting $\mathbf{D} = K\mathbf{E}$ and $\rho = 0$, that both **E** and **H** satisfy the differential equation

$$\nabla^2\mathbf{F} = \frac{K}{c^2}\frac{\partial^2 \mathbf{F}}{\partial t^2},$$

showing that the velocity of propagation in general is $c/\sqrt{K}$.

Finally, we need to add to the above equations one giving the value of the *force per unit charge* acting on the electricity at any point. This will be due partly to the electric intensity $\mathbf{E}$ and partly to the motion of the charge. For the latter component we generalise the result of Art. 122, giving the value of the force on an element of a circuit carrying a current. The element ds of the circuit is acted on by a force $i\mathbf{t}\times\mathbf{H}ds$, where $\mathbf{t}$ is the unit tangent to the path. If v is the speed of the current through the element, the charge on the element is ids/v E.M. units, and therefore the force per E.M. unit charge at that point of the circuit is $v\mathbf{t}\times\mathbf{H}=\mathbf{v}\times\mathbf{H}$, where $\mathbf{v}=v\mathbf{t}$ is the velocity of the charge at the point. Assuming that the result is universally true, we have the force $\frac{1}{c}\mathbf{v}\times\mathbf{H}$ per E.S. unit of charge due to the motion of the electricity. Combining with this the force $\mathbf{E}$ per unit charge due to the electric intensity, we have

$$\mathbf{F}=\mathbf{E}+\frac{1}{c}\mathbf{v}\times\mathbf{H} \quad . \quad . \quad . \quad . \quad . \quad (9)$$

for the total force per E.S. unit of charge acting on the electricity in the neighbourhood of the point considered. This force $\mathbf{F}$ is sometimes called the *electric force* at that point.

The above result has been arrived at on the assumption of air (or the ether) as dielectric. In a medium of permeability μ, the field due to a current i is equivalent to that due to a magnetic shell of strength μi (Art. 116), and the force on the element ds of the circuit is $\mu i\mathbf{t}\times\mathbf{H}ds$. This leads to the component force $\frac{\mu}{c}\mathbf{v}\times\mathbf{H}=\frac{1}{c}\mathbf{v}\times\mathbf{B}$ per E.S. unit charge, due to the velocity of the charge; and the total force per unit charge is then

$$\mathbf{F}=\mathbf{E}+\frac{1}{c}\mathbf{v}\times\mathbf{B} \quad . \quad . \quad . \quad . \quad . \quad (9')$$

126. The electromagnetic potentials. The determination of the values of $\mathbf{E}$ and $\mathbf{H}$, when those of ρ and $\mathbf{v}$ are known as functions of position and time, is most easily effected by means of certain auxiliary functions of the nature of potentials. We shall assume the ether as medium, so that Lorentz's equations take the simple form

$$\operatorname{curl}\mathbf{H}=\frac{1}{c}\left(\frac{\partial\mathbf{E}}{\partial t}+4\pi\rho\mathbf{v}\right) \quad . \quad . \quad . \quad (10)$$

$$\operatorname{curl}\mathbf{E}=-\frac{1}{c}\frac{\partial\mathbf{H}}{\partial t} \quad . \quad . \quad . \quad . \quad . \quad (11)$$

$$\operatorname{div}\mathbf{E}=4\pi\rho \quad . \quad . \quad . \quad . \quad . \quad (12)$$

$$\operatorname{div}\mathbf{H}=0 \quad . \quad . \quad . \quad . \quad . \quad . \quad (13)$$

As in Art. 119, we may satisfy the last equation by putting

$$\mathbf{H} = \text{curl } \mathbf{A} \quad . \quad . \quad . \quad . \quad (14)$$

and substitution of this value in (11) shows that.

$$\text{curl}\left(\mathbf{E} + \frac{1}{c}\frac{\partial \mathbf{A}}{\partial t}\right) = 0.$$

The vector in brackets is therefore the gradient of some scalar function $-\phi$; or

$$\mathbf{E} = -\left(\nabla\phi + \frac{1}{c}\frac{\partial \mathbf{A}}{\partial t}\right). \quad . \quad . \quad . \quad . \quad (15)$$

The function ϕ is called the *electromagnetic scalar potential*, and **A** the *electromagnetic vector potential.* Substituting in (10) the values of **H** and **E** given by (14) and (15), we find

$$\left(\nabla^2\mathbf{A} - \frac{1}{c^2}\frac{\partial^2 \mathbf{A}}{\partial t^2}\right) - \nabla\left(\nabla\cdot\mathbf{A} + \frac{1}{c}\frac{\partial \phi}{\partial t}\right) = -\frac{4\pi}{c}\rho\mathbf{v}.$$

Similarly the same values of **E** and **H** substituted in (12) give a result which may be written

$$\left(\nabla^2\phi - \frac{1}{c^2}\frac{\partial^2 \phi}{\partial t^2}\right) + \frac{1}{c}\frac{\partial}{\partial t}\left(\nabla\cdot\mathbf{A} + \frac{1}{c}\frac{\partial \phi}{\partial t}\right) = -4\pi\rho.$$

It will be shown that we may impose upon the electromagnetic potentials the further condition

$$\nabla\cdot\mathbf{A} + \frac{1}{c}\frac{\partial \phi}{\partial t} = 0 \quad . \quad . \quad . \quad . \quad . \quad (16)$$

Then the last two equations become

$$\left(\nabla^2 - \frac{1}{c^2}\frac{\partial^2}{\partial t^2}\right)\mathbf{A} = -\frac{4\pi}{c}\rho\mathbf{v} \quad . \quad . \quad . \quad (17)$$

$$\left(\nabla^2 - \frac{1}{c^2}\frac{\partial^2}{\partial t^2}\right)\phi = -4\pi\rho \quad . \quad . \quad . \quad (18)$$

These equations are more general than Poisson's, but of a somewhat similar form. Instead of the *Laplacian* ∇^2 we have the *Dalembertian* $\Box^2 \equiv \nabla^2 - \frac{1}{c^2}\frac{\partial^2}{\partial t^2}$; and the functions in (17) and (18) are functions of both position and time. We may express this using $\phi(P, t)$ to denote the value of ϕ at the point P for the instant t. Solutions of (17) and (18) exist, analogous to the solution of Poisson's equation considered in Art. 25. Thus if dv is the volume of an element of space at the point Q, and r the distance from Q to P, the solution of (18) under consideration is given by *

$$\phi(P, t) = \int \frac{\rho\left(Q, t - \frac{r}{c}\right)}{r} dv$$

* See Exercises 1, 2 at the end of this chapter.

where the integration is extended throughout the whole of space. For the sake of brevity we shall use square brackets to indicate that the value of the function is to be taken not at the instant t, but for the previous instant $t-\frac{r}{c}$. Then the above solution of (18) is

$$\phi=\int\frac{[\rho]}{r}dv \quad . \quad . \quad . \quad . \quad . \quad (19)$$

and the corresponding solution of (17) is

$$\mathbf{A}=\frac{1}{c}\int\frac{[\rho\mathbf{v}]}{r}dv \quad . \quad . \quad . \quad . \quad . \quad (20)$$

Functions of this nature are called *retarded potentials*, or sometimes *propagated potentials*. The value of ϕ at P at the instant t depends upon the value of ρ at Q, not at this instant, but at the previous instant $t-\frac{r}{c}$. We may express this roughly by saying that the retarded potentials above are propagated with a velocity c, equal to that of light.

Having thus found the functions ϕ and $\mathbf{A}$, the values of $\mathbf{H}$ and $\mathbf{E}$ are given by (14) and (15). And, further, the relation (16) is satisfied by the above values of ϕ and $\mathbf{A}$. For

$$\nabla\cdot\mathbf{A}=\frac{1}{c}\int\frac{1}{r}[\text{div }\rho\mathbf{v}]dv$$

and

$$\frac{\partial\phi}{\partial t}=\int\frac{1}{r}\left[\frac{\partial\rho}{\partial t}\right]dv,$$

so that

$$\nabla\cdot\mathbf{A}+\frac{1}{c}\frac{\partial\phi}{\partial t}=\frac{1}{c}\int\frac{1}{r}\left[\frac{\partial\rho}{\partial t}+\text{div }\rho\mathbf{v}\right]dv,$$

and the integrand vanishes identically in virtue of the equation of continuity.

127. Radiant vector. Consider the region bounded by a closed surface S. By Art. 115 the values of the electric and magnetic energies within S are

$$\frac{1}{8\pi}\int\mathbf{E}\cdot\mathbf{D}dv, \quad \frac{1}{8\pi}\int\mathbf{H}\cdot\mathbf{B}dv$$

respectively. Hence the rate of increase of the sum of these is

$$\frac{1}{8\pi}\int\frac{\partial}{\partial t}(\mathbf{E}\cdot\mathbf{D}+\mathbf{H}\cdot\mathbf{B})dv.$$

Further, the force $\mathbf{F}$ per unit charge acting on the electricity within S is given by (9′). The rate at which energy is increasing owing to this is

$$\int\rho\left(\mathbf{E}+\frac{1}{c}\mathbf{v}\times\mathbf{B}\right)\cdot\mathbf{v}dv=\int\rho\mathbf{E}\cdot\mathbf{v}dv.$$

Hence the total rate of increase of the energy within S due to all these causes is

$$\frac{1}{4\pi}\int\left[\tfrac{1}{2}\frac{\partial}{\partial t}(\mathbf{E}\cdot\mathbf{D}+\mathbf{H}\cdot\mathbf{B})+4\pi\rho\mathbf{E}\cdot\mathbf{v}\right]dv$$

$$=\frac{1}{4\pi}\int\left[\mathbf{E}\cdot\left(\frac{\partial\mathbf{D}}{\partial t}+4\pi\rho\mathbf{v}\right)+\mathbf{H}\cdot\frac{\partial\mathbf{B}}{\partial t}\right]dv$$

$$=\frac{c}{4\pi}\int(\mathbf{E}\cdot\text{ curl }\mathbf{H}-\mathbf{H}\cdot\text{ curl }\mathbf{E})dv$$

$$=-\frac{c}{4\pi}\int\text{div }\mathbf{E}\times\mathbf{H}dv=-\frac{c}{4\pi}\int\mathbf{n}\cdot(\mathbf{E}\times\mathbf{H})dS,$$

corresponding to a rate of flow of energy

$$\mathbf{R}=\frac{c}{4\pi}\mathbf{E}\times\mathbf{H} \quad . \quad . \quad . \quad . \quad (21)$$

per unit area of a surface perpendicular to $\mathbf{R}$. For this gives a rate of flow inward across the above surface S equal to $-\frac{c}{4\pi}\mathbf{n}\cdot\mathbf{E}\times\mathbf{H}$ per unit area, answering to the total rate of increase just found. The vector $\mathbf{R}$ is called the *radiant vector* or *Poynting's vector*.

128. Electromagnetic stress and momentum. Using the value

$$\mathbf{F}=\mathbf{E}+\frac{1}{c}\mathbf{v}\times\mathbf{B} \quad . \quad . \quad . \quad . \quad (9')$$

for the force per unit charge acting on the electricity within a closed surface S, we have for the total force on the charge within S

$$\int\left(\rho\mathbf{E}+\frac{1}{c}\rho\mathbf{v}\times\mathbf{B}\right)dv.$$

Inserting the values of ρ and $\rho\mathbf{v}$ given by (3) and (1) we may write this

$$\frac{1}{4\pi}\int\left[\mathbf{E}\text{ div }\mathbf{D}+\left(\text{curl }\mathbf{H}-\frac{1}{c}\frac{\partial\mathbf{D}}{\partial t}\right)\times\mathbf{B}\right]dv$$

$$=\frac{1}{4\pi}\int\left[\mathbf{E}\text{ div }\mathbf{D}-\mathbf{B}\times\text{curl }\mathbf{H}-\frac{1}{c}\frac{\partial}{\partial t}(\mathbf{D}\times\mathbf{B})-\frac{1}{c}\mathbf{D}\times(c\text{ curl }\mathbf{E})\right]dv$$

Suppose for simplicity that K and μ are constant throughout the region. Then expanding

$$\nabla(\mathbf{D}\cdot\mathbf{E})=K\nabla(\mathbf{E}\cdot\mathbf{E})$$

and

$$\nabla(\mathbf{B}\cdot\mathbf{H})=\mu\nabla(\mathbf{H}\cdot\mathbf{H})$$

by (19) of Art. 8, and remembering that div $\mathbf{B}=0$, we may write those terms of the integrand which do not involve differentiation with respect to t as

$$(\mathbf{E}\text{ div }\mathbf{D}+\mathbf{D}\cdot\nabla\mathbf{E})+(\mathbf{H}\text{ div }\mathbf{B}+\mathbf{B}\cdot\nabla\mathbf{H})-\tfrac{1}{2}\nabla(\mathbf{D}\cdot\mathbf{E}+\mathbf{B}\cdot\mathbf{H}),$$

which, by Exercise 2 of Chapter VII., is equal to

$$\nabla\cdot(\mathbf{E}\,\mathbf{D} + \mathbf{H}\,\mathbf{B}) - 4\pi\nabla u \qquad \text{ii}$$

where $u \equiv \frac{1}{8\pi}(\mathbf{D}\cdot\mathbf{E} + \mathbf{B}\cdot\mathbf{H})$ is the sum of the electrostatic and magnetic energies per unit volume. Then since $\nabla u = \nabla\cdot(u\mathrm{I})$, we may transform the volume integral of ii to the surface integral

$$\int(\mathbf{E}\,\mathbf{D} + \mathbf{H}\,\mathbf{B} - 4\pi u\mathrm{I})\cdot\mathbf{n}\,dS,$$

the dyadic in brackets being self-conjugate. Thus the portion of the total force i not involving time-differentiation may be represented by a stress over the surface S equal to $\Psi\cdot\mathbf{n}$ where $\mathbf{n}$ is the unit outward normal and

$$\Psi = \frac{1}{4\pi}(\mathbf{E}\,\mathbf{D} + \mathbf{H}\,\mathbf{B}) - u\mathrm{I} \qquad (22)$$

is the stress dyadic. The idea of this stress for the case of the ether is due to Maxwell; and the stress is often called *Maxwell's electromagnetic stress.*

The remaining portion of the total force i is represented by the integral

$$-\frac{1}{4\pi c}\int\frac{\partial}{\partial t}(\mathbf{D}\times\mathbf{B})dv = -\frac{1}{4\pi c}\frac{\partial}{\partial t}\int\mathbf{D}\times\mathbf{B}dv \qquad \text{iii}$$

The vector

$$\mathbf{G} = \frac{1}{4\pi c}\mathbf{D}\times\mathbf{B} \qquad (23)$$

is frequently called the *electromagnetic momentum* per unit volume, a term due to Abraham. In this way the above result may be expressed: The total electromagnetic stress over the surface S is equal to the vector sum of the total electric force on the charge within S and the rate of increase of the electromagnetic momentum of the enclosed region.

II. The Lorentz-Einstein Transformation.

129. Introductory. Origin of the principle of relativity. The purpose of the remaining pages of this book is to furnish a brief introduction to the study of relativity. The general theory of relativity and gravitation, as advanced by Einstein about eight years ago, is quite beyond the scope of this work; and its presentation seems to require some special analysis, such as the absolute differential calculus of Ricci and Levi-Civita. We shall therefore confine our attention to the *restricted* principle of relativity, which deals with systems of reference whose relative motion is a uniform velocity of translation only. Even in this special theory, if we wished to make anything like a complete survey of the field, it would be advantageous to use the properties of *four-vectors*,* or space-time vectors of four components. But for the brief account here given the ordinary vectors of this book will be found sufficient.

The principle of relativity owes its origin primarily to the attempt to express the laws of nature by equations which preserve the same form for all systems of reference; and secondarily to the negative results of all efforts to detect the motion of the earth relative to the ether. It is a matter of common knowledge that the equations of motion of a body, as deduced from Newton's second law, retain their original form when the frame of reference S is replaced by another S' which has uniform velocity $\mathbf{v}$ relative to the former. If time is measured from the instant when a point O fixed in S coincides with the point O' fixed in S', the position vectors $\mathbf{r}$, $\mathbf{r}'$ of any other point relative to O, O' respectively are connected by

$$\mathbf{r}' = \mathbf{r} - t\mathbf{v}$$

where t is the time variable. If the x-axis is taken parallel to the uniform velocity $\mathbf{v}$, this is equivalent to

$$x' = x - vt, \quad y' = y, \quad z' = z.$$

The transformation represented by these relations leaves the Newtonian equations of motion unchanged in form.

This, however, is not the case if the transformation is applied to the fundamental equations of electrodynamics as stated by Maxwell and Lorentz. Observers stationed in the two systems would express the same phenomena by equations not identical, but differing in certain terms of the order v^2/c^2, where c is the velocity of light in free space. All experimental knowledge, however, leads to the conclusion that the actions taking place in S' depend only on the relative velocities of the different parts of that system, and are independent of the relative velocity of S' to any other system S. Starting with the desideratum that the mathematical expression of the laws of physical phenomena should be the same whether these phenomena are referred to S or to another system S' moving uniformly with respect to it, Lorentz and Einstein were led in different ways to the same substitution satisfying the requirements. The development of Einstein's point of view has led to the theory of Relativity.

* *Cf.* two papers by the author on "Four-vector Algebra and Analysis" in the *Messenger of Mathematics*, vol. 49, pp. 155–76, and vol. 50, pp. 49–61 (1920).

130. The principle of relativity, and the Lorentz-Einstein transformation. The celebrated experiment of Michelson and Morley * was made to detect, if possible, a difference in the speeds of propagation of light in different directions relative to the earth's velocity. The negative results of this and other experiments, whose methods were sufficiently accurate to reveal effects of the order v^2/c^2, lead to the conclusion that the velocity of light as accurately determined by an observer in S is the same for all directions, and is independent of the motion of that system relative to other systems. More formally stated this principle is: *Every light disturbance is propagated,* in vacuo, *relative to the system S with a constant speed c, whether it is emitted from a source stationary or in motion relative to S.*

To make the assumption clearer, suppose that P is a point fixed in the system S, and that an arbitrarily moving point-source of light emits a flash just as it is passing through P. Then, to an observer fixed in S, the resulting spherical wave of light will travel out uniformly in all directions from the point P as permanent centre, the radius r at a time t after the flash being equal to ct. Similarly if the point-source emits a flash while passing through a point P' fixed in another system S', then to an observer fixed in S' the spherical wave will have a permanent centre at P', and its radius at a time t' after the flash will be $r' = ct'$.

Considering the system (or frame of reference) S, suppose that at various points of it there are situated clocks which are fixed relative to S. The clocks are said to be synchronous if they satisfy the following condition. Let A, B be two points fixed in S, and suppose that a flash of light is sent from A at an instant when the clock at A registers t_1. Let t_2 be the indication of the clock at B at the instant when the flash arrives at B, to be automatically reflected back to A, arriving there when the clock at A registers t_3. Then if $t_3 - t_2 = t_2 - t_1$, that is, $t_2 = \frac{1}{2}(t_1 + t_3)$, the clocks at A and B are said to be *synchronous*. This definition of synchronism is, of course, based upon the ordinary idea of allowing for the time of transit. We shall suppose that all clocks fixed relative to S have been synchronised, and remain permanently synchronous. We may take it as axiomatic that if the clock at B is synchronous with that at A, then the clock at A is synchronous with that at B. Also that if the clocks at A and B are each synchronous with another clock at C, they are synchronous with each other.

* *Cf.* Michelson, *Light Waves and their Uses*, p. 158. Also Michelson and Morley, *Amer. Jour. of Science*, 3rd ser., vol. 34 (1887); *Phil. Mag.*, 5th ser., vol. 24 (1887).

Let S' be another system (or frame of reference) with another series of clocks fixed relative to it and synchronous with one another. We can choose the units of length and time in the two systems in such a way that, when the systems are in relative rest, they possess equal units of length and equal units of time. Then if the origin of time is the same for each, the clocks of S' are synchronous with those of S.

Suppose now that by some means the system S' has acquired a uniform velocity $\mathbf{v}$ relative to S. Let the origin of time in each system be taken as the instant when the two points O, O', fixed in S, S' respectively, were coincident; and let these points be taken as origins of position vectors (or coordinates) for the two systems. Then at a subsequent instant any one point will have a position vector $\mathbf{r}$ (or coordinates x, y, z) relative to S, and the S-clock instantaneously at that point will indicate a time t; while the same point will have a position vector $\mathbf{r}'$ (or coordinates x', y', z') relative to S', and the S'-clock instantaneously at that point will indicate a time t'.

According to the principle enunciated above, the velocity of light has the same value c when measured with reference to S or S', whether they are at relative rest or in relative motion. Starting with this assumption, Einstein * deduced to the following transformation of coordinates as consistent with the principle. If the x-axis is taken in the direction of the velocity $\mathbf{v}$ of S' relative to S, the transformation may be expressed

$$\left.\begin{aligned} x' &= \beta(x - vt) \\ y' &= y \\ z' &= z \\ t' &= \beta\left(t - \frac{vx}{c^2}\right) \end{aligned}\right\} \quad . \quad . \quad . \quad . \quad (25)$$

where

$$\beta = \frac{1}{\sqrt{1 - \frac{v^2}{c^2}}},$$

and v is the module of $\mathbf{v}$. This is the same transformation that Lorentz had previously deduced from another point of view. The relations are clearly reciprocal. For if the equations are solved for x, y, z, t in terms of the other variables, we find

$$\left.\begin{aligned} x &= \beta(x' + vt') \\ t &= \beta\left(t' + \frac{vx'}{c^2}\right) \end{aligned}\right\} \quad . \quad . \quad . \quad . \quad (26)$$

* *Ann. der Physik*, vol. 17, p. 891 (1905); *Jahrbuch der Radio. und Elek.*, vol. 4, p. 411 (1907). The reader is also referred to Silberstein's *Theory of Relativity*, to which the author is greatly indebted.

as we should expect, seeing that $-\mathbf{v}$ is the velocity of S relative to S'.

131. Interpretation of the transformation. Consider two points A', B' fixed in the system S', and let their coordinates in that system be x_1', y_1', z_1' ; x_2', y_2', z_2'. Relative to the system S at the instant t let the coordinates of the same two points be x_1, y_1, z_1 ; x_2, y_2, z_2. Then from (25) it follows that

$$x_1 - x_2 = \sqrt{1 - \frac{v^2}{c^2}}(x_1' - x_2')$$

$$y_1 - y_2 = y_1' - y_2'$$
$$z_1 - z_2 = z_1' - z_2'.$$

That is to say, to an observer fixed in S the distance between A' and B', measured parallel to the relative velocity $\mathbf{v}$, appears less than it does to an observer fixed in S' in the ratio $\sqrt{1 - \frac{v^2}{c^2}} : 1$; while the distance between the two points measured perpendicular to $\mathbf{v}$ appears the same to both. Thus what appears to the S'-observer to be a sphere, will appear to the S-observer to be a spheroid flattened in the direction of $\mathbf{v}$. And the larger the value of the speed v the greater is the apparent flattening ; and when $v = c$ the figure appears plane to the S-observer.

A body fixed relative to S', and having a volume V' to an S'-observer, will have a volume $\sqrt{1 - \frac{v^2}{c^2}}\, V'$ to an S-observer. For, to the latter, the dimensions measured parallel to $\mathbf{v}$ are $\sqrt{1 - \frac{v^2}{c^2}}$ times what they are to the former ; while the dimensions in the perpendicular directions appear the same to both. We may write this

$$V = \sqrt{1 - \frac{v^2}{c^2}} V'$$

or

$$V' = \beta V \qquad (27)$$

If we choose points A, B fixed in the system S, and consider these from the point of view of the S'-observer at the instant t', we find from (26) in the same way

$$x_1' - x_2' = \sqrt{1 - \frac{v^2}{c^2}}(x_1 - x_2),$$

and so on. The distance between the two points, measured parallel to $\mathbf{v}$, now appears greater to the S-observer than to the S'-observer, as we should expect from the reciprocal nature of the relations (25) and (26).

Consider now an observer fixed in S' at the origin O' of that system. Then since time is measured from the instant when O' coincides with the origin in S, his coordinates relative to S are $x = vt$, $y = 0$, $z = 0$. At a certain instant let t_1' be the time indicated by the S'-clock near the observer, and t_1 that indicated by the S-clock instantaneously at the same place. At another instant let t_2' be the time indicated by the same S'-clock, and t_2 that shown by the (different) S-clock, which is then instantaneously at O'. Then by (25)

$$t_1' = \beta\left(t_1 - \frac{v^2 t_1}{c^2}\right) = \beta t_1\left(1 - \frac{v^2}{c^2}\right) = \frac{t_1}{\beta},$$

so that

$$t_1 = \beta t_1'.$$

Similarly

$$t_2 = \beta t_2',$$

and therefore

$$t_2 - t_1 = \beta(t_2' - t_1').$$

We may, for example, take the above two instants as those determined by two successive strokes of the S'-clock. Then the last equation shows that, to an S-observer, the periodic time of this clock is greater than to the S'-observer in the ratio $\beta : 1$ or $1 : \sqrt{1 - \frac{v^2}{c^2}}$. To the former it appears to go slower than to the latter.

132. Vectorial expression. The transformation (25) may be very neatly expressed by means of vectors, independently of coordinate axes, and therefore without the formal privilege above accorded to the x-axis. Let $\mathbf{r} \equiv x\mathbf{i} + y\mathbf{j} + z\mathbf{k}$, and $\mathbf{r}' \equiv x'\mathbf{i} + y'\mathbf{j} + z'\mathbf{k}$, be the position vectors of a point relative to O and O' respectively. Then the first of equations (25) is equivalent to

$$\mathbf{r}'\cdot\mathbf{i} = \beta(\mathbf{r}\cdot\mathbf{i} - vt) \quad . \quad . \quad . \quad . \quad \text{i}$$

while the second and third are then included in

$$\mathbf{r}' - \mathbf{r}'\cdot\mathbf{i}\,\mathbf{i} = \mathbf{r} - \mathbf{r}\cdot\mathbf{i}\,\mathbf{i} \quad . \quad . \quad . \quad . \quad \text{ii}$$

while the last is

$$t' = \beta\left(t - \frac{v}{c^2}\mathbf{r}\cdot\mathbf{i}\right) \quad . \quad . \quad . \quad . \quad \text{iii}$$

Multiply i by $\mathbf{i}$ and add it to ii. Then since $\mathbf{v} = v\mathbf{i}$ we may write the result

$$\mathbf{r}' = \mathbf{r} + \left(\frac{\beta - 1}{v^2}\mathbf{v}\cdot\mathbf{r} - \beta t\right)\mathbf{v} \quad . \quad . \quad . \quad . \quad \text{iv}$$

It will be found convenient to introduce the self-conjugate dyadic

$$\Phi = \mathrm{I} + \frac{\beta - 1}{v^2}\mathbf{v}\,\mathbf{v} \quad . \quad . \quad . \quad . \quad (28)$$

in terms of which the complete transformation as contained in iii and iv takes the concise form

$$\left.\begin{aligned} \mathbf{r}' &= \Phi\cdot\mathbf{r} - \beta t\mathbf{v} \\ t' &= \beta\left(t - \frac{\mathbf{r}\cdot\mathbf{v}}{c^2}\right) \end{aligned}\right\} \quad . \quad . \quad . \quad . \quad (29)$$

This is the vectorial equivalent of (25).

The dyadic Φ in direct multiplication with a vector parallel to $\mathbf{v}$ leaves its direction unchanged, but increases its length in the ratio $\beta : 1$. On the other hand, direct multiplication by Φ leaves a vector perpendicular to $\mathbf{v}$ unaltered. The dyadic may therefore be described as a *longitudinal stretcher* for vectors parallel to $\mathbf{v}$, the ratio of stretching being $\beta : 1$. The reciprocal dyadic has the value

$$\Phi^{-1} = \Phi - \frac{\beta}{c^2}\mathbf{v}\,\mathbf{v} = \mathrm{I} - \frac{\beta - 1}{\beta v^2}\mathbf{v}\,\mathbf{v} \quad . \quad . \quad . \quad (30)$$

for it is easily shown that this makes $\Phi\cdot\Phi^{-1} = \mathrm{I}$. Similarly the " square " of Φ has the value

$$\Phi^2 = \mathrm{I} + \frac{\beta^2}{c^2}\mathbf{v}\,\mathbf{v} \quad . \quad . \quad . \quad . \quad . \quad (31)$$

as is easily verified.

It was seen above that the relations (25) and (26) are reciprocal, each being obtainable from the other by interchanging accented and unaccented symbols and changing the sign of v. Similarly the equations (29) are equivalent to

$$\left.\begin{aligned} \mathbf{r} &= \Phi\cdot\mathbf{r}' + \beta t'\mathbf{v} \\ t &= \beta\left(t' + \frac{\mathbf{r}'\cdot\mathbf{v}}{c^2}\right) \end{aligned}\right\} \quad . \quad . \quad . \quad (29')$$

We leave it as an exercise for the student to deduce one from the other, making use of (31).

133. Addition of velocities. Consider a particle moving in any manner, and let $\mathbf{r}$ and $\mathbf{r}'$ be its position vectors relative to O and O', and from the points of view of the S-observer and the S'-observer respectively. Then, as viewed by the former, the velocity $\mathbf{u}$ of the particle will be $\frac{d\mathbf{r}}{dt}$; while from the point of view of the latter it will be $\mathbf{u}' = \frac{d\mathbf{r}'}{dt'}$. We naturally inquire how these are related. In ordinary kinematics, since $\mathbf{v}$ is the relative velocity of S' to S, we should have $\mathbf{u} = \mathbf{u}' + \mathbf{v}$. But in the theory of relativity this simple relation no longer holds. Observing that Φ, $\mathbf{v}$, β, and c are constant, we find from (29')

$$d\mathbf{r} = \Phi\cdot d\mathbf{r}' + \beta\mathbf{v}dt'$$

and

$$dt = \beta\left(dt' + \frac{1}{c^2}\mathbf{v}\cdot d\mathbf{r}'\right).$$

Hence the velocity $\mathbf{u}$ is given by

$$\mathbf{u} = \frac{d\mathbf{r}}{dt} = \frac{\Phi\cdot d\mathbf{r}' + \beta\mathbf{v}dt'}{\beta\left(dt' + \frac{1}{c^2}\mathbf{v}\cdot d\mathbf{r}'\right)}.$$

Dividing numerator and denominator by dt' and putting $\mathbf{u}' = \frac{d\mathbf{r}'}{dt'}$, we have the required relation

$$\mathbf{u} = \frac{\Phi\cdot\mathbf{u}' + \beta\mathbf{v}}{\beta\left(1 + \frac{1}{c^2}\mathbf{v}\cdot\mathbf{u}'\right)} \quad . \quad . \quad . \quad . \quad (32)$$

This is the vectorial expression of Einstein's celebrated Addition Theorem. We may look upon $\mathbf{u}$ as the relativistic sum of the two velocities $\mathbf{v}$ and $\mathbf{u}'$, the former being that of S' relative to S, and the latter that of the particle relative to S'. The symbol $\#$ may be used * instead of $+$ to denote such composition of velocities. Then putting $\mathbf{v}_1$ for $\mathbf{v}$, and $\mathbf{v}_2$ for $\mathbf{u}'$, we may write the above result

$$\mathbf{v}_1 \# \mathbf{v}_2 = \frac{\Phi_1\cdot\mathbf{v}_2 + \beta_1\mathbf{v}_1}{\beta_1\left(1 + \frac{1}{c^2}\mathbf{v}_1\cdot\mathbf{v}_2\right)} \quad . \quad . \quad . \quad (32')$$

the suffix unity denoting that the quantities β_1 and Φ_1 are formed in terms of the velocity $\mathbf{v}_1$. Such addition is not commutative. For

$$\mathbf{v}_2 \# \mathbf{v}_1 = \frac{\Phi_2\cdot\mathbf{v}_1 + \beta_2\mathbf{v}_2}{\beta_2\left(1 + \frac{1}{c^2}\mathbf{v}_1\cdot\mathbf{v}_2\right)} \quad . \quad . \quad . \quad (32'')$$

where Φ_2 is the longitudinal stretcher of ratio β_2 for vectors parallel to $\mathbf{v}_2$. The student can verify for himself that the vectors (32′) and (32″), though differing in direction, are equal in length.

The reciprocal formula to (32) is

$$\mathbf{u}' = \frac{\Phi\cdot\mathbf{u} - \beta\mathbf{v}}{\beta\left(1 - \frac{1}{c^2}\mathbf{v}\cdot\mathbf{u}\right)} \quad . \quad . \quad . \quad . \quad (33)$$

These are deducible from each other ; or the latter may be derived from (29) in the same way that the former was derived from (29′).

134. Formulæ of transformation. In the next Art. we shall need expressions for div $\mathbf{F}$ and curl $\mathbf{F}$ (defined in terms of x, y, z, as in Art. 7), in terms of the variables x', y', z', t'. If $\mathbf{F}$ is a vector function

* Following Silberstein.

of position and time,

$$\frac{\partial \mathbf{F}}{\partial x} = \frac{\partial \mathbf{F}}{\partial x'}\frac{\partial x'}{\partial x} + \frac{\partial \mathbf{F}}{\partial y'}\frac{\partial y'}{\partial x} + \frac{\partial \mathbf{F}}{\partial z'}\frac{\partial z'}{\partial x} + \frac{\partial \mathbf{F}}{\partial t'}\frac{\partial t'}{\partial x}$$
$$= \frac{\partial \mathbf{r}'}{\partial x}\cdot\nabla'\mathbf{F} + \frac{\partial \mathbf{F}}{\partial t'}\frac{\partial t'}{\partial x},$$

where $\nabla'\mathbf{F}$ is the dyadic $\Sigma\mathbf{i}\frac{\partial \mathbf{F}}{\partial x'}$ formed with the variables x', y', z'. Hence

$$\operatorname{div}\mathbf{F} = \Sigma\mathbf{i}\cdot\frac{\partial \mathbf{F}}{\partial x}$$
$$= \Sigma\frac{\partial \mathbf{r}'}{\partial x}\cdot\nabla'\mathbf{F}\cdot\mathbf{i} + \frac{\partial \mathbf{F}}{\partial t'}\cdot\Sigma\mathbf{i}\frac{\partial t'}{\partial x}$$
$$= \Sigma\frac{\partial \mathbf{F}}{\partial x'}\cdot\nabla\mathbf{r}'\cdot\mathbf{i} + \frac{\partial \mathbf{F}}{\partial t'}\cdot\nabla t'.$$

But from (29) we easily deduce

$$\nabla\mathbf{r}' = \Phi = \mathbf{I} + \frac{\beta - 1}{v^2}\mathbf{v}\,\mathbf{v}$$

and

$$\nabla t' = -\frac{\beta\mathbf{v}}{c^2}.$$

Substitution of these values in the last equation then gives

$$\nabla\cdot\mathbf{F} = \nabla'\cdot\mathbf{F} + \frac{\beta - 1}{v^2}\mathbf{v}\cdot\nabla'\mathbf{F}\cdot\mathbf{v} - \frac{\beta\mathbf{v}}{c^2}\cdot\frac{\partial \mathbf{F}}{\partial t'} \quad . \quad . \quad (34)$$

In the same way we find

$$\nabla\times\mathbf{F} = \nabla'\times\mathbf{F} - \frac{\beta - 1}{v^2}\mathbf{v}\cdot\nabla'\mathbf{F}\times\mathbf{v} - \frac{\beta\mathbf{v}}{c^2}\times\frac{\partial \mathbf{F}}{\partial t'} \quad . \quad . \quad (35)$$

Lastly, the derivation of $\mathbf{F}$ with respect to t has the value

$$\frac{\partial \mathbf{F}}{\partial t} = \frac{\partial \mathbf{F}}{\partial x'}\frac{\partial x'}{\partial t} + \frac{\partial \mathbf{F}}{\partial y'}\frac{\partial y'}{\partial t} + \frac{\partial \mathbf{F}}{\partial z'}\frac{\partial z'}{\partial t} + \frac{\partial \mathbf{F}}{\partial t'}\frac{\partial t'}{\partial t}$$
$$= \frac{\partial \mathbf{r}'}{\partial t}\cdot\nabla'\mathbf{F} + \beta\frac{\partial \mathbf{F}}{\partial t'},$$

which is equivalent to

$$\frac{\partial \mathbf{F}}{\partial t} = \beta\left(\frac{\partial \mathbf{F}}{\partial t'} - \mathbf{v}\cdot\nabla'\mathbf{F}\right). \quad . \quad . \quad . \quad (36)$$

135. Transformation of the electromagnetic equations. The desideratum that the mathematical expression of electromagnetic phenomena should be of the same form, whether these phenomena are referred to the system S or the system S', is satisfied by the Lorentz transformation (29) if the values $\mathbf{E}'$, $\mathbf{H}'$, ρ' of the electric and magnetic intensities, and the density of charge referred to S', are connected with their values **E**, **H**, ρ referred to S by the relations

$$\left.\begin{aligned}\mathbf{E}' &= \beta\left(\Phi^{-1}\cdot\mathbf{E} + \frac{1}{c}\mathbf{v}\times\mathbf{H}\right)\\ \mathbf{H}' &= \beta\left(\Phi^{-1}\cdot\mathbf{H} - \frac{1}{c}\mathbf{v}\times\mathbf{E}\right)\\ \rho' &= \beta\rho\left(1 - \frac{\mathbf{v}\cdot\mathbf{u}}{c^2}\right)\end{aligned}\right\} \quad . \quad . \quad . \quad (37)$$

In the last of these, **u** is the velocity of the charge relative to S' while its velocity **u′** relative to S' is given by (33). That is to say, the equations (10)–(13) of Art. 126 transform into the equations

$$\left.\begin{aligned}\frac{\partial\mathbf{E}'}{\partial t'} &= c\nabla'\times\mathbf{H}' - 4\pi\rho'\mathbf{u}'\\ \frac{\partial\mathbf{H}'}{\partial t'} &= -\,c\nabla'\times\mathbf{E}'\\ \nabla'\cdot\mathbf{E}' &= 4\pi\rho'\\ \nabla'\cdot\mathbf{H}' &= 0\end{aligned}\right\} \quad . \quad . \quad . \quad (38)$$

where $\nabla' \equiv \mathbf{i}\frac{\partial}{\partial x'} + \mathbf{j}\frac{\partial}{\partial y'} + \mathbf{k}\frac{\partial}{\partial z'}$ is the operator relative to the space S'.

Consider first the equation (12), viz.

$$\nabla\cdot\mathbf{E} = 4\pi\rho.$$

If we use the value of $\nabla\cdot\mathbf{E}$ given by (34), and then the value of $\frac{\partial\mathbf{E}}{\partial t'}$ found from (36), the relation becomes

$$\nabla'\cdot\mathbf{E} + \frac{\beta-1}{v^2}\mathbf{v}\cdot\nabla'\mathbf{E}\cdot\mathbf{v} - \frac{1}{c^2}\left(\mathbf{v}\cdot\frac{\partial\mathbf{E}}{\partial t} + \beta\mathbf{v}\cdot\nabla'\mathbf{E}\cdot\mathbf{v}\right) = 4\pi\rho.$$

But

$$\left.\begin{aligned}\mathbf{v}\cdot\frac{\partial\mathbf{E}}{\partial t} &= \mathbf{v}\cdot(c\nabla\times\mathbf{H} - 4\pi\rho\mathbf{u})\\ &= c\mathbf{v}\cdot\nabla'\times\mathbf{H} - 4\pi\rho\mathbf{v}\cdot\mathbf{u}\\ &= -\,c\nabla'\cdot(\mathbf{v}\times\mathbf{H}) - 4\pi\rho\mathbf{v}\cdot\mathbf{u},\end{aligned}\right\} \quad . \quad \text{by (35)}$$

since **v** is constant. Substituting this value in the above equation we have, on collecting like terms,

$$\nabla'\cdot\mathbf{E} - \frac{\beta-1}{\beta v^2}\mathbf{v}\cdot\nabla'\mathbf{E}\cdot\mathbf{v} + \frac{1}{c}\nabla'\cdot(\mathbf{v}\times\mathbf{H}) = 4\pi\rho\left(1 - \frac{\mathbf{v}\cdot\mathbf{u}}{c^2}\right).$$

Now it is easily shown by the formulæ of Art. 8 that

$$\mathbf{v}\cdot\nabla'\mathbf{E}\cdot\mathbf{v} = \nabla'\cdot(\mathbf{v}\cdot\mathbf{E}\,\mathbf{v}) \quad . \quad . \quad . \quad \text{i}$$

Hence the equation, on multiplication by β, may be written

$$\nabla'\cdot\beta\left[\left(\mathrm{I} - \frac{\beta-1}{\beta v^2}\mathbf{v}\,\mathbf{v}\right)\cdot\mathbf{E} + \frac{1}{c}\mathbf{v}\times\mathbf{H}\right] = 4\pi\rho$$

which, by (30), is equivalent to

$$\nabla' \cdot \mathbf{E}' = 4\pi\rho' \quad . \quad . \quad . \quad . \quad (39)$$

as required. The relation $\nabla' \cdot \mathbf{H}' = 0$ is deducible from $\nabla \cdot \mathbf{H} = 0$ in exactly the same way.

The details of the transformation for the other two equations are rather lengthy, and we shall not burden the reader with them. It is in work like this that the analysis of four-vectors effects a great simplification; and the only proof worth giving in the present instance is by their means.

136. Relations reciprocal. Total charge invariable. The relations (37) are reciprocal. For from them we may easily deduce the forms

$$\left.\begin{aligned} \mathbf{E} &= \beta\left(\Phi^{-1} \cdot \mathbf{E}' - \frac{1}{c}\mathbf{v} \times \mathbf{H}'\right) \\ \mathbf{H} &= \beta\left(\Phi^{-1} \cdot \mathbf{H}' + \frac{1}{c}\mathbf{v} \times \mathbf{E}'\right) \\ \rho &= \beta\rho'\left(1 + \frac{\mathbf{v} \cdot \mathbf{u}'}{c^2}\right) \end{aligned}\right\} \quad . \quad . \quad . \quad (40)$$

obtainable from (37) by interchanging the accented and unaccented symbols and changing the sign of $\mathbf{v}$. "From this standpoint the distinction between electric and magnetic forces becomes indefinite. By a suitable change of moving axes either may be made to vanish, involving a corresponding change in the other. For instance, with a uniformly moving point charge there are important magnetic forces if the motion is relative to the observer, but if the observer moves with the charge, the forces are all electric." *

It is important to observe that, though the density of the charge depends upon the system of reference, the total charge is the same in all cases. Take the system S' as that relative to which the element of charge is at rest, and let $\mathbf{v}$ be the velocity of this system relative to S. Then since for the element of charge $\mathbf{u}' = 0$, we have $\rho = \beta\rho'$ for the relation between the densities of charge relative to the two systems. If dV and dV' are the volumes occupied by the element from the points of view of an S-observer and an S'-observer respectively, it follows from (27) that $dV' = \beta dV$. Hence

$$\rho dV = \rho' dV',$$

showing that the element of charge is the same for both systems. But S' is the system moving with the charge, and S is any other system; so that the total charge is independent of the system of reference. If the charge has velocities $\mathbf{v}_1$ and $\mathbf{v}_2$ relative to the

* Richardson, *The Electron Theory of Matter*, p. 308.

systems S_1 and S_2 respectively, and β_1, β_2 are the corresponding values of β, it follows from the above that

$$\frac{\rho_1}{\beta_1} = \frac{\rho_2}{\beta_2},$$

each being equal to ρ'. This relation is important in the theory of Relativity.

EXERCISES ON CHAPTER X.

1. If $\rho\left(Q, t - \frac{r}{c}\right)$ is a function of the point Q and of the distance r from Q to P, show that

$$V \equiv \frac{\rho\left(Q, t - \frac{r}{c}\right)}{r}$$

satisfies the equation

$$\nabla^2{}_P V - \frac{1}{c^2}\frac{\partial^2 V}{\partial t^2} = 0.$$

By the formula for the gradient of a product of scalar factors

$$\nabla_P V = \frac{1}{r}\nabla_P \rho + \rho \nabla_P \frac{1}{r}.$$

Or, if dashes denote differentiations with respect to the variable $t - \frac{r}{c}$, and $\hat{\mathbf{r}}$ is the unit vector parallel to $\mathbf{r} \equiv \overrightarrow{QP}$, this result may be written

$$\nabla V = -\frac{1}{cr}\rho'\hat{\mathbf{r}} - \rho\frac{\hat{\mathbf{r}}}{r^2} = -\left(\frac{\rho'}{cr^2} + \frac{\rho}{r^3}\right)\mathbf{r}.$$

Then on taking the divergence of both sides, and using formulæ (9) and (15) of Chapter I., we have

$$\begin{aligned} \nabla^2 V &= -\mathbf{r}\cdot\nabla\left(\frac{\rho'}{cr^2} + \frac{\rho}{r^3}\right) - 3\left(\frac{\rho'}{cr^2} + \frac{\rho}{r^3}\right) \\ &= \mathbf{r}\cdot\hat{\mathbf{r}}\left(\frac{\rho''}{c^2r^2} + \frac{2\rho'}{cr^3} + \frac{\rho'}{cr^3} + \frac{3\rho}{r^4}\right) - 3\left(\frac{\rho'}{cr^2} + \frac{\rho}{r^3}\right) \\ &= \frac{\rho''}{c^2 r} = \frac{1}{c^2}\frac{\partial^2 V}{\partial t^2}, \end{aligned}$$

as was to be proved.

2. With the same notation show that the function

$$\phi(P, t) = \int \frac{1}{r}\rho\left(Q, t - \frac{r}{c}\right)dv,$$

where the integration is extended throughout a definite region bounded by S, satisfies the equation

$$\nabla^2\phi - \frac{1}{c^2}\frac{\partial^2\phi}{\partial t^2} = -4\pi\rho(P, t)$$

or zero according as P is within or without the region of integration.

If dv is the volume of an element of space at the point Q, then by the last exercise the function

$$V = \frac{1}{r}\rho\left(Q, t - \frac{r}{c}\right)dv$$

satisfies the equation $\square^2 V = 0$. And therefore, if P is outside the region of integration, it follows by summation that $\phi(P, t)$ satisfies the same equation.

If, however, P is within the region of integration, we may divide this region into two portions, one enclosed by an infinitesimal sphere whose centre is at P, and the other external to this sphere. Let ϕ_1 and ϕ_2 be the two parts of the function ϕ due respectively to integration over these regions. Then $\phi = \phi_1 + \phi_2$. Now, because P is within the sphere,

$$\square^2\phi_2 = 0 \qquad . \quad . \quad . \quad . \quad \text{i}$$

As for the function ϕ_1 due to integration throughout the sphere, $\frac{r}{c}$ is infinitesimal for all positions of Q, and the "retarded" density ρ may be taken as uniform and equal to $\rho(Q, t)$ in this region. Then ϕ_1 is the Newtonian potential due to this space distribution, and therefore satisfies Poisson's equation

$$\nabla^2\phi_1 = -4\pi\rho(P, t).$$

Further, the second derivative of the integrand $\frac{1}{r}\rho\left(Q, t - \frac{r}{c}\right)$ with respect to t is finite, and therefore its volume integral throughout the infinitesimal sphere vanishes. Hence $\frac{\partial^2\phi_1}{\partial t^2} = 0$, which, combined with the last equation, gives

$$\square^2\phi_1 = -4\pi\rho(P, t) \quad . \quad . \quad . \quad . \quad \text{ii}$$

Then in virtue of i and ii we have finally

$$\square^2\phi = \square^2(\phi_1 + \phi_2) = -4\pi\rho(P, t).$$

3. Deduce the form (29′) from the form (29) of the Lorentz transformation.

4. Prove that, with the same notation,

$$\mathbf{r}^2 - c^2t^2 = \mathbf{r}'^2 - c^2t'^2.$$

5. Prove that

$$\nabla^2 - \frac{1}{c^2}\frac{\partial^2}{\partial t^2} = \nabla'^2 - \frac{1}{c^2}\frac{\partial^2}{\partial t'^2}.$$

6. Show that

$$(\mathbf{v}_1 \mathbin{+\!\!\!\!+} \mathbf{v}_2)^2 = (\mathbf{v}_2 \mathbin{+\!\!\!\!+} \mathbf{v}_1)^2 = \frac{(\mathbf{v}_1 + \mathbf{v}_2)^2 - \frac{1}{c^2}(\mathbf{v}_1\times\mathbf{v}_2)^2}{\left(1 + \frac{1}{c^2}\mathbf{v}_1\cdot\mathbf{v}_2\right)^2}.$$

7. If $\mathbf{v}_1$ is parallel to $\mathbf{v}_2$, show that these are also parallel to $(\mathbf{v}_1 \# \mathbf{v}_2)$, and find the value of the last vector.

8. Prove that the relativistic sum of two velocities, each smaller than the velocity of light *in vacuo*, is itself smaller than the velocity of light. But if either mod $\mathbf{v}_1$ or mod $\mathbf{v}_2$ is equal to c, then mod $(\mathbf{v}_1 \# \mathbf{v}_2) = c$.

9. Deduce formula (32′) from (32).

10. From the relation $\rho' = \beta\rho\left(1 - \frac{\mathbf{v}\cdot\mathbf{u}}{c^2}\right)$ deduce its reciprocal $\rho = \beta\rho'\left(1 + \frac{\mathbf{v}\cdot\mathbf{u}'}{c^2}\right)$.

11. Prove that $\nabla\mathbf{r}' = \Phi$.

12. Show that

$$\mathbf{v}\cdot\nabla\times\mathbf{F} = \mathbf{v}\cdot\nabla'\times\mathbf{F}.$$

13. Prove that

$$\nabla'\cdot(\mathbf{v}\cdot\mathbf{E}\,\mathbf{v}) = \mathbf{v}\cdot\nabla'\mathbf{E}\cdot\mathbf{v}.$$

14. Prove the formulæ

$$\nabla F = \Phi\cdot\nabla' F - \frac{\beta\mathbf{v}}{c^2}\frac{\partial F}{\partial t'}$$

and

$$\nabla F = \Phi^{-1}\cdot\nabla' F - \frac{\mathbf{v}}{c^2}\frac{\partial F}{\partial t},$$

where F may be either a scalar or a vector function.

15. Show that

$$\begin{aligned}\mathbf{v}\cdot\nabla'\mathbf{E}\times\mathbf{v} &= -\mathbf{v}\cdot\nabla'(\mathbf{v}\times\mathbf{E}) \\ &= \nabla'\times[\mathbf{v}\times(\mathbf{v}\times\mathbf{E})] - \mathbf{v}\nabla'\cdot(\mathbf{v}\times\mathbf{E}) \\ &= \nabla'\times(\mathbf{v}\,\mathbf{v}\cdot\mathbf{E} - \mathbf{v}^2\mathbf{E}) - \mathbf{v}\nabla'\cdot(\mathbf{v}\times\mathbf{E}).\end{aligned}$$

16. Prove that, with the notation of Art. 134,

$$\Sigma\frac{\partial\mathbf{r}'}{\partial x}\cdot\nabla'\mathbf{F}\cdot\mathbf{i} = \nabla'\cdot(\Phi\cdot\mathbf{F})$$

and

$$\Sigma\mathbf{i}\times\left(\frac{\partial\mathbf{r}'}{\partial x}\cdot\nabla'\mathbf{F}\right) = \nabla'\cdot(\Phi\times\mathbf{F}).$$

17. Show that

$$\begin{aligned}\nabla'\cdot\mathbf{H} &= \beta\frac{\mathbf{v}}{c^2}\cdot\frac{\partial\mathbf{H}}{\partial t'} - \frac{\beta-1}{v^2}\mathbf{v}\cdot\nabla'\mathbf{H}\cdot\mathbf{v} \\ &= \beta\frac{\mathbf{v}}{c^2}\cdot\frac{\partial\mathbf{H}}{\partial t'} - \frac{\beta-1}{v^2}\nabla'\cdot(\mathbf{v}\,\mathbf{v}\cdot\mathbf{H}).\end{aligned}$$

18. From the relations (37) deduce the equivalent relations (40).

19. Write down the reciprocal formulæ to (34), (35), and (36) in the text.

20. Prove the relations

$$\nabla' \cdot \mathbf{H}' = 0$$

$$\frac{\partial \mathbf{H}'}{\partial t'} = -c\nabla' \times \mathbf{E}'.$$

by the method of Art. 135.

NOTATION AND FORMULÆ

OF THE FOUR CHAPTERS, I., II., V., VII., WHICH DEAL WITH THE THEORY OF VECTOR ANALYSIS.

The formulæ are numbered as in the text.

The Differential Operators.

The *position vector* of a point is

$$\mathbf{r} = r\hat{\mathbf{r}} = x\mathbf{i} + y\mathbf{j} + z\mathbf{k}.$$

Scalar point-functions are denoted by letters in italics, *e.g.*

$$F, G, H, U, V, W, u, v, w \ldots$$

Vector point-functions by Clarendon symbols :

$$\mathbf{F}, \mathbf{G}, \mathbf{H}, \mathbf{U}, \mathbf{V}, \mathbf{W}, \mathbf{u}, \mathbf{v}, \mathbf{w} \ldots$$

The **gradient** of a scalar function V is

$$\text{grad } V = \nabla V = \frac{\partial V}{\partial n}\mathbf{n}$$

$$= \frac{\partial V}{\partial x}\mathbf{i} + \frac{\partial V}{\partial y}\mathbf{j} + \frac{\partial V}{\partial z}\mathbf{k} \quad . \quad . \quad . \quad (4)$$

where $\mathbf{n}$ is a unit normal to the level-surface of V, and $\frac{\partial V}{\partial n}$ is the derivative of V in this direction. The derivative of V in the direction of $\hat{\mathbf{a}}$ is

$$\hat{\mathbf{a}}\cdot\nabla V = a_1\frac{\partial V}{\partial x} + a_2\frac{\partial V}{\partial y} + a_3\frac{\partial V}{\partial z} \quad . \quad . \quad . \quad (6)$$

The **divergence** and **curl** of a vector point-function $\mathbf{F} = F_1\mathbf{i} + F_2\mathbf{j} + F_3\mathbf{k}$ are

$$\text{div } \mathbf{F} = \nabla\cdot\mathbf{F} = \Sigma\mathbf{i}\cdot\frac{\partial \mathbf{F}}{\partial x} = \frac{\partial F_1}{\partial x} + \frac{\partial F_2}{\partial y} + \frac{\partial F_3}{\partial z} \quad . \quad (11), (13)$$

and

$$\text{curl } \mathbf{F} = \text{rot } \mathbf{F} = \nabla\times\mathbf{F} = \Sigma\mathbf{i}\times\frac{\partial \mathbf{F}}{\partial x} \quad . \quad . \quad . \quad . \quad . \quad (12)$$

$$= \left(\frac{\partial F_3}{\partial y} - \frac{\partial F_2}{\partial z}\right)\mathbf{i} + \left(\frac{\partial F_1}{\partial z} - \frac{\partial F_3}{\partial x}\right)\mathbf{j} + \left(\frac{\partial F_2}{\partial x} - \frac{\partial F_1}{\partial y}\right)\mathbf{k}. \quad (14)$$

and the derivative of $\mathbf{F}$ in the direction of $\hat{\mathbf{a}}$ is

$$\hat{\mathbf{a}}\cdot\nabla\mathbf{F} = a_1\frac{\partial\mathbf{F}}{\partial x} + a_2\frac{\partial\mathbf{F}}{\partial y} + a_3\frac{\partial\mathbf{F}}{\partial z} \quad . \quad . \quad . \quad (10)$$

The following formulæ of expansion are very useful:

$$\nabla\cdot(u\mathbf{v}) = \nabla u\cdot\mathbf{v} + u\nabla\cdot\mathbf{v} \quad . \quad . \quad . \quad (15)$$

$$\nabla\times(u\mathbf{v}) = \nabla u\times\mathbf{v} + u\nabla\times\mathbf{v} \quad . \quad . \quad . \quad (16)$$

$$\nabla\cdot(\mathbf{u}\times\mathbf{v}) = \mathbf{v}\cdot\nabla\times\mathbf{u} - \mathbf{u}\cdot\nabla\times\mathbf{v} \quad . \quad . \quad . \quad (17)$$

$$\nabla\times(\mathbf{u}\times\mathbf{v}) = \mathbf{v}\cdot\nabla\mathbf{u} - \mathbf{u}\cdot\nabla\mathbf{v} + \mathbf{u}\nabla\cdot\mathbf{v} - \mathbf{v}\nabla\cdot\mathbf{u} \quad . \quad . \quad (18)$$

$$\nabla(\mathbf{u}\cdot\mathbf{v}) = \mathbf{v}\cdot\nabla\mathbf{u} + \mathbf{u}\cdot\nabla\mathbf{v} + \mathbf{v}\cdot\nabla\times\mathbf{u} + \mathbf{u}\cdot\nabla\times\mathbf{v} \quad . \quad . \quad (19)$$

The *second order differential functions* are

$$\left.\begin{aligned}\nabla\cdot\nabla\times\mathbf{F} &= \text{div curl }\mathbf{F} = 0\\ \nabla\times\nabla V &= \text{curl grad } V = 0\end{aligned}\right\} \quad . \quad . \quad . \quad (20)$$

$$\nabla\cdot\nabla V = \text{div grad } V = \nabla^2 V \quad . \quad . \quad . \quad (21)$$

$$\nabla\times\nabla\times\mathbf{F} = \nabla\nabla\cdot\mathbf{F} - \nabla^2\mathbf{F} \quad . \quad . \quad . \quad (22)$$

and

$$\nabla\nabla\cdot\mathbf{F} = \text{grad div }\mathbf{F}.$$

For the function r^m

$$\nabla r^m = mr^{m-1}\hat{\mathbf{r}} = mr^{m-2}\mathbf{r} \quad . \quad . \quad . \quad (8)$$

$$\nabla^2 r^m = \nabla\cdot\nabla r^m = m(m+1)r^{m-2} \quad . \quad . \quad . \quad (23)$$

More generally, if u is any scalar function of r,

$$\nabla u = u'\hat{\mathbf{r}} \quad . \quad . \quad . \quad (9)$$

$$\nabla^2 u = u'' + \frac{2u'}{r} \quad . \quad . \quad . \quad (24)$$

dashes denoting differentiations with respect to r. In terms of **orthogonal curvilinear coordinates** u, v, w with arcual parameters h_1, h_2, h_3, and unit vectors $\mathbf{a}$, $\mathbf{b}$, $\mathbf{c}$ parallel to the coordinate axes at any point, the expressions for gradient, divergence, and curl are:

$$\text{grad } V = \frac{\mathbf{a}}{h_1}\frac{\partial V}{\partial u} + \frac{\mathbf{b}}{h_2}\frac{\partial V}{\partial v} + \frac{\mathbf{c}}{h_3}\frac{\partial V}{\partial w} \quad . \quad . \quad (25)$$

$$\text{div }\mathbf{F} = \frac{1}{h_1h_2h_3}\left[\frac{\partial}{\partial u}(h_2h_3F_1) + \frac{\partial}{\partial v}(h_3h_1F_2) + \frac{\partial}{\partial w}(h_1h_2F_3)\right] \quad . \quad (26)$$

$$\text{curl }\mathbf{F} = \Sigma\frac{\mathbf{a}}{h_2h_3}\left[\frac{\partial}{\partial v}(h_3F_3) - \frac{\partial}{\partial w}(h_2F_2)\right] \quad . \quad . \quad (28)$$

while the Laplacian is

$$\nabla^2 V = \frac{1}{h_1h_2h_3}\left[\frac{\partial}{\partial u}\left(\frac{h_2h_3}{h_1}\frac{\partial V}{\partial u}\right) + \frac{\partial}{\partial v}\left(\frac{h_3h_1}{h_2}\frac{\partial V}{\partial v}\right) + \dots\right] \quad . \quad (27)$$

Line, Surface, and Space Integrals.

The **tangential line integral** of a vector function **F** along a curve from A to B is

$$\int_A^B \mathbf{F}\cdot\mathbf{t}ds = \int_A^B \mathbf{F}\cdot d\mathbf{r}$$

where **t** is the unit tangent to the curve, and $d\mathbf{r} = \mathbf{t}ds$ the vector element of the curve. In particular

$$\int_A^B \nabla V\cdot d\mathbf{r} = V_B - V_A \quad . \quad . \quad . \quad (1)$$

and if V is single-valued the integral round a closed curve vanishes; that is,

$$\int_0 \nabla V\cdot d\mathbf{r} = 0 \quad . \quad . \quad . \quad . \quad (1')$$

The **normal surface integral** of a vector function **F** is

$$\int \mathbf{n}\cdot\mathbf{F}dS = \int \mathbf{F}\cdot d\mathbf{S}$$

where **n** is the unit normal and $d\mathbf{S} = \mathbf{n}dS$ the vector area of the element of the surface. If the surface is closed, and **n** is the unit *outward* normal, the following relations hold between integrals over S and integrals throughout the enclosed space:

$$\int \nabla V dv = \int \mathbf{n} V dS \quad . \quad . \quad . \quad . \quad (5)$$

$$\int \nabla\cdot\mathbf{F}dv = \int \mathbf{n}\cdot\mathbf{F}dS \quad . \quad . \quad . \quad . \quad (2)$$

$$\int \nabla\times\mathbf{F}dv = \int \mathbf{n}\times\mathbf{F}dS \quad . \quad . \quad . \quad . \quad (6)$$

The second of these is Gauss's **Divergence Theorem.**

If C is a closed curve and S an open surface bounded by it, **Stokes's Theorem** states that

$$\int \mathbf{n}\cdot\nabla\times\mathbf{F}dS = \int_0 \mathbf{F}\cdot d\mathbf{r} \quad . \quad . \quad . \quad (9)$$

where the sense of **n** is positive relative to the description of the curve C. The theorem

$$\int \mathbf{n}\times\nabla V dS = \int_0 V d\mathbf{r} \quad . \quad . \quad . \quad (10)$$

is easily deducible from (9).

Green's Theorem for the region bounded by a closed surface S may be expressed

$$\int \nabla U\cdot\nabla V dS = \int U\mathbf{n}\cdot\nabla V dS - \int U\nabla^2 V dv \quad . \quad . \quad (14)$$

$$= \int V\mathbf{n}\cdot\nabla U dS - \int V\nabla^2 U dv \quad . \quad . \quad (14')$$

If P is a point within the surface S, **Green's Formula** states that

$$4\pi V_P = \int\left(\frac{1}{r}\frac{\partial V}{\partial n} - V\frac{\partial}{\partial n}\frac{1}{r}\right)dS - \int\frac{1}{r}\nabla^2 V dv \quad . \quad . \quad (17)$$

while, if P is outside the region, the right-hand side is equal to zero (16).

Gauss's Integral $-\int \mathbf{n}\cdot\nabla\frac{1}{r}dS$ has the value 4π or zero according as P is inside or outside the closed surface S (18) and (18′).

Potential Theory.

The *potential* V due to a number of discrete particles is

$$V = \Sigma\frac{m}{r} \quad . \quad . \quad . \quad . \quad (1')$$

and the *intensity* of force at any point is

$$\mathbf{F} = \nabla V = \nabla\Sigma\frac{m}{r} \quad . \quad . \quad . \quad . \quad (2')$$

At points not occupied by the attracting matter,

$$\nabla^2 V = 0 \quad . \quad . \quad . \quad . \quad . \quad (3)$$

For a continuous *space distribution* of volume density ρ the potential is

$$V = \int\frac{\rho dv}{r} \quad . \quad . \quad . \quad . \quad . \quad (4)$$

and the intensity

$$\mathbf{F} = \nabla V \quad . \quad . \quad . \quad . \quad . \quad (5)$$

as before. At all points the potential satisfies **Poisson's equation**

$$\nabla^2 V = -4\pi\rho \quad . \quad . \quad . \quad . \quad . \quad (7)$$

The theorem of *total normal intensity* over a closed surface S is

$$\int\mathbf{n}\cdot\mathbf{F}dS = -4\pi\int\rho dv \quad . \quad . \quad . \quad (6)$$

The potential due to a *surface distribution* of area density σ is

$$V = \int\frac{\sigma}{r}dS \quad . \quad . \quad . \quad . \quad (13)$$

This is continuous at the surface; but its normal derivative has the discontinuity

$$\left(\frac{\partial V}{\partial n}\right)_e - \left(\frac{\partial V}{\partial n}\right)_i = -4\pi\sigma \quad . \quad . \quad . \quad (14)$$

Helmholtz's formula expressing a vector $\mathbf{F}$ as the sum of lamellar and solenoidal components is

$$\mathbf{F} = \nabla\phi + \nabla\times\mathbf{H} \quad . \quad . \quad . \quad . \quad (10)$$

where

$$\phi = -\frac{1}{4\pi}\int\frac{\text{div } \mathbf{F}}{r}dv \quad . \quad . \quad . \quad (11)$$

and

$$\mathbf{H} = \frac{1}{4\pi}\int\frac{\text{curl } \mathbf{F}}{r}dv \quad . \quad . \quad . \quad . \quad (12)$$

the integration being extended throughout all space.

Dyadics

(Chapter V.).

Any **linear vector function** of **r** is expressible in the form

$$\Phi\cdot\mathbf{r} \quad \text{or} \quad \mathbf{r}\cdot\Phi_c$$

where Φ is a *dyadic* used as a prefactor to **r**, and Φ_c its *conjugate* used as a postfactor. The terms of a dyadic are *dyads*, each being the " indeterminate " product of two vectors called the *antecedent* and the *consequent*. The distributive law applies to dyads and dyadics in " direct " multiplication. The **nonion form** of a dyadic is

$$\left.\begin{aligned}\Phi = a_{11}\mathbf{i}\,\mathbf{i} + a_{12}\mathbf{i}\,\mathbf{j} + a_{13}\mathbf{i}\,\mathbf{k} \\ + a_{21}\mathbf{j}\,\mathbf{i} + a_{22}\mathbf{j}\,\mathbf{j} + a_{23}\mathbf{j}\,\mathbf{k} \\ + a_{31}\mathbf{k}\,\mathbf{i} + a_{32}\mathbf{k}\,\mathbf{j} + a_{33}\mathbf{k}\,\mathbf{k}\end{aligned}\right\} \quad . \quad . \quad . \quad (6)$$

consisting of nine terms. But any dyadic is expressible as the sum of three dyads, of which either the antecedents or the consequents are three arbitrarily chosen non-coplanar vectors.

If

$$\Phi = \mathbf{a}_1\mathbf{b}_1 + \mathbf{a}_2\mathbf{b}_2 + \ldots$$

its *scalar* is

$$\Phi_s = \mathbf{a}_1\cdot\mathbf{b}_1 + \mathbf{a}_2\cdot\mathbf{b}_2 + \ldots \quad . \quad . \quad . \quad . \quad (7)$$

$$= \mathbf{i}\cdot\Phi\cdot\mathbf{i} + \mathbf{j}\cdot\Phi\cdot\mathbf{j} + \mathbf{k}\cdot\Phi\cdot\mathbf{k} \quad . \quad . \quad . \quad . \quad (7'')$$

and its *vector* is

$$\Phi_v = \mathbf{a}_1\times\mathbf{b}_1 + \mathbf{a}_2\times\mathbf{b}_2 + \ldots \quad . \quad . \quad . \quad . \quad (8)$$

$$= -(\mathbf{i}\cdot\Phi\times\mathbf{i} + \mathbf{j}\cdot\Phi\times\mathbf{j} + \mathbf{k}\cdot\Phi\times\mathbf{k}) \quad . \quad . \quad . \quad (8'')$$

The *associative law* holds for direct products of dyadics. Thus

$$(\Phi\cdot\Psi)\cdot\Omega = \Phi\cdot(\Psi\cdot\Omega) \quad . \quad . \quad . \quad . \quad (10)$$

and so on for several factors.

The **idemfactor** or *identical dyadic*

$$\mathrm{I} \equiv \mathbf{i}\,\mathbf{i} + \mathbf{j}\,\mathbf{j} + \mathbf{k}\,\mathbf{k} \quad . \quad . \quad . \quad . \quad (15)$$

in direct multiplication with a vector or a dyadic, leaves the vector or dyadic unchanged. Thus

$$\mathrm{I}\cdot\mathbf{r} = \mathbf{r}$$

and

$$\mathbf{I}\cdot\Phi = \Phi.$$

Reciprocal dyadics are such that their direct product is equal to the idemfactor. We use the notation

$$\Phi\cdot\Phi^{-1} = \mathbf{I}.$$

The reciprocal of the product of two dyadics is equal to the product of their reciprocals taken in the opposite order. Thus

$$(\Phi\cdot\Psi)^{-1} = \Psi^{-1}\cdot\Phi^{-1}.$$

Any dyadic is expressible as the sum of a *self-conjugate* and an *anti-self-conjugate* part:

$$\Phi = \tfrac{1}{2}(\Phi + \Phi_c) + \tfrac{1}{2}(\Phi - \Phi_c) \quad . \quad . \quad . \quad (20)$$

and

$$\Phi\cdot\mathbf{r} = \tfrac{1}{2}(\Phi + \Phi_c)\cdot\mathbf{r} - \tfrac{1}{2}\Phi_v\times\mathbf{r} \quad . \quad . \quad . \quad (21)$$

$$\mathbf{r}\cdot\Phi = \tfrac{1}{2}\mathbf{r}\cdot(\Phi + \Phi_c) - \tfrac{1}{2}\mathbf{r}\times\Phi_v \quad . \quad . \quad (21')$$

The necessary and sufficient condition that a dyadic be self-conjugate is that its vector be equal to zero.

The dyadic $\mathbf{I}\times\mathbf{a} \equiv \mathbf{a}\times\mathbf{I}$ is anti-self-conjugate, and

$$\mathbf{r}\times\mathbf{a} = \mathbf{r}\cdot(\mathbf{I}\times\mathbf{a}) = \mathbf{r}\cdot(\mathbf{a}\times\mathbf{I}) \quad . \quad . \quad . \quad (22')$$

$$\mathbf{a}\times\mathbf{r} = (\mathbf{I}\times\mathbf{a})\cdot\mathbf{r} = (\mathbf{a}\times\mathbf{I})\cdot\mathbf{r} \quad . \quad . \quad . \quad (22)$$

Theorem. *Any self-conjugate dyadic may be expressed in the form*

$$a_1\mathbf{i}\,\mathbf{i} + a_2\mathbf{j}\,\mathbf{j} + a_3\mathbf{k}\,\mathbf{k}.$$

Dyadics involving ∇

(Chapter VII.).

The operator ∇ applied to a vector yields a dyadic. Thus

$$\nabla\mathbf{V} = \mathbf{i}\frac{\partial\mathbf{V}}{\partial x} + \mathbf{j}\frac{\partial\mathbf{V}}{\partial y} + \mathbf{k}\frac{\partial\mathbf{V}}{\partial z} \quad . \quad . \quad . \quad (1)$$

and

$$\mathbf{V}\nabla = \frac{\partial\mathbf{V}}{\partial x}\mathbf{i} + \frac{\partial\mathbf{V}}{\partial y}\mathbf{j} + \frac{\partial\mathbf{V}}{\partial z}\mathbf{k} \quad . \quad . \quad . \quad (1')$$

are conjugate dyadics; and each is invariant with respect to the choice of rectangular axes. Just as in the case of a scalar function, we have

$$d\mathbf{r}\cdot\nabla\mathbf{V} = d\mathbf{V} \quad . \quad . \quad . \quad . \quad (3)$$

The scalars and vectors of the above dyadics are

$$(\nabla\mathbf{V})_s = \nabla\cdot\mathbf{V} = (\mathbf{V}\nabla)_s \quad . \quad . \quad . \quad . \quad (4)$$

$$(\nabla\mathbf{V})_v = \nabla\times\mathbf{V} = -(\mathbf{V}\nabla)_v \quad . \quad . \quad . \quad (5)$$

The dyadic $\nabla\nabla V$ is self-conjugate because its vector is zero.

The operator ∇ applied to a dyadic in direct or cross multiplication yields

$$\nabla\cdot\Phi = \mathbf{i}\cdot\frac{\partial\Phi}{\partial x} + \mathbf{j}\cdot\frac{\partial\Phi}{\partial y} + \mathbf{k}\cdot\frac{\partial\Phi}{\partial z} \quad . \quad . \qquad (7)$$

and

$$\nabla\times\Phi = \mathbf{i}\times\frac{\partial\Phi}{\partial x} + \mathbf{j}\times\frac{\partial\Phi}{\partial y} + \mathbf{k}\times\frac{\partial\Phi}{\partial z} \quad . \quad . \quad . \qquad (8)$$

while $\Phi\cdot\nabla$ and $\Phi\times\nabla$ are similarly defined by (7′) and (8′).

The relations

$$\nabla\times\nabla\mathbf{V} = 0 \qquad (9)$$

$$\nabla\cdot\nabla\times\Phi = 0 \qquad (10)$$

$$\nabla\cdot\nabla\mathbf{V} = \nabla^2\mathbf{V}. \qquad (11)$$

$$\nabla\times\nabla\times\Phi = \nabla\nabla\cdot\Phi - \nabla^2\Phi \qquad (12)$$

are analogous to results in Chapter I. ; while

$$\nabla\cdot(\mathbf{V}\nabla) = \nabla\nabla\cdot\mathbf{V} \qquad (11')$$

The following formulæ of expansion are useful :

$$\nabla(\mathbf{u}\cdot\mathbf{v}) = \nabla\mathbf{u}\cdot\mathbf{v} + \nabla\mathbf{v}\cdot\mathbf{u} \qquad (13)$$

$$\nabla(\mathbf{u}\times\mathbf{v}) = \nabla\mathbf{u}\times\mathbf{v} - \nabla\mathbf{v}\times\mathbf{u} \qquad (14)$$

$$\nabla(u\mathbf{v}) = \nabla u\,\mathbf{v} + u\nabla\mathbf{v}\,. \qquad (15)$$

$$\nabla\cdot(u\Phi) = \nabla u\cdot\Phi + u\nabla\cdot\Phi \qquad (16)$$

$$\nabla\times(u\Phi) = \nabla u\times\Phi + u\nabla\times\Phi \qquad (17)$$

In particular, if $\Phi = \mathrm{I}$, the last two become

$$\nabla(u\mathrm{I}) = \nabla u \qquad (16')$$

$$\nabla\times(u\mathrm{I}) = \nabla u\times\mathrm{I} \qquad (17')$$

Occasionally we need the formulæ

$$\nabla\cdot(\mathrm{I}\times\mathbf{v}) = \nabla\times\mathbf{v}\,. \qquad (18)$$

$$\nabla\times(\mathrm{I}\times\mathbf{v}) = \mathbf{v}\nabla - \mathrm{I}\nabla\cdot\mathbf{v}\,. \qquad (19)$$

$$\nabla\times u\mathrm{I}\times\nabla = \nabla\nabla u - \nabla^2 u\mathrm{I} \qquad (20)$$

Transformation of Integrals.

As in the case of Chapter II., the following relations hold between line integrals round a closed curve and surface integrals over an open surface bounded by the curve :

$$\int \mathbf{n}\times\nabla\mathbf{V}dS = \int_0 d\mathbf{r}\,\mathbf{V} \qquad (23)$$

$$\int \mathbf{n}\cdot\nabla\times\Phi dS = \int_0 d\mathbf{r}\cdot\Phi\,. \qquad (22)$$

Also the formula

$$\int_0 d\mathbf{r}\times\mathbf{V}=\int[\mathbf{n}\cdot(\mathbf{V}\nabla)-\mathbf{n}\nabla\cdot\mathbf{V}]dS \quad . \quad . \quad . \quad (24)$$

will be found useful.

In the case of a closed surface S we have the results

$$\int \nabla\mathbf{V}dv=\int\mathbf{n}\mathbf{V}dS \quad . \quad . \quad . \quad . \quad (25)$$

$$\int \nabla\cdot\Phi dv=\int\mathbf{n}\cdot\Phi dS \quad . \quad . \quad . \quad . \quad (28)$$

$$\int \nabla\times\Phi dv=\int\mathbf{n}\times\Phi dS \quad . \quad . \quad . \quad . \quad (29)$$

analogous to the theorems of Chapter II

APPENDIX I.

[Reprinted by permission from the *Mathematical Gazette*, January 1917.]

A PLEA FOR A MORE GENERAL USE OF VECTOR ANALYSIS IN APPLIED MATHEMATICS.

THAT the advantage of using vector analysis in mathematical physics has met with so little recognition by British applied mathematicians must appear rather strange to those of other countries. There are probably not more than half a dozen among us who habitually use vector methods and notation, at any rate in published work. The fact is still more surprising when we recall the work of Maxwell * and Heaviside, seeing that the former gave a sort of authority to the *curl* and *divergence*, while the latter had so much to do with the systematic development of the vectorial calculus.

Perhaps the chief reason † why vector analysis has not come into more general favour with us is that our leaders in applied mathematics have not felt the need of it. It has often been remarked, and perhaps with some degree of truth, that nothing can be accomplished by vector methods that cannot also be done by Cartesian analysis; and therefore, it is argued, the change is unnecessary and useless. If we had to deal only with minds of special mathematical ability and analytical insight, this conclusion might be accepted. But with the average student so much of his attention is occupied in dealing with the complex array of symbols of partial differentiation to which he is often led in Cartesian analysis, that he is unable to grasp the inner meaning of the work. It is difficult for him in many cases even to see exactly what is expressed in the formulæ obtained, involving as they do the three components of a vector quantity in combinations not easy to visualise. And even if the student succeeds in following the argument, it is often almost impossible for him to remember either the train of reasoning or the result arrived at. He does not perhaps see why his equations should be differentiated partially with respect to x, y, z and added, or with respect to z, y and subtracted.

* There is no doubt that Maxwell would have gone much further in the vectorial method if he had had ready to hand a system of analysis such as to-day is at our disposal. Unfortunately, at that period there was only the theory of quaternions, which he wisely did not employ except in passing reference.

† See, however, the Note at the end of this paper.

Working, however, with the aid of vector analysis, we no longer have three unsymmetrical equations to carry in our thoughts, but a single equation involving only the vector quantity as a whole; and we thus form the habit of regarding this as one complete quantity rather than as a group of three. The analytical transformations are reduced to a minimum, and the student is able to devote a much greater part of his attention to the meaning of his equations. The reason, too, for a particular step in the analysis is often quite apparent. Suppose, for instance, that we desire to eliminate from our equation a certain vector of which only the *gradient* is present. The obvious course is to take the *curl* of both members. Or, if it is the curl of the undesirable vector that is present, we immediately take the *divergence* of both sides. The Cartesian equivalent of the former of these eliminations is much more involved.

It is on the strength of personal experience that I advocate the adoption of vector analysis. As a student first at Sydney and then at Cambridge, I had some leaning toward the applied subjects; but it was not until the last few years that I gained any knowledge of vector methods.* The newer analysis completely altered my mathematical outlook, and made mathematical physics to me a new subject. An almost dying interest gave place to a keen enthusiasm, and most of the old difficulties vanished in the new light thrown upon the work. It is to save the average students of the coming generation any unnecessary difficulties, and to help them to form clearer conceptions of physical quantities and mathematical processes, that I am advocating the change which has been delayed too long. It is not a matter of vital importance which particular notation we use—whether the dot and cross or the bracket notation, although the former has many advantages. Nor does it make much difference whether we teach in terms of *dyadics* or of *tensors*.

But it is not only the student of average mathematical intelligence who would gain by the change. The vector methods are in themselves so much quicker; and in these days we cannot afford to waste time either in writing or in unnecessary mechanical thought. Associated with this is the great gain in condensation. It is laborious and often irksome to wade through three pages of Cartesian analysis when one page of vectorial would suffice. And the expenditure of mental effort is balanced by no corresponding gain; but rather the shorter analysis affords a clearer mental picture of the meaning of the equations and the significance of the transformations. The argument of condensation is certainly worth serious consideration. In this connection it may be remarked how few English mathematical books are written vectorially. One thinks of a couple of recent works in Relativity, one or two in Mechanics, and Heaviside's Electromagnetic treatise, which can hardly be called recent, but the number is soon exhausted. And yet there is no dearth of ex-

* In undertaking the study of vector analysis, I followed the example of my learned colleague at Melbourne University—Prof. J. H. Michell, F.R.S.—who adopted it several years previously.

cellent treatises on a great variety of subjects. No doubt the chief reason why a larger number of authors have not adopted the vector methods and notation is the lack of familiarity with these methods among their readers. This recalls the practice of "dodging the calculus" so common in elementary text-books, and of course unavoidable when the necessary knowledge is not possessed by the student. Yet everyone admits the great advantages to be derived from the use of the infinitesimal calculus, and the early mastery of the elements of it. The case for the vector calculus is exactly parallel; and the student who acquires familiarity with it delights in the facility with which he can make the various transformations, and in the clearer understanding of the main ideas beneath them. To him the more laborious Cartesian analysis appears exactly like dodging the calculus.

It will hardly be seriously objected that to become familiar with the new analysis involves a certain expenditure of time and the effort of learning more formulæ. Precisely the same objection may be raised to learning the infinitesimal calculus itself. And, just as in this case, the amount of time and labour saved in the long run is vastly greater than that spent in acquiring the necessary knowledge. Even in the proofs of many of the theorems of the integral calculus vector methods lead to a considerable shortening of detail, and the final results are expressible in forms that are neater and easier to remember than the old ones. Take, for instance, some of the theorems expressing the transformation of integrals connected with lines, surfaces, and volumes.

In vector notation we have

$$\int_0 \phi d\mathbf{s} = \iint \mathbf{n} \times \text{grad}\, \phi\, dS,$$

$$\int_0 \mathbf{R} \cdot d\mathbf{s} = \iint \mathbf{n} \cdot \text{curl}\, \mathbf{R}\, dS,$$

$$\iint \mathbf{n} \phi dS = \iiint \text{grad}\, \phi\, dv,$$

$$\iint \mathbf{n} \cdot \mathbf{R} dS = \iiint \text{div}\, \mathbf{R}\, dv,$$

$$\iint \mathbf{n} \times \mathbf{R} dS = \iiint \text{curl}\, \mathbf{R}\, dv.$$

These forms are very simple, while in comparison their Cartesian equivalents are clumsy.

There is another great gain which would almost certainly follow upon the change under consideration. Looking down the tables of contents in our mathematical journals one is struck with the preponderance of papers in pure over those in applied subjects, and notices how few of the latter are really three-dimensional. We have seen a far greater number of our brilliant students take up the pure in preference to the applied; while many who have a leaning toward the latter choose laboratory work in physics, and in some cases forget the mathematical claims of the subject in their devotion to the experimental. The writer is confident that an early training in vector thought and vector analysis would go far toward inducing a much larger proportion of our students to cultivate the study of physical mathematics, and then to undertake research in this domain. The practice of visualising inculcated by such a training leads to the same kind of conceptions as those which Faraday formed of the condition of the electric field.*

The place of Vector Analysis in a University course would depend to a certain extent upon the earlier mathematical curriculum. Speaking generally, however, the purely algebraic part of the subject, including the different kinds of products of two or more vectors, and perhaps the elementary part of the theory of linear vector functions,† might be given in the first year. A considerable application of this may be made to the theory of elementary mechanics, without any introduction of the infinitesimal calculus. The differential and integral calculus of vectors might be postponed till the second year, where it would still be in plenty of time for use in those applied subjects for which it is so admirably fitted. The teaching of analytical solid geometry, which is often begun at this stage, would be rendered much easier by the vector knowledge thus gained; and many of the proofs in this subject are greatly simplified by vector methods.

In conclusion, let it be distinctly stated that *nothing is further from my thoughts than the abolition of Cartesian analysis. Such a thing is impossible.* But this analysis is an incomplete instrument in itself, and that whose adoption I have been pleading goes a long way toward completing it. In some respects the older analysis suggests the reading of a book by spelling every word on each page. In vector analysis we deal with words rather than letters, and in so doing can give more of our attention to the thoughts. But we never forget that in written language the primary elements are the letters; and the vector analyst often finds it instructive to spell his words, resolving his vectors into components and expanding his single equations into Cartesian trios. Thus *the new analysis has not come to destroy the old, but to fulfil it.*

NOTE.—Since writing this paper I have read those portions of Heaviside's *Electromagnetic Theory* dealing with vectorial algebra and analysis, and giving incidentally ‡ some idea of the controversy toward the close of the last century for and against the use of quaternions in mathematical physics. I am very glad that before beginning the study of vector analysis I had no knowledge of quaternions beyond the name and a few vague ideas about the controversy referred to. I was thus able to approach the subject quite unbiassed and *from the Cartesian point of view.* This, I believe, makes all the difference to one's reception of the vectorial method; for, as stated at the close of my paper, the Cartesian and vectorial analyses are inseparably connected. Since writing those lines, I was pleased to

* *Cf* Coffin, *Vector Analysis*, Preface, p. vi.

† This is purely algebraic.

‡ In a manner often blunt and amusing, but always interesting.

find the same thought expressed by Heaviside. "The quaternionists," he says, "want to throw away the 'Cartesian trammels,' as they call them. This may do for quaternions, but with vectors would be a grave mistake. My system, so far from being inimical to the Cartesian system of mathematics, is its very essence." *

The unfortunate idea that vector analysis is a sort of modified system of quaternions is perhaps largely responsible for its tardy adoption in Great Britain. The consideration of my own experience may therefore be of some value, chiefly because there were no initial conceptions and associations to bias me. The first book I studied on the subject was the French edition of *Le Calcul Vectoriel*, by Burali-Forti and Marcolongo. I found their system interesting and helpful, though not always natural. While waiting for other books by mail I read Silberstein's *Vectorial Mechanics*, in which Heaviside's notation and analysis are employed. Speaking only of the chapter on vector algebra and analysis, I thought it simple and direct, but found the symbol *V* used to denote a vector product very confusing. I have since, of course, learnt that this is only a survival of the quaternionic notation, and yet adopted, strange to say, by such a pronounced anti-quaternionist as Heaviside. Then I had the pleasure of reading Gibbs's *Vector Analysis*, by E. B. Wilson, explaining a system substantially the same as that of Heaviside, from which it differs chiefly in notation. It appeared to me at once most natural in both method and notation, and afforded me the inspiration already referred to. The bracket notation for products of vectors has since come under my notice in many works, but while reading this with equal facility I prefer that of Gibbs. Not only does this leave the brackets free for ordinary algebraic purposes, but the dot and cross are now hardly needed in algebra to indicate a product.

C. E. WEATHERBURN.

23rd September 1916.

* *Loc. cit.*, vol. i. p. 305.

APPENDIX II.

[Reprinted by permission from the *Mathematical Gazette*, December 1920.]

VECTOR ANALYSIS IN A UNIVERSITY COURSE.

SINCE due recognition is now being more and more widely given to the importance of Vector Analysis for three-dimensional work in mechanics, geometry, and mathematical physics, the time is opportune to consider the place which that subject merits in a University degree course. A student who undertakes anything like research work in applied subjects is considerably handicapped if he has had no training in Vector Analysis ; but the need for it is felt much earlier than the stage at which research is generally begun. Every University course contains subjects which are less useful than Vector Analysis ; and on the ground of utility alone there is no question that the latter deserves a place in the curriculum. It will, however, be found quite unnecessary to displace anything else, because the time occupied in teaching the essential parts of vector algebra and calculus will be saved, even during a three years' course, by the application of this method to the three-dimensional parts of mechanics and mathematical physics.

It is, perhaps, not generally recognised that the subject of Vector Analysis belongs essentially to the domain of *pure* mathematics. The fundamental length-vector is a geometrical quantity whose magnitude is a length ; and vector algebra involves nothing but elementary geometry, algebra, and trigonometry. Certainly its most important applications are in mechanics and physics, but the same is true of certain other branches of pure mathematics. The differential and integral calculus of vectors involves only geometry and the algebraic calculus. In the analysis itself there is no need to make mention of a single physical quantity. The theory of the linear vector function, whether it employs dyadics, tensors, or matrices, is purely algebraic, and in no way dependent upon mixed mathematics, though it has extremely important applications in elasticity and the electromagnetic theory.

The time for teaching the different parts of the subject will depend to some extent upon local conditions. Generally, however, it will be found advisable to give a short course in *vector algebra* to "honour" students in their first year, and to "pass" students either at the end of the first or at the beginning of the second year. As remarked above, this part of the subject is quite elementary, and may be disposed of in six or seven lectures. These would treat of sums of vectors, the various products of two or three vectors, and some geometrical applications. A little later, when the student possesses a fair knowledge of the algebraic calculus, differentiation of vectors with respect to a single variable may be treated. In elementary applications the single variable will usually be the time variable t or the arc-length s.

Even this elementary knowledge of Vector Analysis will be found exceedingly useful in mechanics, and to some extent also in solid geometry. By means of it practically all the important principles of *mechanics* are just as easily proved for three dimensions as for two, and a great simplification is introduced into the work. The vector moment or torque about the origin, of a force * $\mathbf{F}$ localised in a line through the point whose position vector is $\mathbf{r}$, is given by the vector product $\mathbf{r}\times\mathbf{F}$; and the (scalar) moment about any axis through the origin is the resolved part of the vector moment in that direction. Similarly the moment of any other localised vector may be defined. The moment of the velocity of a particle is represented by $\mathbf{r}\times\mathbf{v}$, which is twice the areal velocity about the same point. The angular momentum or moment of momentum of the particle is $\mathbf{r}\times(m\mathbf{v})$; and the A.M. about any axis through the origin is the resolved part of this vector in the direction of the axis. The work of a force $\mathbf{F}$, during a displacement $\mathbf{d}$ of the particle acted upon, is given by the scalar product $\mathbf{F}\cdot\mathbf{d}$; and it is merely a corollary that the work of the resultant of several forces is the sum of the works of the components. The activity of a force $\mathbf{F}$ at any instant is $\mathbf{F}\cdot\mathbf{v}$, where $\mathbf{v}$ is the velocity of the particle acted upon.

The relative position of one point P with respect to another, O, is determined by the vector $\mathbf{r}=\overrightarrow{OP}$. The velocity of P relative to O is the rate of change of its relative position, and is therefore given by the vector $\mathbf{v}=\frac{d\mathbf{r}}{dt}$. The relative acceleration is similarly the rate of increase of the relative velocity, so that

$$\mathbf{a}=\frac{d\mathbf{v}}{dt}=\frac{d^2\mathbf{r}}{dt^2}.$$

The theorems of the vector addition of velocities or accelerations are an immediate consequence. In the case of a system of particles the importance of the centre of mass, and the theorems connecting the velocity and acceleration of this point with the momenta of the separate particles and the vector sum of the forces acting on the system, follow directly from the formula

$$\bar{\mathbf{r}}=\frac{\Sigma m\mathbf{r}}{\Sigma m},$$

which defines the centre of mass. The formulæ associated with rotating axes can be proved vectorially almost in one line; and the

* In printing, vectors are usually denoted by Clarendon symbols. For manuscript and blackboard work, Greek letters and script capitals will be found convenient.

single vector formula is much easier to remember than the triad of scalar ones. In three-dimensional Statics the equations of equilibrium for a rigid body are reduced to two ; and all the spatial work, such as Poinsot's reduction of a system of forces on a rigid body, is wonderfully abbreviated and simplified.

In *solid geometry* the essential things are vector quantities. Each point is specified by its position vector relative to an assigned origin, and each element of a surface by its position vector and vector area. The equation of a plane takes the simple form $\mathbf{r}\cdot\mathbf{n} = p$, where $\mathbf{n}$ is a unit vector perpendicular to the plane, and $\mathbf{r}$ the position vector of a current point on the plane. The whole geometry of the plane may be deduced very concisely from this equation. The vector equation of the straight line through the point $\mathbf{a}$ parallel to the vector $\mathbf{b}$ is $\mathbf{r} = \mathbf{a} + t\mathbf{b}$; and the geometry of non-intersecting lines involves nothing beyond the scalar triple product of vectors, corresponding to the determinant of 3×3 elements in coordinate geometry. The coordinate equivalent of any vectorial result is a mere corollary, whether the axes are rectangular or oblique. Thus the heavy, artificial, and lengthy argument in the case of oblique axes becomes unnecessary ; for it is as easy to expand our formulæ in terms of any three non-coplanar vectors $\mathbf{a}$, $\mathbf{b}$, $\mathbf{c}$ as in terms of the mutually perpendicular vectors $\mathbf{i}$, $\mathbf{j}$, $\mathbf{k}$. The standard equation of a sphere may be written $\mathbf{r}^2 - 2\mathbf{r}\cdot\mathbf{c} + k = 0$, from which the geometry of the sphere may be neatly and concisely deduced. Finally, the curvature and torsion of curves are very easily investigated in terms of the derivatives of the position vector of a current point on the curve, with respect to the arc-length s. The method is perfectly elementary, and the results appear in a form which is easy to remember.

The *advanced part* of Vector Analysis naturally begins with the differential operations which yield the gradient of a scalar point-function, and the divergence and curl of a vector point-function. We are confronted with these as soon as we enter upon higher applied mathematics ; and the student who has to do so without the vectorial equipment finds himself seriously handicapped. There is here, after all, only a very little to learn. All that is really important about the differential operations would make only one chapter of reasonable size ; while another of the same size could contain the theorems on line, surface, and volume integrals which are continually employed in advanced mathematics. These are Gauss's divergence theorem, Stokes's theorem, and a few others which are immediately deducible from them. Such matters belong to the domain of pure mathematics ; and their teaching should not be consigned to lectures or books in mixed mathematics. The student is thereby apt to gain the impression that the theorem is part of the applied subject under discussion. Lectures on advanced calculus are their appropriate setting ; and six or seven lectures could supply all the necessary information. An " honour " student will probably need these at the end of his second year, in readiness for the higher applied work he is likely to have in his third. " Pass " students may not reach a standard, during their degree course, at which this work will be necessary. But that will depend upon the nature of the course.

Linear vector functions are hardly met till this stage; but their treatment is quite elementary and almost entirely algebraic. The theory may be developed in terms either of dyadics or of tensors, which belong to the province of multiple algebra. The resolved form of a dyadic is really equivalent to a matrix, and the theory of dyadics is parallel with that of matrices. But the dyadic has certain advantages, among others that it need not be expressed in resolved form, but in a shorter form as the sum of three dyads. Linear vector functions are of constant occurrence in elasticity and the electromagnetic theory; and the student will experience far fewer difficulties in these subjects if he has had an earlier and separate introduction to the linear function. Without such a preparation he must find the theory of elasticity very heavy. The variable dyadic is a great help in the treatment of heterogeneous strain. The geometry of central quadric surfaces is also rendered more compact by the use of dyadics. So also is the treatment of moments and products of inertia, and the motion of a rigid body about a fixed point.

It is a mistake for the student to leave the consideration of vector methods till he has finished his course. Not only does he lose much before this stage, but he will be all the longer in acquiring that familiarity with these methods which is necessary for their effective employment, and which comes only with time and practice. Macaulay has remarked that "no noble work of imagination was ever composed by any man, except in a dialect which he had learned without remembering how or when." The two cases are hardly parallel; but we may safely say that the earlier a student begins to learn the vectorial mode of thought and expression, the greater will be his facility in three-dimensional calculations, and the better will be the quality of his later work in this direction.

C. E. WEATHERBURN.

August 1920.

INDEX.

The numbers refer to the articles.

The numbers refer to the articles.

The numbers refer to the articles.

Printed by PHOTOTYPE LTD., LONDON

ADVANCED VECTOR ANALYSIS

WITH APPLICATION TO MATHEMATICAL PHYSICS

BY

C. E. WEATHERBURN

M.A. (CAMBRIDGE), D.SC. (SYDNEY)

PROFESSOR OF MATHEMATICS
UNIVERSITY OF WESTERN AUSTRALIA

LONDON

G. BELL AND SONS, LTD.

1951

To

PROFESSOR H. S. CARSLAW, Sc.D.

THIS BOOK IS GRATEFULLY DEDICATED

BY A FORMER PUPIL

First published January, 1924
Reprinted 1928, 1937, 1943,
1944, 1947, 1949, 1951